OUTLINE OF ASTRONOMY

2722

Outline of astronomy

VOLUME I

by

HANS-HEINRICH VOIGT
Professor at the University of Göttingen

translated by
L. PLAUT
Kapteyn Laboratory, University of Groningen

NANCY HOUK
Department of Astronomy, University of Michigan

NOORDHOFF INTERNATIONAL PUBLISHING LEYDEN

ISBN 90 01 71270 3

Library of Congress Catalog Card Number 72-97241

Original edition published in 1969 under the title "*Abriss der Astronomie*" at Mannheim – Bibliographisches Inst. AG.

Printed in the Netherlands

TABLE OF CONTENTS

SHORT SURVEY of VOLUME 2 (CHAPTERS 6 to 10):

AUTHOR'S PREFACE

The origin of this book goes back to key-word-like summaries of the subjects to be treated, distributed among the students at the beginning of each class of a two-semester course in introductory astronomy. In this way, copying by the students should be avoided and a stronger concentration on the subject itself be made possible. This "abstract" has been used for the preparation of classes and lectures at other universities and at Göttingen has served for a long time as a foundation in preparing for examinations. However, I have not taken up the suggestion, made more than once, to write a coherent "introduction to astronomy", because a continuous text would not comply with the original idea and would, in addition, overlap too much with other books. However, at the time when the Bibliographisches Institut declared its willingness to publish this review in its series of textbooks with retention of the key-word-like, telegraphic style I wholly revised and greatly extended the original version, so that the "outline" now available is far more extensive than an "introduction".

What the book is or is not follows from this history: it is not a textbook of astronomy for the beginner, who still is unfamiliar with the material; for this purpose a supplementary oral course, for instance, is needed. Rather it is a concise and, hopefully, clearly arranged summary of what has already been heard or read in detail. Moreover the book is not a collection of astronomical data.

To this end there exist other and better reference books, some of which are mentioned below. No emphasis was put on getting the most comprehensive, exact and most up-to-date numerical data. Numerical data should serve only as an illustration and explanation. Rather the aim of this book is to define the astronomical concepts, to derive important equations and to explain the fundamental methods and relations. Individual observational results and the description of specific astronomical objects are, relatively, of less importance and are conceived, too, more as an illustration than for their own significance.

Concerning the distribution of weight over the various sections I followed the trend of treating somewhat more comprehensively those fields which generally were mentioned very briefly in general astronomy books. On the other hand, I tried to shorten greatly those topics which already are extensively described in the popular literature. However, it is obvious that the special interests of the author also are reflected in the distribution of weights.

I want to thank Prof. Kippenhahn, who has given the introductory course in astronomy during last year and who discussed several chapters with me in connection with this. I especially thank Dr. L. Plaut of Groningen and Dr. Nancy Houk of Ann Arbor for their translation and furthermore that they pointed out some errors in the German edition and that they extended the contents and brought them up-to-date. Thanks are also due to Mr. Craig Chester for his help in up-dating the original manuscript.

H. H. Voigt

Göttingen, August, 1972.

REFERENCES

The references quoted in the individual chapters are not to be considered as a complete literature list. In general, only a few important books and reviews are quoted, which were consulted while preparing the chapter considered. Original papers are mentioned only if they were used explicitly and if they are not yet quoted in the relevant books and reviews.

Some reference books and textbooks covering the whole field of astronomy are given below. These books are not mentioned again in the individual chapters.

A. Unsöld 1967, *The New Cosmos* (translated by W.H. McCrea). Longmans/Springer, New York.

L. Motz and A. Duveen 1966, *Essentials of Astronomy*, Blackie and Son, London.

L.H. Baker and L.W. Frederick, *An Introduction to Astronomy*, Van Nostrand, Princeton, N.J.

C.W. Allen 1963, *Astrophysical Quantities*, 2nd edition, Athlone Press, London.

Landolt-Börnstein 1965, *Numerical Data and Functional Relationships in Science and Technology* (new series). group VI, Vol.I. *Astronomy and Astrophysics*, edited by H.H. Voigt, Springer, New York.

1

SPHERICAL ASTRONOMY

References:

Smart, W.M. 1962, *Text-Book on Spherical Astronomy*, 5th ed., Cambridge University Press, Cambridge.

Woolard, E.W. and Clemence, G.M. 1966, *Spherical Astronomy*, Academic Press, New York.

Explanatory Supplement to the Astronomical Ephemeris and the American Ephemeris and Nautical Almanac, 1961, H.M.S.O., London.

§ 1 Coordinate systems

Defining of stellar position on the (apparent) celestial sphere: two spherical coordinates (analogous to the terrestrial coordinates). Third coordinate (= distance) is not considered here; only the "direction" is of interest.

Each system is defined by:

1) A fundamental plane = great circle (equator) with corresponding poles and latitude circles

⟹ First coordinate : distance from fundamental circle (terrestrial or geographic latitude) or distance from pole

2) Longitude circles = great circles from pole to pole. A zero-longitude point serves as a starting point (meridian through Greenwich).

⟹ Second coordinate : distance of longitude circle through the object from zero-longitude circle (terr. or geogr. longitude).

1.1 *Horizon system* (natural system of observation)

Fundamental circle: horizon — upper pole: zenith; lower pole: nadir

Longitude circles: great circles through zenith = verticals
Zero-longitude circle: vertical through south point = meridian

Coordinates:

Altitude h above the horizon or zenith distance $z = 90^\circ - h$

Azimuth A = angle between vertical through the object and meridian; from S westward up to 360°. Also defined in several other ways, so definition should always be given.

Theodolites and many large radio telescopes are mounted "azimuthally".

1.2 *Equatorial system* = projection of the terrestrial grid from the earth's center onto the celestial sphere

A) Fixed equatorial system (for observation at the telescope)

Fundamental circle: celestial equator

north and south pole = extension of the terrestrial axis

north pole very close to "Polaris" = α Ursae Minoris

Zero-longitude circle: great circle pole-zenith-south point = meridian

Coordinates:

Declination δ = distance from equator (to $\pm 90^\circ$)

Hour angle t = angle between the longitude circle through the star and the meridian; from S westward up to 360° or westward and eastward from the meridian

Because of the rotation of the earth, t goes through all values in the course of a single day, δ remains unchanged. On account of this cycle t is usually measured not in degrees but in time:

$24^h \mathrel{\hat=} 360^\circ$ therefore: $1^h \mathrel{\hat=} 15^\circ$ $1^\circ \mathrel{\hat=} 4^m$

$1^m \mathrel{\hat=} 15'$ $1' \mathrel{\hat=} 4^s$

$1^s \mathrel{\hat=} 15''$ $1'' \mathrel{\hat=} 0\overset{s}{.}07$

Meridional cross section:

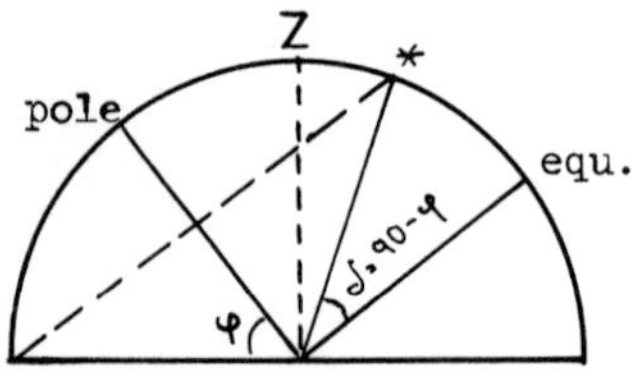

$\delta = 0^\circ$ stars 12^h above horizon

$\gtrless 0^\circ$ " $\gtrless 12$ " "

$> 90^\circ - \phi$ circumpolar stars

ϕ = geographic latitude
= zenith distance of the equator
= altitude of the pole

t = time since meridian passage of the star

= 0^h: upper culmination, star on meridian

= 12^h: lower culmination

At the north pole of the earth: all stars north of the equator circumpolar, all southern stars never visible

At the earth's equator: all stars always 12 hours above and below the horizon

Most telescopes are mounted "equatorially".
One axis (= polar axis) parallel to the axis of the earth.
Compensation of rotation of the earth by rotation in opposite direction around this axis.

B) Moving equatorial system (for cataloging)

Fundamental circle: celestial equator, as above

Zero-longitude circle: hour circle through the vernal equinox or the first point of Aries (vernal equinox ♈

= position of sun at beginning of spring

= point of intersection of ecliptic and equator)

Coordinates:

Declination δ, as above

Right ascension α = distance between hour circle through vernal equinox ♈ and hour circle through star; measured eastward from ♈.

The coordinates α and δ are "fixed" on the celestial sphere, independent of the daily motion.

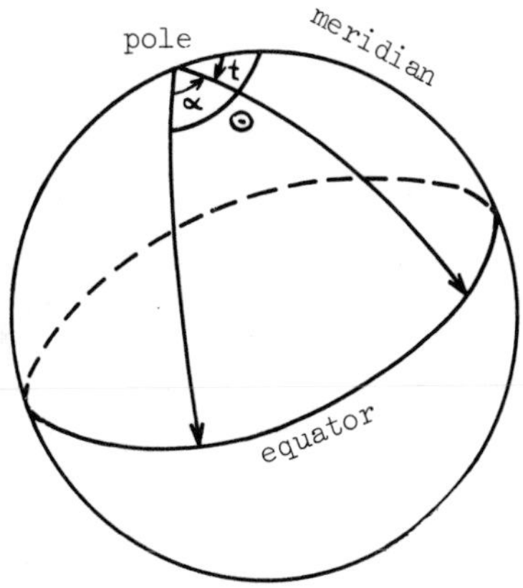

Local sidereal time

θ = hour angle of vernal equinox

$$\boxed{\theta = t + \alpha}$$

$\theta = 0$ vernal equinox on meridian

Star on meridian:

$t = 0$

hence $\theta = \alpha$

This means, e.g., at 7^h local sidereal time stars with $\alpha = 7^h$ are on the meridian

1.3 *Ecliptical system* (celestial mechanics of the solar system)

Fundamental circle: ecliptic = apparent orbit of the sun in the course of a year
= orbit of the earth
= line of eclipses (from the Greek)

Zero-longitude circle: great circle through vernal equinox ♈.
= intersection of equator and ecliptic

Coordinates:

Celestial latitude β

Celestial longitude λ

ε = inclination of the ecliptic to the equator
= obliquity of the ecliptic
= distance north pole to pole of ecliptic
= $23\overset{\circ}{.}5$

1.4 *Galactic system* (galactic research)

Fundamental circle: galactic equator = plane of the Milky Way

Zero-longitude circle:

old system (I) : intersection with the celestial equator
new system (II) : center of galaxy

Coordinates:

Galactic latitude b^{I}, b^{II}, respectively

Galactic longitude l^{I}, l^{II}, respectively

The I.A.U. at the 1970 meeting decided to use only the new system and to omit the superscripts, so: new system:

galactic latitude l
galactic longitude b
(see also 9.3).

1.5 *Transformation from one system to another*

Most simply by means of the spherical triangle formed by the star and the poles of the two systems, e.g., δ, $t \longleftrightarrow z$, A (equatorial system into horizon system and vice versa)

P = celestial pole
Z = zenith
S = star

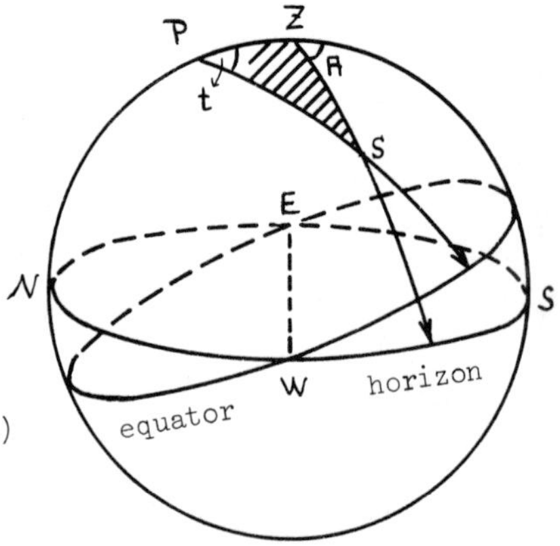

Triangle PZS =

astronomical or nautical triangle

q = parallactic angle

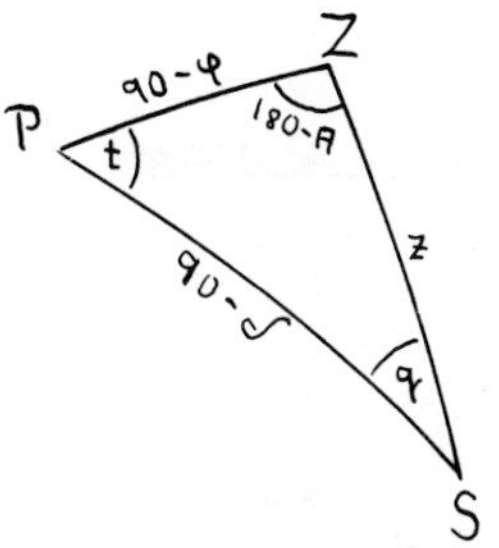

Then, by means of the well-known formulae of spherical trigonometry:

(see Smart, loc. cit., pages 1-24),

$\underline{\delta, t \longrightarrow z, A}$

$$\sin z \sin A = \cos\delta \sin t$$
$$\cos z = \sin\phi \sin\delta + \cos\phi \cos\delta \cos t$$
$$-\sin z \cos A = \cos\phi \sin\delta - \sin\phi \cos\delta \cos t$$

$\underline{z, A \longrightarrow \delta, t}$

$$\cos\delta \sin t = \sin z \sin A$$
$$\sin\delta = \sin\phi \cos z - \cos\phi \sin z \cos A$$
$$\cos\delta \cos t = \cos\phi \cos z + \sin\phi \sin z \cos A$$

Numerical example:

Sunrise for Göttingen ($\phi = +51^0 30'$, $\tan\phi = +1.26$)

Hour angle at sunrise = semi-diurnal arc = t_o

At sunrise $h = 0$ or $z = 90^0$;

then, from the middle equation of the first system it follows that

$$\cos t_o = -\tan\phi \tan\delta$$

Longest day:

$\delta = +23^0 30'$, $\tan\delta = +0.43$ and from this

$$\cos t_o = -0.54$$

$$t_o = 180^0 - 57^0 = 123^0 = 8^h 12^m$$

Sunrise: $12^h - 8^h 12^m$ = <u>3:48 a.m. local time</u>

Shortest day:

$\delta = -23^0 30'$, $t_o = +57^0 = 3^h 48^m$

Sunrise: $12^h - 3^h 48^m$ = <u>8:12 a.m. local time</u>

§ 2 Time (basic concepts)

A) Sidereal time θ = hour angle of vernal equinox ♈ (defined by the equatorial system; § 1.2)

Sidereal day = time between two meridian passages of ♈
= 24 sidereal hours

Because of precession, $0^s.0084$ shorter than the actual rotation time of the earth.

Sidereal time unsuitable for civil use, because the sun moves (apparently) and therefore $\theta = 0$ takes place during the various times of day.

B) Apparent solar time = actual hour angle of the sun $+12^h$ (to let the day begin at night)

Non-uniform measure of time, because

1) velocity of the sun variable
2) sun is moving on the ecliptic, hence inclined with respect to the equator of the earth.

C) Mean solar time

One defines a "mean sun", which moves with constant period of rotation and with constant velocity on the equator.

Difference: **apparent - mean time = equation of time**

(earlier: opposite sign!)

a) Period of a whole year because of changing velocity

summer = 186 days } northern
winter = 179 days } hemisphere

b) Period of half a year because of the effect of projection on the equator:

if $a = b$, then $a' < b'$

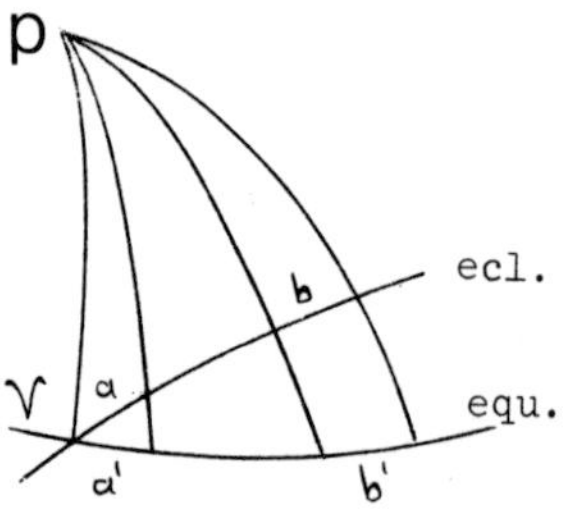

The periods are superposed on one another:

Maxima:	$+ 3^m.8$	approx.	May 14	Dates ± a few days because of leap years
	+16.4		November 3	
Minima:	-14.4		February 12	
	- 6.4		July 26	

Plot of equation of time

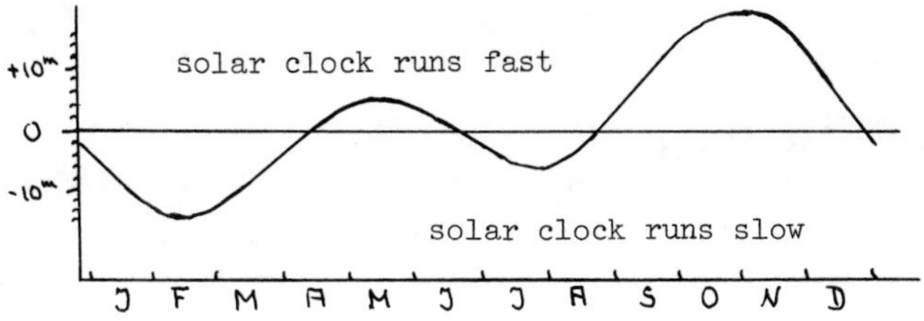

The sun appears to move among the stars from west to east as the earth revolves around it; hence after a single true (sidereal) rotation of the earth the sun is retarded and <u>not yet</u> on the meridian.
Only after 4^m is the sun, too, on the meridian.

⟹ **solar day > sidereal day**

24^h solar time = $24^h\ 03^m\ 56^s.555$ sidereal time

24^h sidereal time = 23 56 04.091 solar time

> During the year the sun revolves once;
> hence 365 solar days = 366 sidereal days

Every terrestrial longitude has its own specific solar time.

D) <u>Zone Time</u> (= Standard Time)

By agreement, same civil time for strips of (in general) 15^0 longitude,

e.g., $l = 0^0$ (Greenwich) G.M.T. (Greenwich Mean Time = Western European Time)
$= 75^0$ W (New York) E.S.T. (Eastern Standard Time)
$= 90^0$ W (Chicago) C.S.T. (Central Standard Time)

> Ann Arbor, Mich. (E.S.T.-zone): $l = 83^0\ 45'$ W,
> hence meridian passage of sun 35^m after noon E.S.T.
>
> Including equation of time:
>
> February: meridian passage $12^h 50^m$ (long afternoons)
>
> November: " " 12 20

For convenience some countries and most states of the USA have also introduced "Daylight Savings Time", i.e., set clocks one hour ahead of zone time for the summer months.

At $l = 180^0$ International Date Line

crossing toward east: one day counted twice
crossing toward west: one day omitted

E) <u>Universal Time</u> = <u>UT</u> = <u>Greenwich Time</u>

For timing of astronomical events (see § 10)

F) Year = period of apparent revolution of the sun

1) Tropical year: revolution from vernal equinox to vernal equinox = $365^d5^h48^m46^s$ = $365^d.24220$ mean solar days

The tropical year determines the seasons; the calendar should be adapted to it.

In order to be independent of the place of observation, the beginning of the tropical year is by definition when $\alpha_\odot = 280^0 = 18^h40^m$ (e.g., 1972 Jan. 1: $6^h2^m53^s$ UT).

2) Sidereal year: revolution from fixed star to fixed star

about 20 min longer, because the first point of Aries moves on the sky (see § 7) = $365^d6^h9^m10^s$ = $365^d.25636$.

3) Anomalistic year: revolution from perihelion to perihelion

(The position of the orbital ellipse of the earth is not fixed in space, see 2.2) = $365^d6^h13^m53^s$ = $365^d.25946$.

4) Julian year (established by Julius Caesar in 46 B.C.) = 356^d6^h = $365^d.2500$ (leap year every four years)

11 min longer than the tropical year: in the 16th century already an error of 10 days. Pope Gregory XIII, therefore, ordained that October 4th, 1582, should be followed by October 15th, 1582.

5) Gregorian year since 1582 = $365^d5^h49^m12^s$ = $365^d.2425$ = $365 + \frac{1}{4} - \frac{3}{400}$

(years ending with 00 are not leap-years, unless divisible by 400, e.g., the year 2000).

Still 26^s too long (3 units in the 7th decimal place); that is, one day in 3300 years.

G) Calendar:

Units : days, months, years.

Problem : the tropical year is not an integral multiple of the day

Nomadic people of the Orient: purely lunar calendar year = 12 synodic months (from new moon to new moon)
The beginning of the year shifts 11 to 12 days every year.

Egypt: solar year

Jewish, ancient Greek and Roman Calendar: Combination, so-called luni-solar year: adjustment by means of leap months

e.g., Metonic: 19-year cycle
12 years with 12 months
7 years with 13 months

At present : purely solar calendar: months only historical
no connection with lunar orbit
= Gregorian calendar (see above).

Planned reform: same weekday on same date.
Last day of the year and - in leap years - a day in the middle of the year will be weekdays without a name or date.

No astronomical reform; length of the year remains the same.

Julian Days = consecutive numbering of days

Zero point: January 1, 4713 B.C.

e.g., Jan. 1, 1968, 0^h UT = JD 2439856.5

Jan. 1, 1974, 0^h UT = JD 2442048.5

(The Julian Days begin at noon, in order to have no change of date at night).

Peculiarity of the historical chronology:

⟹ There is no year 0.

In astronomy years B.C. are counted as negative; then, because of the mathematics, a year "zero" must exist.

Astr.		Hist.	
Year 0	=	1 B.C.	e.g., the two-thousandth anniversary
-1	=	2 B.C.	of the death of Caesar
-n	=	(n+1) B.C.	(44 B.C. = -43) was 1957, not 1956.

Easter = Sunday after the first full moon in spring. Exact calculation complicated. Previously, considerable discrepancies between the Greek Orthodox and Roman Catholic Church. Today use simplified lunar theory (Gauss' rule); the results only seldom deviate from the strict rule. Extremes: March 22 and April 25

§ 3 Stellar positions (measurement of coordinates)

3.1 *Designations*

a) 88 Constellations (list in all reference books; see preface)
Northern hemisphere mostly by Ptolemy (from mythology)
Southern hemisphere mostly by navigators
In astronomy: Latin names, three-letter abbreviations

Zodiac (belt 18^0 wide centered on ecliptic) includes:

Ram	Aries	Ari	Scales	Libra	Lib
Bull	Taurus	Tau	Scorpion	Scorpius	Sco
Twins	Gemini	Gem	Archer	Sagittarius	Sgr
Crab	Cancer	Cnc	Goat	Capricornus	Cap
Lion	Leo	Leo	Watercarrier	Aquarius	Aqr
Virgin	Virgo	Vir	Fish	Pisces	Psc

b) Stars: some named (most Arabic), e.g., Vega

J. Bayer (*Uranometria*, 1603): Greek letter + constellation

e.g., Sirius = α CMa
Vega = α Lyr
Rigel = β Ori

Schurig-Götz, *Tabulae Caelestes*;
new edition by K. Schaifers 1960
Bibliographisches Institut, Mannheim

Norton A.P. 1966, *Star Atlas and Reference Handbook*;
Sky Publishing Co., Cambridge, Mass.

Faint stars: numbers from a catalogue
or specification of accurate coordinates (see § 8)

3.2 *Meridian circle* (Olaf Roemer 1689)

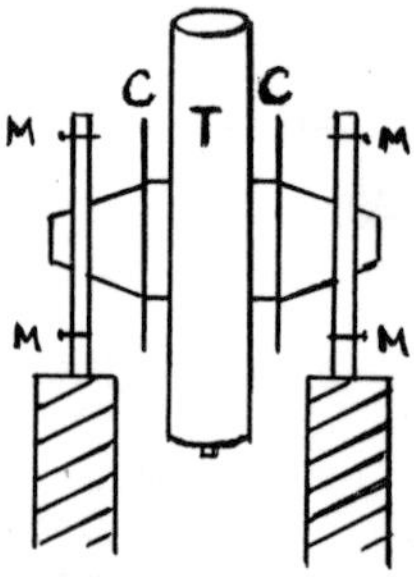

T telescope

horizontal E-W axis

M microscopes

C graduated circles

Telescope moves along the meridian.
It can be lifted out of its mounting
and reversed.

At the transit (i.e., meridian passage) of the star, measure:

a) zenith distance z (circles) $\pm 0\overset{''}{.}05$
b) clock-time of transit T $\pm 0\overset{s}{.}005$
→ precision in the case of numerous observations.

(Eye-ear method; telegraph-type signal;
impersonal micrometer; photoelectrically recorded).

Mounting errors

1) Inclination errors (axis not horizontal)
correction: spirit levels

2) Azimuthal errors (axis not east-west) correction: stars near the pole at upper and lower culmination

Instrumental errors

3) Collimation errors (optical axis not perpendicular to the rotation axis)
correction: stars near the pole at two positions

4) Graduation errors of the circle
correction: 8 microscope readings

5) Eccentricity error (point of rotation not in center)
correction: readings at two diametrically opposed points

6) Zenith-point error (zero-point of circle erroneous)
correction: mirror image in mercury horizon

Errors 1) to 3) influence mainly the measurement of time
4) to 6) influence mainly the zenith distance

3.3 *Relative positions*

Get positions with respect to stars whose coordinates are accurately known (so-called fundamental or time stars)
Then, we have

$$\Delta\delta = \Delta z \qquad \Delta\alpha = \Delta T$$

Determination of relative positions on photographic plates: conversion of rectangular coordinates x, y on the plate to spherical coordinates (central projection). To determine the scale (expansion), the orientation (rotation) and the zero point (translation) one needs at least six constants, hence three "reference stars" with known coordinates:

$$\Delta x = ax + by + c \qquad \Delta y = a'x + b'y + c'$$

If possible, one uses more reference stars and determines the constants by a least squares solution.

3.4 *Absolute positions*

Assume knowledge of the:

altitude of the pole (= terrest. latitude) ϕ

obliquity of the ecliptic ε

clock error (clock correction) ΔT

// Altitude of the pole ϕ follows from upper and lower culmination of the same star:

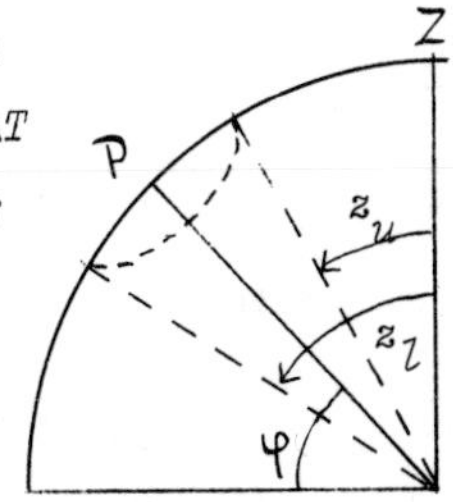

$$\tfrac{1}{2}(z_u + z_l) = 90^0 - \phi$$
$$\phi = 90^0 - \tfrac{1}{2}(z_u + z_l)$$

// Obliquity of the ecliptic
= declination of the sun at the furthest point from equator:
$\varepsilon = (\delta_\odot)_{max} = \phi - (z_\odot)_{min}.$

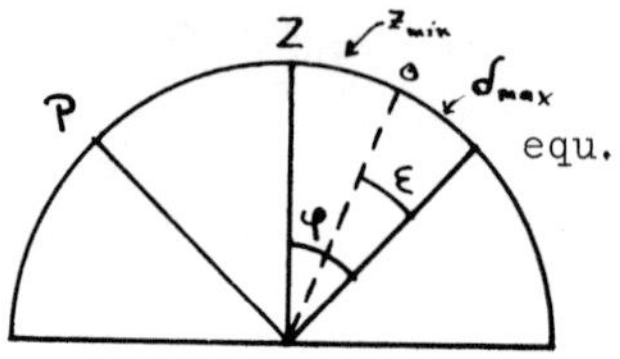

// Calibration of the clock:
From the rectangular spherical triangle (Napier's rule):

$$\sin\alpha_\odot = \frac{\tan\delta_\odot}{\tan\varepsilon}$$

and from this get $\alpha_\odot$.

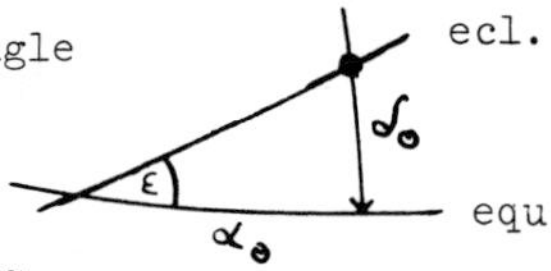

At the meridian passage of the sun we have:

$\alpha_\odot = \theta = T_\odot + \Delta T$ θ = sidereal time (see § 1.2)

hence $\Delta T = \alpha_\odot - T_\odot$ $T_\odot$ = time as read off from the clock (affected by error)

ΔT = error of the clock

a) Absolute declination:

For stars south of the zenith: $\delta = \phi - z$

For stars north of the zenith: $\delta = \phi + z$

b) Absolute right ascension:

From the clock reading and the known clock correction at meridian passage: $\alpha_* = T_* + \Delta T$

For other astrometric instruments see § 10.1

Up to now it has been assumed that nothing "happens" to the light. Motion of the earth and influence of the atmosphere of the earth have been neglected.
In practice one must take into account:

Refraction	(bending of radiation in the atmosphere)	§4
Aberration	(influence of the motion of the earth)	§5
Parallax	(change in position of observer)	§6
Precession	(top-like motion of the earth's axis)	§7
Nutation	(superposed variations in the direction of the earth's axis)	

§ 4 Refraction

= bending of radiation in the earth's atmosphere.

Plane atmosphere

Snell's law of refraction

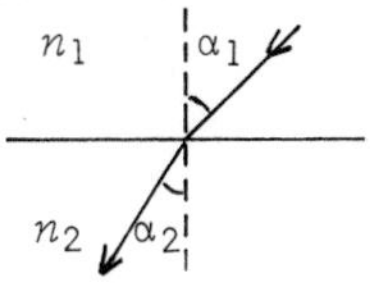

$$\frac{\sin \alpha_1}{\sin \alpha_2} = \frac{n_2}{n_1} \text{ or } n_i \sin \alpha_i = \text{const.}$$

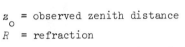

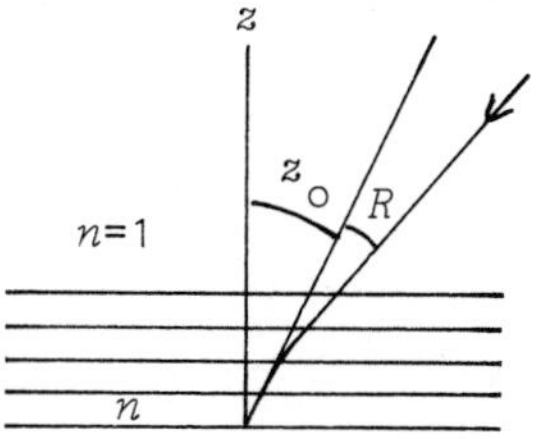

z_o = observed zenith distance

R = refraction

$z = z_o + R$ = true zenith distance

From the law of refraction: $\sin(z_o + R) = n \sin z_o$

Additional theorem: $\sin z_o \underbrace{\cos R}_{\approx 1} + \cos z_o \underbrace{\sin R}_{\approx R} = n \sin z_o$

R small, hence:

and: $$\boxed{R = (n - 1) \tan z_o}$$

Since density of atmosphere increases downward, radiation will be bent downward. Hence apparent altitudes exceed true altitudes.
At large z, R is no longer small; in addition the curvature of the earth's atmosphere must be taken into account.

Note: In order to compute R, one does not need to know along the whole path, but only the value at the earth's surface!

At 0° C and 760 mm pressure: $(n - 1) = 0.000293$

This happens to correspond to 1', hence: $R\,[']= \tan z_o$.

z	R
10°	10."6
45	1'
85	10'
90	35'

n, hence R, increases with increasing density of the air, hence with decreasing temperature and with increasing pressure.
(use refraction tables)

Anomalous refraction: surfaces of equal density (n = const.) inclined or bent

a) Azimuthal refraction (lateral displacement)
b) Zenith refraction
c) Room refraction (refraction at the slit of the dome)
d) Scintillation (rapid changes in refraction due to turbulence, etc.)

One differentiates between: scintillation in direction,
scintillation in brightness.

The scintillation in direction (disturbance of the air or "seeing") plays an important role in the selection of sites for new observatories.
The lowest atmospheric layers have great influence.

Atmospheric Dispersion:

the index of refraction increases with decreasing wave length:

image of a star ⟶ small spectrum

blue toward zenith
red toward horizon.

§ 5 A b e r r a t i o n

Combined effect of the velocity of the arriving light signal and the motion of the observer.

The light appears to come from a different direction; the telescope must be inclined by an angle α toward the direction of the motion.

For $v \perp c$ and $v \ll c$,

we have
$$\boxed{\alpha = \frac{v}{c}}$$

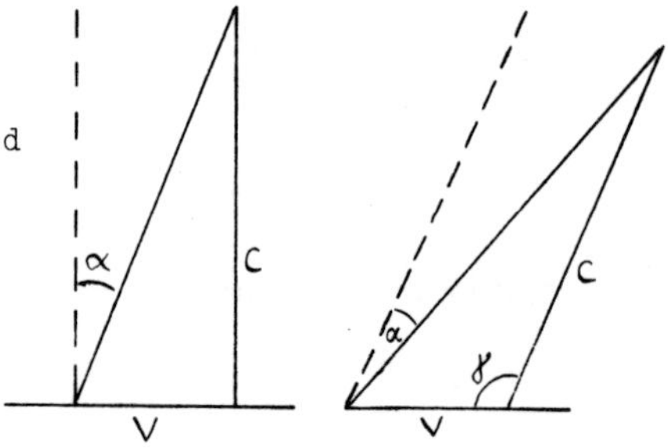

// If v is not perpendicular to c,
we have $\alpha = \frac{v}{c} \sin \gamma$, where γ = angle between v and c.

// If v is not small with respect to c, the equations of the special theory of relativity have to be used.

Note: the derivation often given in text-books for which the time which the light needs to travel through the telescope is related to the motion of the telescope during the same time, is erroneous.
According to it a different angle would result in the case of a tube filled with water. The telescope, on the contrary, must stand perpendicular to the arriving wave front.

Mechanical analogy to aberration:
The rain drops, which in a moving car apparently fall slanting from the front and run downward inclined along the window.

1) Annual aberration (motion of the earth around the sun)

$$\alpha = \frac{v}{c} \sin \gamma \qquad \left. \begin{array}{l} c = 300\,000 \text{ km/sec} \\ v = 30 \text{ "} \end{array} \right\} v/c = 10^{-4}$$

γ = angle between v and c

Measured in "arc: $$\alpha^{['']} = \frac{10^{-4}}{\sin 1''} \sin\gamma = k \sin\gamma$$

$k = 20''.47$ = constant of aberration
(large in comparison to the precision of the determination of stellar positions!)

For a star of celestial latitude β,
γ varies during a year between β and 90^0.

Hence, the star describes an ellipse with

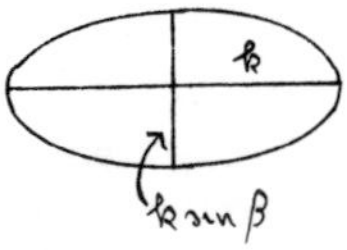

- semimajor axis k
- semiminor axis $k \sin\beta$

At the pole of the ecliptic: circle with a radius k

On the ecliptic : straight line of length $2k$

2) Diurnal aberration (rotation of the earth)

$V = V_{\text{equator}} \cos\phi$, $V_{\text{equ.}} = 465$ m/sec } Constant of diurnal aberration $= 0''.32 \cos\phi$

At culmination the star is displaced eastwards by $0^s.021 \cos\phi \sec\delta$, i.e., crosses the meridian late.

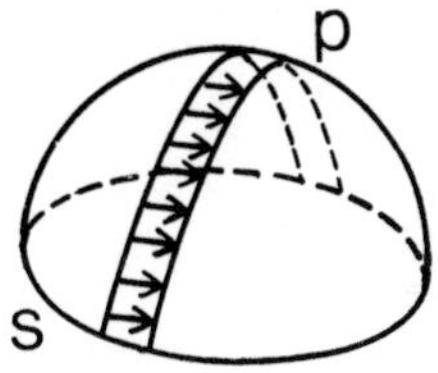

Note: on the meridian all stars are displaced by the same amount as measured in arc. The difference as measured in time results from the singularity at the pole.

3) Secular aberration (motion of the sun)

Motion (in historical times) uniform;
aberration therefore constant, not accessible to observation

⟹ constant displacement of stellar positions

Because of galactic rotation, extragalactic systems at the pole of the Milky Way describe an aberrational circle of a little more than 2' in about 10^8 years.

§ 6 Parallax

= change of coordinates by displacement of the origin of the coordinates

1) Diurnal parallax (topocentric → geocentric)

The zenith distance of a star can be measured as

z = zenith distance at the place (on earth) of observer
or z_0 = zenith distance at the center of the earth.

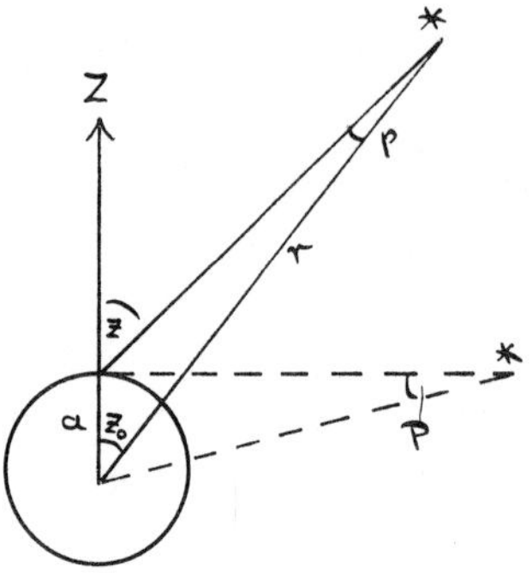

Parallax $p = z - z_o$

$$\sin p = \frac{a}{r} \sin z$$

where: a = radius of the earth
r = distance to star

Maximum at $z = 90^0$
(i.e., star on horizon)

→ P = horizontal parallax

= angular radius of the earth as seen from the star

$$\boxed{\sin P = \frac{a}{r}}$$ from this, distance r

More precisely: equatorial horizontal parallax: $\sin P = \frac{a_{equ}}{r}$

Moon: (average value) = $57'02''.45$ (nearly 2 full-moon diameters)

In 150 A.D. Ptolemy found $P = 58'.3$.

Sun: $P = 8''.79$; from this, $r = 149.6 \times 10^6$ km

Solar parallax not directly observable. Trigonometric determination from the observation of asteroids which approach the earth very closely (Eros, Amor).
If one distance is known in the solar system, all others can be determined easily by means of Kepler's third law (see 2.2.2).

Modern determinations: by radar echoes from Venus

Stars: diurnal parallax imperceptibly small

2) Annual parallax (geocentric → heliocentric)

Displacement of the stars because of the motion of the earth around the sun

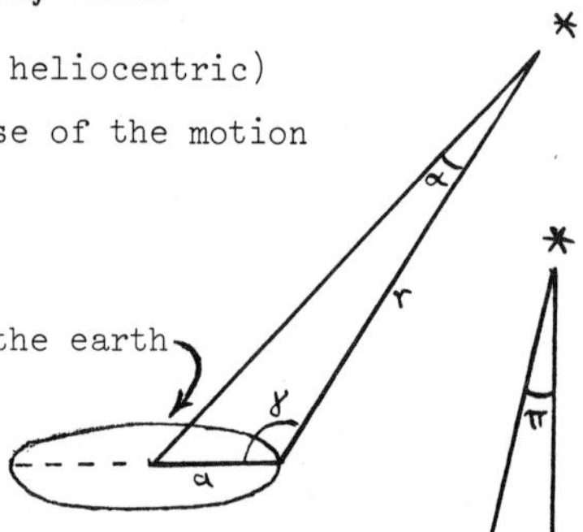

$$\sin \alpha = \frac{a}{r} \sin \gamma$$

a = radius of the orbit of the earth

r = distance

γ varies during a year between the celestial latitude β of the star and $180^0 - \beta$

i.e., stars describe ellipses with semiaxes π and $\pi \sin \beta$,

where π = parallax of the star

= maximum value of α (for $\gamma = 90^0$)

= angular radius of the orbit of the earth as seen from the star

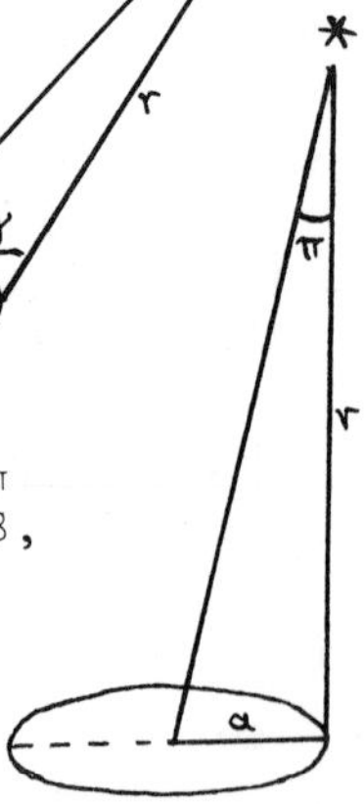

$$\boxed{\sin \pi = \frac{a}{r}}$$ (analogous to the horizontal parallax P)

A parallax π = 1" corresponds to a distance: 206 265 radii of the earth's orbit
= 30.8×10^{12} km = 3.26 light years

This distance serves as a unit in astronomy = 1 parsec = 1 pc

1 kpc = 1000 pc
1 Mpc = 1 000 000 pc

A parallax of 0".1 corresponds to a distance of 10 pc etc.

In general:

$$\pi'' = \frac{1}{r\ [pc]}$$

Measurement of the annual parallax thus means trigonometric determination of distance. The measurement generally is not absolute, but is made relative to faint background stars.

Maximum: Proxima Centauri: π = 0".762; = 1.3 pc

Limit of measurement : ≈ 0".01, e.g., 100 pc
≈ 300 light years
(several hundred stars)

Distance determination by non-trigonometric methods are often also called parallaxes;
(e.g., spectroscopic parallax, dynamical parallax; see 9.2).

Note: The aberration– and the parallax ellipses are shifted in phase to one another by 90°. Moreover, the aberration ellipse is independent of distance whereas the parallax ellipse is dependent on the distance.

3) Secular parallax

The sun is moving - relative to the system of nearby stars - with a velocity of about 20 km/sec in the direction of the constellation Hercules (see 9.4.2). This causes an apparent motion of the stars in the opposite direction. Because this effect cannot be separated from the proper motion of the stars, only mean parallaxes for large groups of stars can be determined (statistical parallaxes: see 2.2.1).

§ 7 Precession and nutation

Up to now assumed: coordinate system fixed in space

i.e., a) axis of the earth (and celestial poles) fixed in space

b) orbit of the earth (ecliptic) fixed in space

This is not the case; the earth is a spinning top, which is exposed to external forces (sun, moon, planets).

1) Luni-solar precession

Attraction by sun and moon on the equatorial bulge of the earth
⟹ torque, which tends to shift the axis of the earth

Consequence: Axis of the earth describes a cone,
with a semiangle of $23^\circ.5$,
around the pole of the ecliptic.
The vernal equinox moves westward
of the ecliptic i.e.,
opposite to the annual motion of the sun
(discovered by Hipparchus, 130 B.C.).

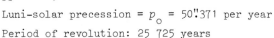

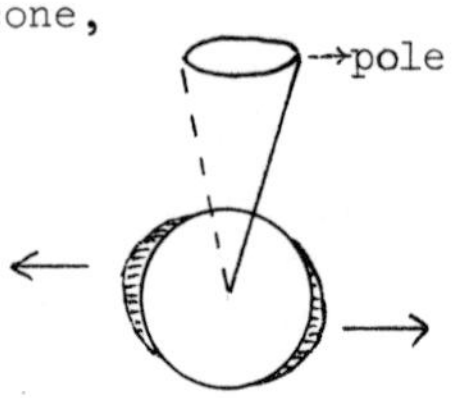

Luni-solar precession = p_o = $50''.371$ per year

Period of revolution: 25 725 years

> In about 12000 years Vega will be the pole star. Since time of Hipparchus motion of about 30^0 i.e., approximately one constellation. The zodiac sign Aries and the vernal equinox are no longer in the constellation of Aries, but now in the constellation Pisces.

2) <u>Planetary precession</u>

Because of perturbing forces by the planets the orbit of the earth in space is shifting,
i.e., the pole of the ecliptic is moving (very much slower).

Consequences: a) eastward shifting of the vernal equinox
planetary precession = p_{pl} = $0''.125$ per year

b) change of the obliquity of the ecliptic;
at present decreases by $0''.47$ annually.

3) <u>General precession</u>

Combined influence of sun, moon and planets

Let:

$(Equ)_o$ = equator at the beginning of the year

Equ = equator at the end of the year

E_o = ecliptic " " beg. " " "

E = " " " end " " "

V_o = vern. equinox beg. " " "

V = " " end " " "

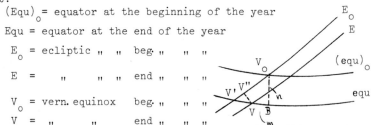

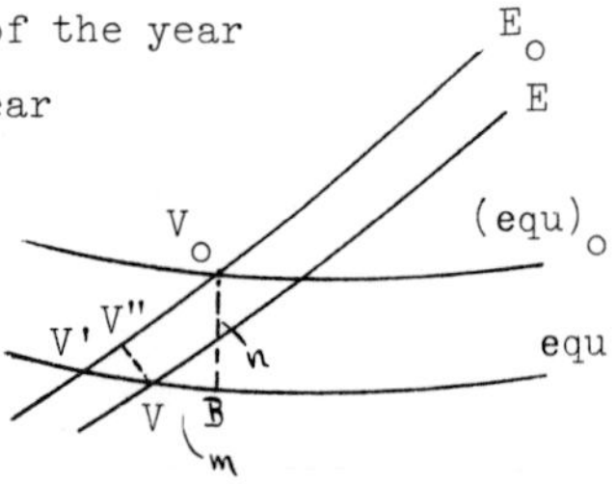

then:

p_o $=V_oV'$=luni-solar precession (equator moves on ecliptic)

$p_{pl}$$=V'V$ = planetary precession (ecliptic moves on equator)

$p \;=V_oV'' = p_o - p_{pl} \cos \varepsilon_o$ = $50''.256$ per year
= <u>general precession in longitude</u>

Since 1900 approximately $0^\circ.7$

Further, from the figure, (because all quantities are small, the triangles can be considered as plane)

General precession in declination:

$$n = V_oB = p_o \sin \varepsilon_o = 20''.047 \text{ per year}$$

General precession in right ascension:

$$m = BV = p_o \cos \varepsilon_o - p_{pl} = 46''.085 \text{ per year}$$
$$= 3^s.0723 \text{ per year}$$

Then, the general precession in longitude becomes:

$$p = m \cos \varepsilon + n \sin \varepsilon_o .$$

Then, from elementary geometric considerations, the change in the coordinates α, δ of a star because of precession is:

$$\Delta\alpha = m + n \tan \delta \sin \alpha$$
$$\Delta\delta = n \cos\alpha$$

When giving coordinates it must be stated to which "equinox" they are referred. There is some confusion about the term "epoch".
Epoch is often used for any fixed or well-defined time or, sometimes, interval of time. In star catalogues it is defined as the time at which the observation was made.

"Equinox" can be 1) first point of Aries, vernal equinox

or 2) the coordinate system to which the observations (made at some epoch) are referred. This coordinate system is fixed by a time, called the "equinox" because the position of the vern. equ. changes with time.

Secular variations:

All quantities given are in themselves time-dependent.
At present, the following values are valid:

General precession in longitude:

$$p = 50''.2564 + 0''.0222\, T \quad \text{per year}$$

Obliquity of the ecliptic:

$$\varepsilon = 23^o27'08''.26 - 46''.84\, T$$

T = time in tropical centuries from 1900

The position of the celestial pole corrected only for the precession is called the "mean pole".

4) <u>Nutation</u> = superposed periodic oscillations of the pole

Main term: caused by the motion of the nodes of the lunar orbit

Nodes = the 2 points where lunar orbit cuts the ecliptic

i = inclination of orbital plane

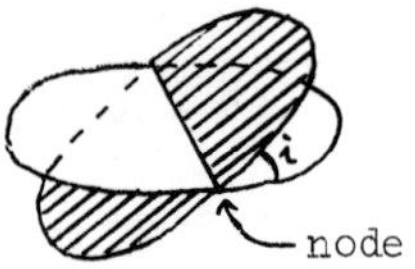

Lunar orbit inclined by 5^0 to the ecliptic
Sun tends to shift the lunar orbit,
lunar orbit reacts like a spinning top.

Consequence:

The pole of the lunar orbit describes a circle with a radius of 5^0 around the pole of the ecliptic.

The line of nodes regresses westward; period 18.6 years

Consequence of this:

Periodic change in the direction of the perturbation by the moon

Consequence of this:

The true celestial pole describes a nutation ellipse around the mean pole:

major axis 9.″21 = constant of nutation N

minor axis 6.″86

Because the mean pole moves as a result of the precession, the true pole describes a wavy line on the celestial sphere.

Nutation changes the position of the vernal equinox and the obliquity of the ecliptic. Therefore, have:

nutation in longitude $d\lambda = -17.''24 \sin \Omega$

nutation in obliquity $d\varepsilon = 9.''21 \cos \Omega$

Ω = longitude of the moon's node (see 2.2.1)

= distance of the moon's ascending node from the vernal equinox

Second-order terms:

All further periodic perturbations in the position of the vernal equinox and the obliquity of the ecliptic (e.g., on account of the position of the sun on the ecliptic) are smaller by several orders of magnitude.

5) <u>Problems with regard to precession</u> (determination of the numerical values)

a) Planetary precession:
known accurately enough by celestial mechanics

b) Luni-solar precession:
cannot be calculated exactly, because the distribution of mass in the interior of the earth is not known accurately. Here, there is a new possible solution by determination of orbits of artificial satellites.

Up to now: empirical determination from change of coordinates of the stars

Problem: stars are moving. To determinate their motion, we need an accurate system of coordinates, and to get this we need the precession

successive approximations: e.g., assume random distribution of stellar motions

Goal: establishing an inertial system connected to extragalactic objects

Remark:

Astronomy: precession = long-period change
nutation = short-period changes

Physics: precession = regular motion of the axis of moment of inertia
nutation = oscillation of the force-free top (e.g., difference between the geometrical axis and the instantaneous axis of rotation; in the case of the earth about 10 m)

Astronomical nutation is physically a forced oscillation.

§ 8 Astronomical constants

The numerous astronomical constants mentioned in the previous sections and determined by various methods are not independent of each other.

Hence, one distinguishes:

a) Fundamental (mutually independent) constants:

Velocity of light $c = 2.9979250 \times 10^{10}$ cm sec^{-1}

equatorial radius of the earth
$R = 6.378\ 165 \times 10^{8}$ cm

astronomical unit $AU = 1.49\ 598 \times 10^{13}$ cm

geocentric gravitational constant
(E = earth's mass in gm) $GE = 3.98\ 603\ 361 \times 10^{20}$ cm^3 sec^{-2}

ratio of the mass of the moon
to the mass of the earth $\mu = 1/81.30$

general precession in longitude
$p = 5025''.640$ per century (for 1900)

constant of nutation $N = 9''.210$ (for 1900).

Numerical values are from Landolt-Börnstein:
Numerical Data and Functional Relationships in Science and Technology. New Series, 1965, Group 6:
Astronomy, Astrophysics and Space Science, Sections 2, 3, 4.
ed. H.H. Voigt, Springer Verlag, Berlin, Heidelberg, New York

See also Allen, C.W. 1960,
Astrophysical Quantities, The Athlone Press, 2nd ed., London.

b) Derived constants

All other constants . . .

Parallax of the sun; light time of the astronomical unit; constant of aberration; heliocentric gravitational constant; sun/earth mass ratio; moon-earth distance, and others
. . . are determined from the fundamental ones.

By changing them on the basis of new observations, without correspondingly correcting the system of fundamental constants, one obtains an internally contradictory system.

§ 9 Star catalogues

One defines:

1) Observed position, corrected for instrumental errors, refraction, daily aberration i.e., with respect to the center of the earth } apparent place

2) Apparent position corrected for annual aberration and parallax i.e., with respect to the center of the sun } true place

3) True position after applying the nutation and correcting for precession to a specified date (so-called equinox) } mean place

In catalogues mean places are given.
In comparison of two catalogues, take account of the precession between the equinoxes!

Historical catalogues

Ptolemy : "Almagest" 150 A.D. 1022 stars

Tycho Brahe: last catalogue
before invention of the telescope: 16th century
More than 700 carefully measured positions.

Modern catalogues of positions

1) Fundamental catalogues: to fix the inertial system
Precise absolute positions
(compiled from many observations)

Internal accuracy : $\Delta\delta \approx 0''.05$

$\Delta\alpha \approx 0^s.005 \sec\delta$

FK 4: Fourth Fundamental Catalogue, 1963 Heidelberg
Basis of the computation of ephemerides;
about 1500 positions of highest accuracy.
Equinox 1950.0 and 1975.0.

GC : General Catalogue, B. Boss
33 342 positions, not as accurate as FK 4.

2) Zone catalogues:

Accurate relative positions; connected to fundamental stars.

AGK 1: First catalogue of the Astronomische Gesellschaft 1863 and following, nearly 200 000 stars, various epochs and equinoxes

AGK 2: Repetition, 1928/32 epoch ~1930, equinox 1950.0

AGK 3: Repetition, 1956/63 epoch ~1950, equinox 1950.0
(only proper motions)

From comparison of the catalogues ⟹ proper motions

3) Survey catalogues:

many stars with moderate accuracy,
(complete to a certain mag.limit: in the cases below ≈ 9th mag.)

a) for statistical investigations
b) for the identification of stars

BD: Bonner Durchmusterung, epoch ~1855, equinox 1855.0
458 000 stars $+90^0$ to -23^0

CD or CoD: Cordoba Durchmusterung, epoch ~1875, equinox 1875.0
614 000 stars -22^0 to -90^0

BD and CD with charts

CPD: Cape Photographic Durchmusterung -18^0 to -90^0
455 000 stars epoch ~1890, equinox 1875.0

(Annals of the Cape Observatory vol. 3, 4, 5, 1896 - 1900)

HD: Henry Draper Catalogue, equinox 1900.0
223 000 stars
covering the whole sky, e.g., HD 54351 = BD + 15^0 1482

Annals of the Harvard College Observatory, vols. 91 to 99, Cambridge (Mass.) 1918 - 1924.

Star Charts:

National Geographic Society - Palomar Observatory Sky Survey:
1954, Pasadena, Calif.
Contact copies of the plates taken with the big Schmidt telescope on Palomar Mountain

879 fields (for each a blue and a red exposure),

plates 35.4 × 35.4 cm ($6\overset{\circ}{.}6 \times 6\overset{\circ}{.}6$)

Tabulae Caelestes: Bibl. Institut (Mannheim) Schurig-Götz, 1960, new edition by K. Schaifers

Atlas Coeli: A. Becvar 1958, Skalnate Pleso, Prague.

A.P. Norton '66, *Star Atlas and Reference Handbook*, Harvard College Observatory, Cambridge, Mass.: Sky Publishing Co.

Index of all important charts and catalogues: Landolt-Börnstein, New Series, Vol. VI/I *Astronomy and Astrophysics*.

§ 10 Determination of time and geographic position

10.1 *Instruments*

a) Meridian circle (see 1.3.2): for highest accuracy

b) Astrolabe:

Horizontal, rotatable telescope; in front of it a 60° prism with two semi-transparent sides

Star light divided; one image directly into the telescope, one via the mercury horizon *MH*

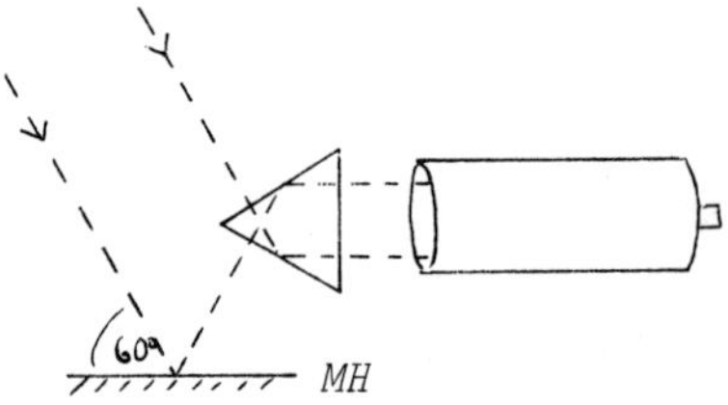

The stellar images meet in the ocular if $z = 30°$

Very accurate instrument.

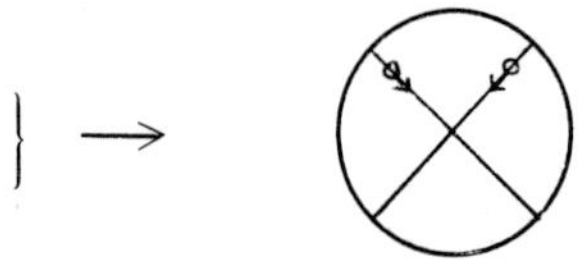

// Advantage over meridian circle: very stable, no flexure, etc.

// Disadvantage: only stars within limits of 60° in declination (30° north and 30° south of the zenith) can be reached.

Detailed description: A. Danjon 1960 in *Telescopes, Stars and Stellar Systems*, vol. I, p.115.

c) Universal theodolite: for use on expeditions.

Small, azimuthally mounted telescopes with graduated circles to read off zenith distance and azimuth.

d) Sextant: used at sea, to measure altitudes of stars

Horizon and stars (via two mirrors) are brought simultaneously into the field of view.

Necessary correction: dip of the horizon = D = angle between true and apparent horizon

$$D\ ['] \cong \sqrt{[H(ft)]}$$

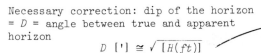

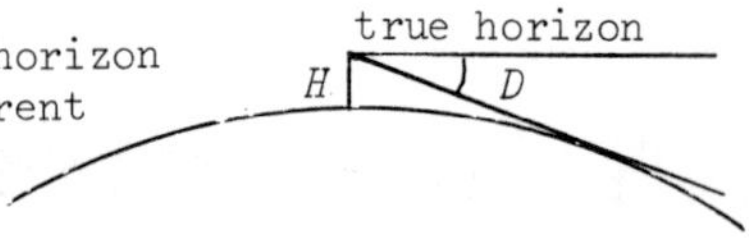

10.2) *The most important methods*

1) Determination of latitude (= altitude of the pole) ϕ:

Basic equation (see 1.3.4)

$\delta_1 = \phi - z_1$ for * south of zenith

$\delta_2 = \phi - z_2$ for * north of zenith

e.g., by altitude measurements on the meridian (= maximum altitude), at noon

Most exact: Horrebow-Talcott method

Two stars, which transit the zenith one closely after the other with about the same z, one north of the zenith, the other south of it.

Then:

$$\phi = \tfrac{1}{2}(\delta_1 + \delta_2) + \tfrac{1}{2}(z_1 - z_2)$$

Advantage: only small differences;
refraction and other uncertainties cancel out

Special instrument for doing this:
zenith tube (a vertical rotatable telescope)

With it measurements of the variation of latitude
discovered: 1888
by Küstner (Bonn) Maximum values: 0"7 = 10 m

Period of 1 year: meteorological origins; snow load, ice at the poles . . .

Period of 14 months: according to Euler from the theory of the rotation of a solid body. Period should be 10 months: longer because of elasticity of the earth.

2) Determination of time

With a meridian circle : $\theta = \alpha$

Without a meridian circle: from the equation of the nautical triangle (see 1.1.5)

$$\cos z = \sin\phi \;\sin\delta + \cos\phi \;\cos\delta \;\cos t$$

From this get t, and then $\theta = t + \alpha$

3) Determination of longitude

For two locations we have: $\Delta\lambda = \Delta\theta$

i.e., if local time is known for a specified meridian (e.g., Greenwich) the difference in longitude follows from the measured local time.

$$\lambda = \theta_{\mathrm{Greenwich}} - \theta$$

Today: Universal Time can always be obtained from radio broadcasts (e.g., for U.S.A., WWV; for Canada, CHU).

Previously: determination of longitude one of the most difficult problems
Solved by specifying "lunar distances" = distance of the moon from bright stars. From this, Universal Time (moon moves by its own diameter in 50 minutes); or by giving the time of the eclipses of Jovian satellites (see 2.9.1).

4) Method of position lines

Determination of ϕ and λ at a known time from zenith distances

// Principle: a special star (α, δ) is at a certain known time θ_G (= local sidereal time Greenwich) in the zenith of a specified place with the coordinates:

$$\lambda_z = \theta_G - \alpha; \qquad \phi_z = \delta$$

All positions, for which this star at this time has the zenith distance z, are situated on a circle around the zenith with the radius z = position circle

= position line

(portion of circle on which have any chance of being located is so small that can be replaced by straight line)

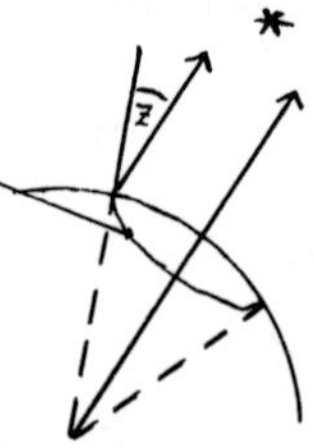

Two position lines follow from the observed z of two stars.

The place searched for = intersection of the position lines.

// In practice: assume an approximate place, estimated by "dead reckoning", ϕ_o, λ_o.

For this position the zenith distance z_{comp} is calculated for the time of observation.

$\Delta z = z_{comp} - z_{obs}$ = distance from the true position line (the position line is always perpendicular to the direction to the star).

$\Delta z < 0$, hence $z_{obs} > z_{comp}$: true position more distant than estimated position

$\Delta z > 0$, viz. $z_{obs} < z_{comp}$: true position nearer than estimated position

Intersection point of new position lines yields the true position ϕ, λ

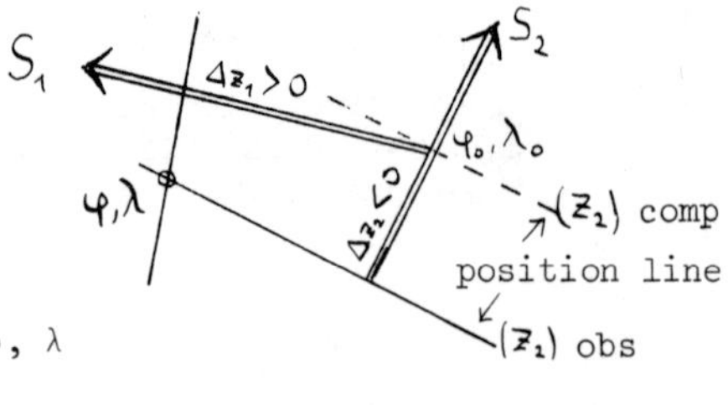

Aviation: prepared charts with position lines indicated for specified stellar latitudes for different stars and times. After measuring the altitudes, the position can be read off without further calculations.

5) Precise determination of time

Previously: time obtained from stellar observations, i.e., rotation of the earth as a measure of time (Changes and irregularities of the rate of rotation of the earth were not detectable by pendulum clocks)

Today : quartz clocks and atomic clocks; over short time intervals more accurate than the earth

Result : measurement of fluctuations in the rate of rotation of the earth

a) annual variation, amplitude ≈ 22 msec
meteorological origin

b) 6-month period, amplitude ≈ 10 msec
solar tidal forces

c) period of 13.8 and 27.6 days, very small amplitude
lunar tidal forces

The large amplitudes arise from cumulative effects.

The deviations in the length of a day itself are very small; extreme values (June, July) about - 0.6 msec.

Since one day = 86 400^s, this is an error of 10^{-8}

May : earth is slow by about 30 msec.

September: earth is fast by about 25 msec.

Secular change in the rotation rate of the earth

Theory : retardation by tidal friction

Observation: secular acceleration of the moon (see 2.7.1)

Sidereal time of revolution of the moon decreases by 8" (= 0.5 sec) per century.

Of this, 6" originates from the secular decrease of the eccentricity of the orbit of the earth.

The rest of 2" (observed analogously also for the planetary orbits) originates from change of the unit of time.

Direct evidence not yet available. It is estimated that the rate at which the day is lengthened by tidal friction is of the order of magnitude of one second per 100 000 years.

Change of the length of a day: The secular, periodic and

partially irregular variations of the rotation of the earth (the causes of which are partly still unexplained) imply - disregarding the annual variations - at present a decrease of the length of the day of $4.8 \cdot 10^{-8}$ sec between two consecutive days which amounts to a decrease in the length of the day of 0.0016 sec in 100 years

= decrease of the length of the day by $\approx 1^s$ in 60 000 years.

10.3 *Ephemeris time*

Changes in the rotation rate of the earth make a new definition necessary of a constant measure for the time (postulate for Newtonian mechanics)

Length of the astronomical second at the beginning of the 20th century was chosen.

Exact definition:

$$\text{Second of time} = \frac{1}{31\,556\,925.975} \text{ of the tropical year}$$

for 1900 January 0, 12^h Ephemeris Time

The time correction:

Ephemeris Time - mean solar time in 1970

amounts to approximately $+40^s$ (cumulative effect!)

The exact value of the correction can be determined only afterwards from accurate measurements of time.

Modern designations:

UT 0: Universal Time derived from astronomical determination of time, as defined in § 1.2.

UT 1: UT 0 corrected for the motion of the pole.

UT 2: UT 1 corrected for seasonal variations in the rate of rotation of the earth.

ET : = Ephemeris Time = UT 2 reduced to the ephemeris - second of time as defined above.

AT : = time as given by atomic clocks. Good approximation to Ephemeris Time.

THE SOLAR SYSTEM

§ 1 to 8: Problems of mechanics of the solar system

§ 9 : Physical properties of the members

The physics of the sun, which represents the prototype of a normal star, will be treated together with the physics of stars in Chapters 4 to 6.

References (for the mechanics of the solar system):

Brouwer, D. and Clemence, G.M. 1961, *Methods of Celestial Mechanics*, Academic Press, New York.

Danby, J.M.A. 1962, *Fundamentals of Celestial Mechanics*, Macmillan, New York.

Fitzpatrick, P.M. 1970, *Principles of Celestial Mechanics*, Academic Press, New York.

Kurth, R. 1959, *Introduction to the Mechanics of the Solar System*, (transl. A.H. Batten) Pergamon Press, New York.

McCuskey, S.W. 1963, *Introduction to Celestial Mechanics*, Addison-Wesley Publ. Co., Reading, Mass.

Moulton, F.R. 1914, *An Introduction to Celestial Mechanics*, Macmillan, New York, 2nd rev. ed.

§ 1 Summary

Solar system = large number of celestial objects which are bound together by the gravitation of the central star, i.e., the sun

1) Sun: radius $R_\odot$ = 696,000 km = 109 $R_♁$

mass $\mathcal{M}_\odot$ = 2 · 10^{33} g = 332,000 $\mathcal{M}_♁$

= 0.999 of the mass of the whole system

♁ = symbol for earth

Gravitational acceleration at the surface

$$g_\odot = 2.74 \cdot 10^4 \text{ cm sec}^{-2} = 28\, g_♁$$

Distance earth-sun = 1 astronomical unit = 1 A.U. = 149.6 × 10^6 km

2) Major planets: (see 2.9.1) Nine planets known.

Nearly circular orbits, almost in the ecliptic

Total mass = $448\,M_{♃} = \dfrac{M_{\odot}}{743}$

3) Asteroids (= minor planets, planetoids) (see 2.9.2)
Elliptical orbits, predominantly between Mars and Jupiter

4) Moons or satellites = companions of the planets (see 2.9.1)
32 known; mostly small relative to the planet

5) Comets (see 2.9.3)
Isotropically distributed, nearly parabolic ellipses:
"Cloud of comets" reaches far out beyond the system of planets

6) Interplanetary material

Meteorites: small members of the planetary system (see 2.9.4)

Zodiacal light: dust particles and electrons in the ecliptic (see 2.9.5)

Interplanetary gas, particles of the solar wind (see 2.9.5)

Summary of celestial mechanics data

<table>
<tr><th>Object</th><th>Dimensions</th><th>Shape of orbit</th><th>Position of orbit</th></tr>
<tr><td>Sun</td><td>10^6 km</td><td>–</td><td>–</td></tr>
<tr><td>Planets</td><td>$10^3 - 10^5$ km</td><td>nearly circular ellipses</td><td rowspan="3">concentrated to the ecliptic</td></tr>
<tr><td>Asteroids</td><td>$1 - 10^2$ km</td><td rowspan="2">ellipses</td></tr>
<tr><td>Short-period comets</td><td rowspan="2">(1)</td></tr>
<tr><td>Long-period comets</td><td>nearly parabolic ellipses</td><td>random</td></tr>
<tr><td>Meteors</td><td>$10^{-4} - 10$ mm</td><td>all kinds of conic sections</td><td>some random
some concentrated to ecliptic</td></tr>
<tr><td>Particles comprising the zodiacal light</td><td>dust: 10^{-2}mm
electrons</td><td>nearly circular</td><td>strongly concentrated to ecliptic</td></tr>
<tr><td>Solar wind</td><td>protons
electrons</td><td colspan="2">radially, outwards</td></tr>
</table>

(1) Nucleus: $1 - 10^2$km; coma: $10^4 - 10^5$km; tail: $10^6 - 10^8$km (see 2.9.3)

§ 2 Planetary orbits

In these paragraphs we start from Kepler's laws. In § 4 we give the derivation from the law of gravitation

Kepler's first law	Planetary orbits are ellipses with the sun at one focus.

2.1 *Definitions, orbital elements*

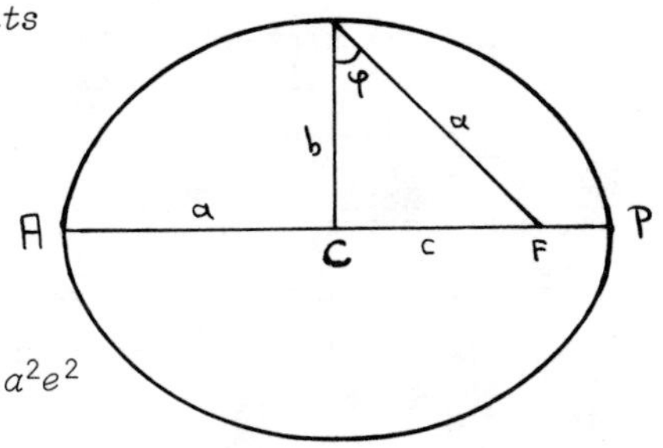

a = semimajor axis

b = semiminor axis

$c = \overline{FC}$ = center-to-focal-point distance

$e = \dfrac{c}{a} = \sin\phi$ = eccentricity

Then: $a^2 = b^2 + c^2 = b^2 + a^2e^2$

$b^2 = a^2(1 - e^2)$

P = perihelion distance of perihelion $= \overline{PF} = a - c = a(1 - e)$

A = aphelion distance of aphelion $= \overline{AF} = a + c = a(1 + e)$

$\overline{AP}$ = line of apsides

a) Shape of the ellipse: determined by two quantities,

usual in astronomy: **a and e**

b) Position of the orbital plane:

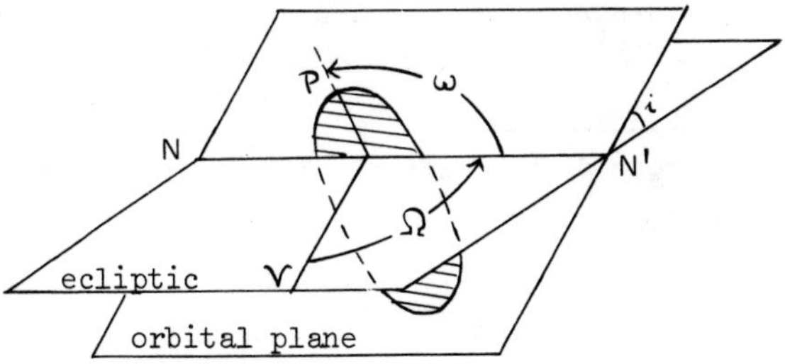

NN' = line of nodes = intersection with ecliptic

N = ascending node (planet moves northward)

N' = descending node

i = inclination of the orbit with respect to the ecliptic

Ω = longitude of the ascending node

= angular distance from vernal equinox ♈

Position of the orbit defined by: **Ω and i**

$i < 90^\circ$: orbit direct, i.e., counterclockwise as seen from the north, (as projected on the ecliptic: like the earth)

$i > 90^\circ$: orbit retrograde

c) Position of the ellipse with respect to the ecliptic

characterized by position of the perihelion

ω = argument of perihelion = angle in the orbital plane from line of nodes to perihelion point

$\boxed{\tilde{\omega}}$ = longitude of perihelion = ♈ FN + NFP = $\Omega + \omega$

Notice: angle composed of two angles in different planes

d) Position of the planet in the orbit

Orbital motion is determined by laws of motion (section 2.2)

therefore need to fix only a zero point in time

$\boxed{T}$ = time of passage of the planet through perihelion

The quantities in boxes above, sections a-d, are the

six orbital elements

Ω, i, $\tilde{\omega}$: position of the ellipse in space — dependent on the system of coordinates; change because precession; state equinox!

a, e: shape of the ellipse
T : position in time
} independent of the coordinate system

Remark: for nearly parabolic orbits $e = 1$ therefore only 5 orbital elements necessary

Numerical data

a: mean distance from the sun, see Table on p. 80

The law of Titius and Bode: $a = 0.4 + 0.3 \cdot 2^n$ yields for $n = -\infty, 0, 1, \ldots, 7$ to a good approximation (except for Neptune) the distances of the planets in astronomical units:

	n	a_{comp}	a_{obs}		n	a_{comp}	a_{obs}
Mercury	$-\infty$	0.4	0.39	Jupiter	4	5.2	5.20
Venus	0	0.7	0.72	Saturn	5	10.0	9.55
Earth	1	1.0	1.0	Uranus	6	19.6	19.20
Mars	2	1.6	1.52	Neptune			30.09
asteroids	3	2.8	2.9	Pluto	7	38.8	39.5

Recently even better laws of distances found, which take account of the mass.

The particular form of this law has no special meaning and can be easily replaced by even better ones. It only indicates that the distances roughly follow a geometric progression.

e: eccentricity: in most cases very small for planets

Earth: 0.0167, ϕ = 57' i.e., $b = a \cdot \cos\phi = 0.9998\,a$ i.e., semiminor axis smaller by 2×10^{-4} (≈ 0.2 mm for a circle with a radius of 1 m!) Difference in distance at perihelion and aphelion, however, 4% (sun at the focal point, not in the center)

More extreme cases:

Mercury:	e = 0.206	ϕ = 11°52'	b = 0.979a
Pluto:	0.248	14 23	0.969a

Distance at perihelion for Pluto 25% smaller than mean distance (perihelion 30 AU, aphelion 50 AU).
Orbit of Pluto "intersects" orbit of Neptune.

⟹ Planetary orbits, to a good approximation, are eccentric circles

i: orbital inclinations small, 0° to 3°

appreciable values only for	Mercury	i = 7°0
	Pluto	17.1

Ω, T, $\tilde{\omega}$: randomly distributed

The peculiarities mentioned ....

a) Series of Titius-Bode
b) nearly-circular orbits
c) concentration to the ecliptic

... are not caused by the laws of mechanics.
They can be explained only by a cosmogony of the solar system (see 2.9.6).

2.2 *Orbital motion of a planet*

a) Orbital coordinates

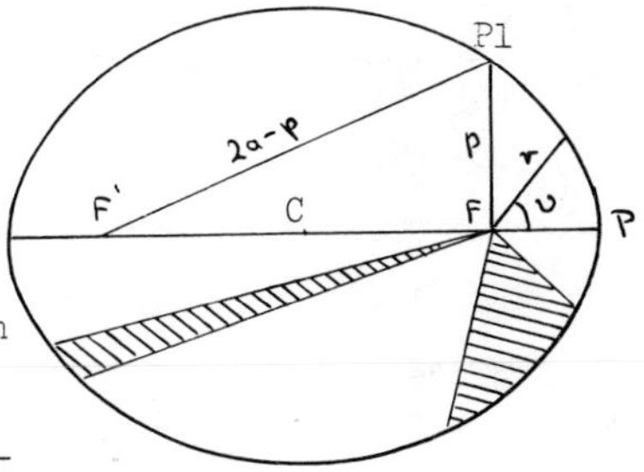

r = radius vector

ν = true anomaly

tied together by the equation of an ellipse:

$$r = \frac{p}{1 + e\cos\nu} = \frac{a(1-e^2)}{1 + e\cos\nu}$$

where p = semi latus rectum = ordinate at $F = a\,(1-e^2)$

(from the triangle F-Pl-F' and definition in section 2.1)

b) Velocity

Kepler's second law — Constant areal velocity

The radius vector sweeps out equal areas in equal times (figure)

Areal velocity
$= \text{area/period} = \frac{\pi\, ab}{P} = \frac{\pi\, a^2\sqrt{1-e^2}}{P}$
(according to 2.1)

c) Determination of position in the orbit (Kepler's Problem)

Orbital elements given

t = time since perihelion passage
A = total area
S = sector of ellipse, which is traversed, hence S known

$\frac{S}{A} = \frac{t}{P}$ (2nd Law of Kepler)

Problem: to determine the angle υ (true anomaly) from S

Construction:
Eccentric circle with $2a$ as a diameter

At each point the ratio of the ordinates of the ellipse to the ordinates of the circle is $\frac{b}{a}$

Pl = position of the planet

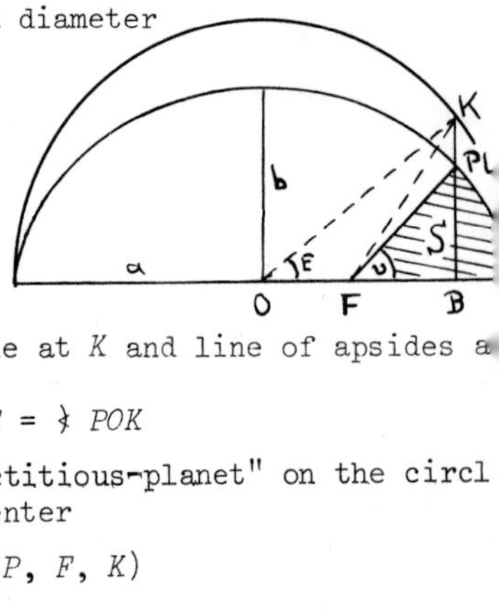

Ordinate at Pl intersects circle at K and line of apsides a

Definition: Eccentric anomaly $E = \measuredangle POK$
= anomaly of the "fictitious-planet" on the circl
as seen from the center

Sector S = Sector $P, F, Pl = \frac{b}{a}(P, F, K)$

This area (P, F, K)

= circle-sector (P, O, K) - triangle (F, O, K)

$= \frac{E}{2\pi}\pi a^2 - \frac{1}{2}a^2 e \sin E$

$= \frac{1}{2} a^2 (E - e \sin E)$

base line $c = ae$
height $= a \sin E$

hence:
$S = \frac{1}{2} ab\, (E-e \sin E)$

on the other hand, from Kepler's 2nd law:
$S = \frac{\pi\, abt}{P}$

$\rightarrow (E-e \sin E) = \frac{2\pi t}{P}$

<u>Definition</u>: <u>Mean anomaly</u> $M = \frac{2\pi}{P}\, t$

= angle, analogous to υ but which is increasing with constant speed from 0° to 360° during the period P

hence:

Kepler's Equation $\boxed{E - e \sin E = M}$ (I)

= transcendental equation; solution by iteration, graphically or by series

Further, we have (figure):

$$\overline{OB} = \overline{OF} + \overline{FB}$$

$$a \cos E = ae + r \cos \upsilon$$

and, moreover, the equation of the ellipse:

$$r = \frac{a(1-e^2)}{1+e \cos \upsilon}$$

Substitute, divide by a:

$$\cos E = e + \frac{(1-e^2) \cos \upsilon}{1+e \cos \upsilon} = \frac{e + \cos \upsilon}{1+e \cos \upsilon}$$

From this: $$1 - \cos E = \ldots = \frac{(1-e)(1-\cos \upsilon)}{1+e \cos \upsilon}$$

$$1 + \cos E = \ldots = \frac{(1+e)(1+\cos \upsilon)}{1+e \cos \upsilon}$$

Dividing: $$\tan^2\left(\frac{E}{2}\right) = \frac{1-e}{1+e} \tan^2\left(\frac{\upsilon}{2}\right) \qquad \left[\tan \alpha = \sqrt{\frac{1-\cos 2\alpha}{1+\cos 2\alpha}}\right.$$

or: $$\boxed{\tan\left(\frac{\upsilon}{2}\right) = \sqrt{\frac{1+e}{1-e}} \tan\left(\frac{E}{2}\right)} \qquad \text{(II)}$$

Finally, r:

From the equation of the ellipse, $re \cos \upsilon = a - ae^2 - r$

and the above equation: $re \cos \upsilon = ea \cos E - ae^2$

Thus, we have $\boxed{r = a(1-e \cos E)}$ (III)

<u>Summary</u>

The orbital elements are known, hence the period of revolution P and the time since the perihelion passage t,

consequently $M = \frac{r\pi}{P} \cdot t$ is known.

Hence, from (I) $\longrightarrow E$
from (II) $\longrightarrow \upsilon$
from (III) $\longrightarrow r$

r and υ are the heliocentric orbital coordinates in the plane of the orbit of the planet.

From this by transformation of coordinates:
$\longrightarrow$ heliocentric ecliptic coordinates
From this by translation of the origin:
$\longrightarrow$ geocentric coordinates (λ, β) or (α, δ).

so-called <u>ephemeris</u>

Ephemeris = calculation of geocentric coordinates from the orbital elements

<u>Relationship between period of revolution and semimajor axis</u>

Kepler's 3rd Law The cubes of the semimajor axes are proportional to the equares of the periods of revolution

$$\frac{a_1^3}{a_2^3} = \frac{P_1^2}{P_2^2} \; ; \quad \frac{a^3}{P^2} = \text{const}$$

as long as $(\text{mass})_{pl} \ll (\text{mass})_\odot$

Exact form (with $M_\odot = 1, M_{pl} = m$):

$$\frac{a_1^3}{a_2^3} = \frac{(1 + m_1)\, P_1^2}{(1 + m_2)\, P_2^2}$$

2.3 *Orbit of the earth*

Mean distance = 1 AU $a = 149.6 \cdot 10^6$ km
eccentricity $e = 0.0167$
minor axis $b = 0.9998a$

perihelion distance $a(1-e) = 147 \cdot 10^6$ km
aphelion distance $a(1+e) = 152 \cdot 10^6$ km
} $\Delta = 5 \cdot 10^6$ km (≈ 3.3 %)

time of perihelion (at present):
beginning of January, velocity = 30.3 km/sec

time of aphelion (at present):
beginning of July = 29.3 "
⟶ summer nearly 8 days longer

mean diurnal motion: $\mu = 59'08''.2 \approx 1^\circ$

sidereal period of revolution of the perihelion:
111,270 years (direct)

(anomalistic year 4.7 min longer than sidereal year; see 1.2

sidereal period of revolution of the first point of Aries
(precession): 25,800 years (retrograde)

(tropical year 20 min shorter than sidereal year)

tropical period of revolution of the perihelion:
20,900 years (direct)

Perihelion shifts (advances) relative to the seasons annually by a quarter of an hour in the sense that it occurs later each year.

About 700 years ago the time of perihelion coincided with the time of the (northern) winter solstice.

<u>Seasons</u>

Axis of the earth not perpendicular to the orbit of the earth; inclined by $23\overset{\circ}{.}5$ (= obliquity of the ecliptic)

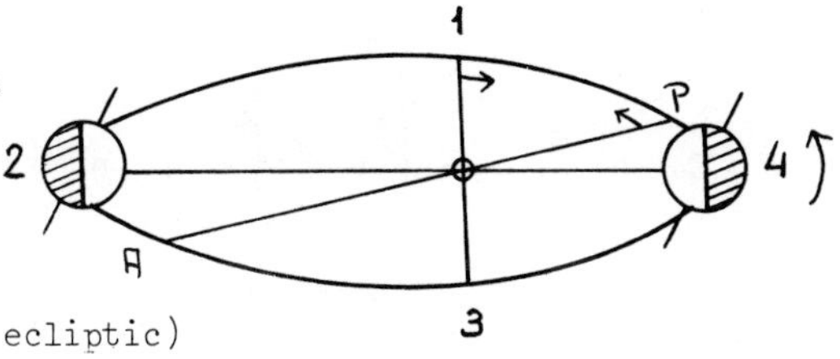

1) spring 2) summer 3) autumn 4) winter
= seasons for the northern hemisphere (figure)

1,3: vernal and autumnal equinox
2,4: summer and winter solstice $\overline{1\text{–}3}$ = line of equinoxes
P,*A*: perihelion and aphelion $\overline{PA}$ = line of apsides

Motion of the earth:
seen from the north: direct / mathematically positive / counterclockwise

Vernal equinox:
retrograde motion Perihelion: direct motion

2.4 *Geocentric (apparent) planetary orbits*

Superposition of the orbital motion of the earth and the planets leads to complicated apparent motions.

a) <u>Basic concepts</u>

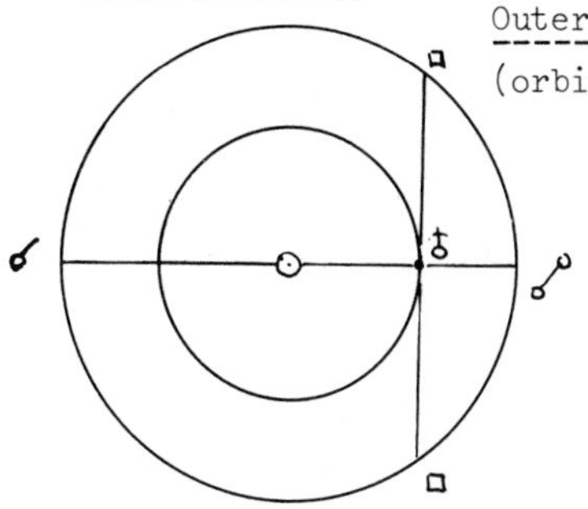

<u>Outer planets</u>

(orbit outside the orbit of the earth)

Opposition ☍
Conjunction ☌
Quadrature □
with respect to ⊙

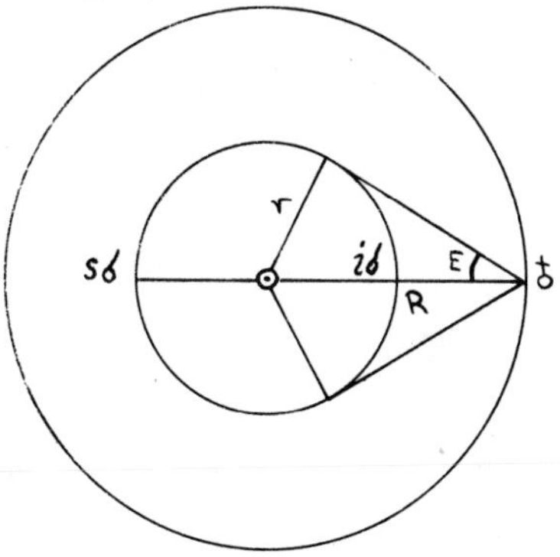

<u>Inner planets</u>

(Orbit inside the orbit of the earth)

Superior conjunction *s*☌

Inferior conjunction *i*☌

greatest {western / eastern} elongation E_g

Also see 2.9.3). For circular orbits: $r = R \sin E_g$

All orbits direct, i.e., counterclockwise as seen from the north. On the sky: from west to east

b) Geocentric orbits

1) Outer planet: opposition (Fig. I)

Earth *A*, *B*, *C* } position at three times
Planet *a*, *b*, *c* } *Bb* = opposition

Planet moves (apparently) from "left" (*a*') to "right" (*c*') (east to west), thus retrograde (Earth overtakes the planet)

At "*S*" (approximately the tangent) the planet becomes stationary

Because the orbits are not situated in a plane, a loop or *S*-curve will result (opposition loop).

2) Inner planet: inferior conjunction

Fig. I; changed in that

Earth *a*, *b*, *c*

Planet *A*, *B*, *C*

aA: planet "left" of ⊙
i.e., in east (evening sky)

cC: planet "right" of ⊙
i.e., in west (morning sky)

Planet disappears in evening twilight, emerges again in the morning sky.

Relative to the background stars the planet moves from left to right, thus retrograde.

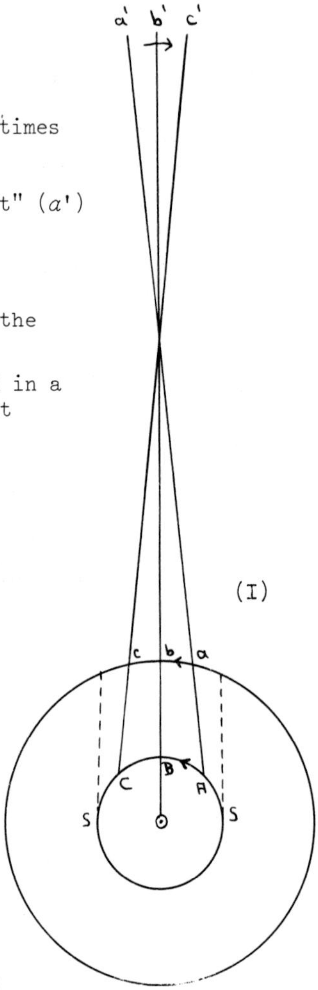

(I)

3) Outer planet: conjunction (Fig. II)

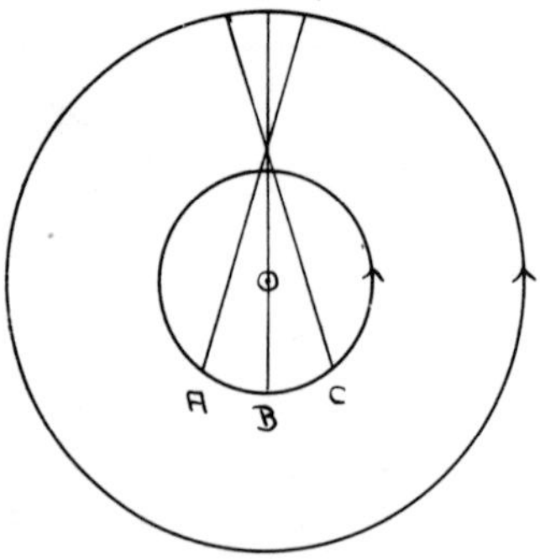

Earth *A*, *B*, *C*; planet *a*, *b*, *c*

Planet from left of ⊙ (*Aa* = eastern, evening sky) to right (*Cc* = western, morning sky)

In contrast to (2) the solar and planet motion is direct, but the sun faster, overtakes planet.

4) Inner planet: superior conjunction

Fig. II; changed in that

Earth *a*, *b*, *c*; planet *A*, *B*, *C*

In this case planet faster than ⊙; planet overtakes ⊙; planet at first at right (western/morning sky), then left (eastern/evening sky)

Exact description

Vectorial addition of the planetary orbit and the orbit of the earth. Earth fixed, sun describes ellipse around the earth, planets describe ellipses around the sun.

⟶ Result: epicyclic orbits (see 2.3)

Kinematically totally equivalent, only a question of usefulness.

Physically: heliocentric picture more meaningful, because of the simpler and uniform law of force

"Proof" of the heliocentric picture: parallax and aberration

§ 3 Historical development

Right through the Middle Ages: geocentric world view of Ptolemy

Then it was shown by:	Copernicus	that the earth is moving
	Kepler	how the earth is moving
	Newton	why the earth is moving

3.1 *Ptolemy*, about 150 A.D.

His "Almagest" was the standard reference for 1400 years. Although his theories are out of date, they show many features of modern celestial mechanics.

Assumptions

a) Geocentric, i.e., earth = center

The idea sun = center already occured to the Greeks, but did not prevail

b) Uniform circular motions

(Dogma of Aristotle)

Because of the actual non-uniformity Ptolemy considered eccentric circles (as Hipparchus already had 300 years earlier)

i.e., sun is moving around the earth in a circle, the center of which is outside the earth. Representation very good, deviation less than 1 in 10^3 (see 2.2.1). Planets are moving in superposed circles (= epicycles), which are invented by Apollonius, 200 B.C.

Description of a planetary orbit

Fictitious point *M* (= center of epicycle) is moving on an eccentric circle (= deferent). Planet *Pl* is moving on a small circle (= epicycle) around *M*.

⟹ Loop orbits

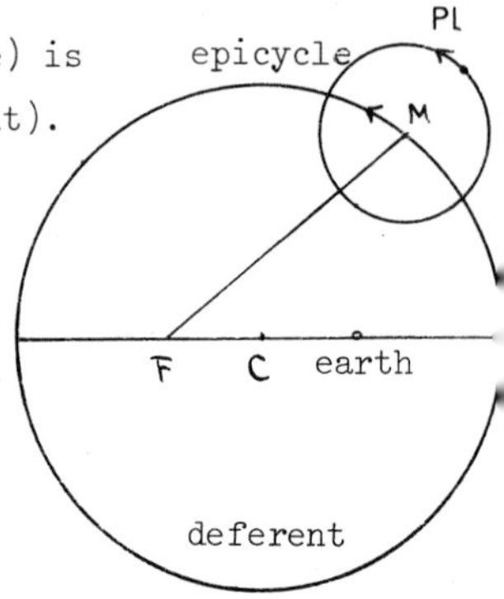

Assumption of uniform motion of *M* is not sufficient; therefore, *M* must be guided by a radius vector $\overline{FM}$, which circles around *F* with a constant speed.

Thus, motion of *M* is non-uniform, but varies in such a manner that it appears uniform as seen from *F*.

F = Punctum equans (as long as the eccentricity is small, *F* corresponds to the 2nd focal point)

In this way get a good description of the orbits of Venus, Mars, Jupiter and Saturn. Mercury bad (high eccentricity); for it, Ptolemy had a special, very complicated theory.

Comparison with modern theory:

Outer planets: deferent ⟶ planetary orbit
epicycle ⟶ orbit of the earth

Inner planets: deferent ⟶ orbit of the earth
epicycle ⟶ planetary orbit

Physical point of view played no role

3.2 *Copernicus* 1473-1543

1510 Hand-written manuscript

1543 First printing of "De revoluticnibus orbium celestium"

Transition geocentric ⟶ heliocentric (the reverse of treatment in 2.2.4)

Retained: a) eccentric circles
b) observed data from Ptolemy

[No interest in "reality", but only in the best formal representation in order to compute the tables.

By the transition to heliocentric view he eliminated several epicycles; however for a better representation at another place he had to introduce new ones (epicycle on epicycles). Essentially, Copernicus was not the beginning of new era, but the closing of an old era!

This Copernican representation not better; one needed new observational data.
This was supplied by

Tycho Brahe 1546 - 1601

Interpretation of the new material was made by Kepler

Literature: A. Köstler, *The Sleepwalkers*

Interesting and - especially in the case of Kepler - detailed description of the development of the world view.

3.3 *Kepler* 1571-1630

Direct determination of the orbit:

Y = sidereal year (period of earth)

P = sidereal period of a planet

S = synodic period of a planet (e.g., from opposition to opposition)

From observations over long time intervals, Y and the mean value of S are well known.

After one synodic period the "lead" of the earth with respect to an outer planet has grown to 360°.

Diurnal motion of a planet: $360^\circ/P$ (P in days)

Diurnal motion of the earth: $360^\circ/Y$ (Y in days)

Thus: Diurnal lead of the earth: $\frac{360^\circ}{Y} - \frac{360^\circ}{P}$

This diurnal increase is identical with the diurnal synodic motion; thus

$$\frac{360^\circ}{Y} - \frac{360^\circ}{P} = \frac{360^\circ}{S} \quad \text{or} \quad \frac{1}{P} = \frac{1}{Y} - \frac{1}{S} \qquad \boxed{P = \frac{S\cdot Y}{S-Y}} \quad \text{From this}$$

Analogous for inner planets:

$$\boxed{P = \frac{S\cdot Y}{S+Y}} \quad P$$

E.g., Mars: S = 2.135 years, hence: $P = \frac{2.135}{1.135} = 1.881$ years

i.e., after every 1.881 years Mars is at the same position in space, but as seen from the earth, in different directions. Intersection of the directions is the actual position.

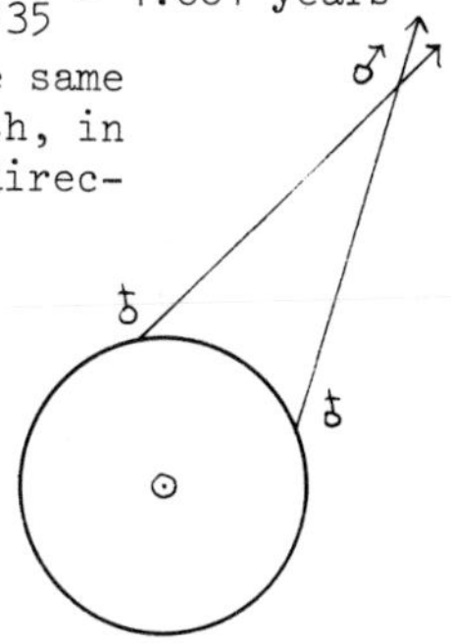

In this manner Kepler determined by tedious calculations several points on the orbit and found that shape of the orbit is an ellipse (after having first tried ovals for a long time).

In the same way - purely empirically - he found the two other laws of Kepler (2.2). (He himself did not yet recognize the implications of the laws).

The significance of the third law of Kepler: if a <u>single</u> distance in the solar system is known in km, then all are known (because the periods of revolution are easily determined). Important for the determination of the astronomical unit (1.6)

Kepler also introduced physical conceptions: force of the sun which moves the planets in their orbits and which decreases with distance. However, wrong interpretation of the inertia (Kepler: inertia = rest). He postulates a force to keep a body in motion, a lateral force ("broom"), the influence of which decreases outwardly.

True interpretation of inertia: Galileo

<u>Objections</u> to the heliocentric system:

No measurable parallax for a star; therefore, the distances had to be improbably large. Tycho Brahe had specified diameters of 3';
hence, the true diameters also had to be improbably large.

Therefore, <u>Tycho Brahe</u> mixed view:

Earth fixed, sun describes an ellipse around earth, planets describe ellipses around sun.

3.4 *Newton* 1643-1727

The force with which two bodies attract one another is proportional to the product of the masses of the bodies and inversely proportional to the square of their distances.

Newton showed that this law is also valid for the planets in their orbits.

Discussion of the law of gravitation: 2.4

<u>Two approaches:</u>

// a) The laws of Kepler follow from the law of gravitation (deductive way)

⟹ see following § 2.4.

// b) The law of gravitation follows from the laws of Kepler (historical way)

// From the law of areas (Kepler's 2nd law) a central force follows.

Elementary derivation:

The curved orbit *ABD* is approximated in the limiting case by the polygonal track.

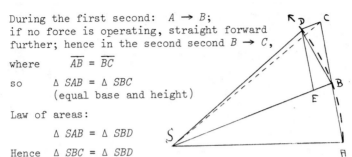

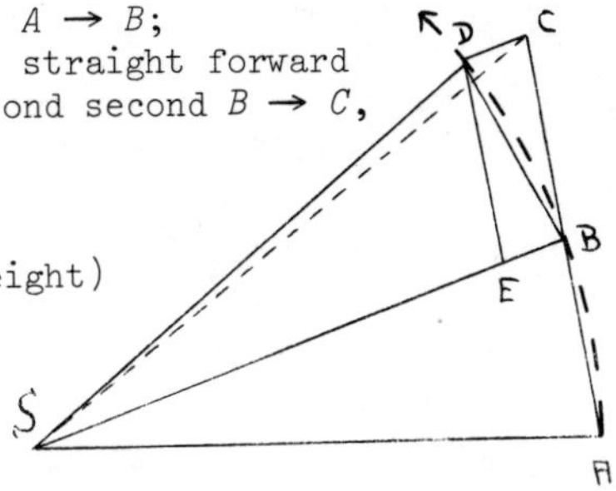

During the first second: $A \rightarrow B$;
if no force is operating, straight forward further; hence in the second second $B \rightarrow C$,

where $\overline{AB} = \overline{BC}$

so $\Delta\ SAB = \Delta\ SBC$
(equal base and height)

Law of areas:

$\Delta\ SAB = \Delta\ SBD$

Hence $\Delta\ SBC = \Delta\ SBD$

Because these triangles have the same base $\overline{SB}$, their heights are also equal;
i.e., D and C are at equal distances from $\overline{SB}$.

Hence: $\overline{DC}\ //\ \overline{SB}$
But now $\overline{DE}\ //\ \overline{CB}$, hence $EBCD$ = parallelogram

$\overline{BC}$ and $\overline{BE}$ are components of the true motion $\overline{BD}$.

Component $\overline{BC}$ = inertia
Component $\overline{BE}$ points to the center

hence central force

//From Kepler's 3rd law a quadratic distance law follows

Simplification: circular orbit:

Acceleration $a = v^2/r$

Velocity $v = 2\pi r/P$ $\longrightarrow$ $a = \dfrac{4\pi^2 r}{P^2}$

Hence, for two bodies: $\dfrac{a_1}{a_2} = \dfrac{r_1 P_2^{\,2}}{r_2 P_1^{\,2}}$

3rd law of Kepler: $\dfrac{P_1^{\,2}}{P_2^{\,2}} = \dfrac{r_1^{\,3}}{r_2^{\,3}}$

Substitution yields: $\dfrac{a_1}{a_2} = \dfrac{r_2^{\,2}}{r_1^{\,2}}$

that is, a quadratic distance law.

§ 4 The two-body problem

4.1 *Law of gravitation, equations of motion*

Newton's law of gravitation:

$$\boxed{\mathbf{F}_m = -\,G\,\frac{Mm}{r^2}\,\mathbf{r}} \qquad (I)$$

[bold type = vectors]

$\mathbf{F}_m$ = Force exerted on m by M
m, M = masses of the bodies
$\mathbf{r}$ = distance $M \rightarrow m$
G = gravitational constant
$= 6.668 \cdot 10^{-8}$ dyn cm^2 g^{-2}

Force exerted on M by $m \equiv \mathbf{F}_M = - \mathbf{F}_m = + G \frac{Mm}{r^3} \mathbf{r}$ (Newton's 3rd law)

x, y, z rectangular coordinate system

α, β, γ angles between the direction of the force and the axes of the coordinates

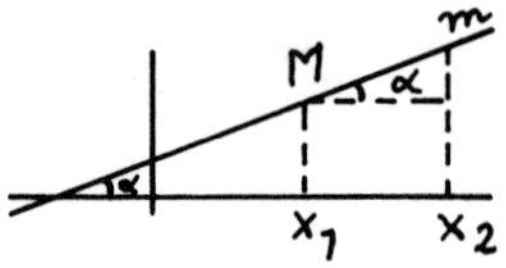

Subscript 1: coordinates of M
Subscript 2: " " m

Then, (using: Force = mass × acceleration) the equations of motion of M read as

$M\ddot{x}_1 = F_{Mx} = F_M \cos\alpha = + G \frac{Mm}{r^2} \cos\alpha = G \frac{Mm}{r^3} (x_2 - x_1)$

$M\ddot{y}_1$ and $M\ddot{z}_1$ analogous

Equations of motion of m, correspondingly:

$m\ddot{x}_2 = \ldots = - G \frac{Mm}{r^3} (x_2 - x_1)$; $m\ddot{y}_2$ and $m\ddot{z}_2$ analogous

Divide by M and m, respectively, and (by substraction) introduce relative coordinates

$$x_2 - x_1 = x, \text{ etc.}$$

i.e., ||transfer the origin to (the center of) mass M to obtain the equations of motion for the two-body problem with respect to (the center of) the mass M:

$$\left.\begin{aligned} \ddot{x} &= - G(M+m) \frac{x}{r^3} \\ \ddot{y} &= - G(M+m) \frac{y}{r^3} \\ \ddot{z} &= - G(M+m) \frac{z}{r^3} \end{aligned}\right\} = \text{three second-order differential equations}$$

or vectorially:

$$\boxed{\ddot{\mathbf{r}} = \frac{d^2\mathbf{r}}{dt^2} = - G \frac{M + m}{r^3} \mathbf{r}} \qquad \text{(II)}$$

Consequently, 6 integrations are necessary for the solution of the system of differential equations. They are all strictly soluble and yield:

1st to 3rd integration:	relative motion in a plane (2.4.2)
4th " :	law of areas (conservation of angular momentum)(2.4.2)
5th " :	law of conservation of energy (2.4.4)
6th " :	orbit = conic section (2.4.3)

If $M >> m$, one can substitue M for M+m in (II)

and get the equations of motion of the "one-body problem"

4.2) *Angular momentum, law of areas* (Kepler's 2nd law)

Vectorial (i.e., cross) product of (II) with $\mathbf{r}$:

$$\ddot{\mathbf{r}} \times \mathbf{r} = -G\frac{M+m}{r^3}\mathbf{r} \times \mathbf{r} = 0$$ Valid generally for central forces

On the other hand:

$$\mathbf{r} \times \ddot{\mathbf{r}} \equiv \frac{d}{dt}(\dot{\mathbf{r}} \times \mathbf{r})$$

Hence

$$\boxed{\mathbf{r} \times \dot{\mathbf{r}} \equiv \mathbf{r} \times \frac{d\mathbf{r}}{dt} = \text{const.} \equiv \mathbf{h} \equiv \frac{\mathbf{L}}{m}} \qquad \text{(III)}$$

Since $m(\mathbf{r} \times \dot{\mathbf{r}}) \equiv m(\mathbf{r} \times \mathbf{v}) \equiv$ angular momentum,

equation (III) represents the

law of conservation of angular momentum.

$\mathbf{h}$ is the angular momentum vector corresponding to unit mass.

$\mathbf{L}$ " " " " " .

From the figure (polar coordinates) we have the change in area

$d\mathbf{A} = \frac{1}{2}[\mathbf{r} \times (\mathbf{r} \times d\mathbf{r})] = \frac{1}{2}(\mathbf{r} \times d\mathbf{r}) = \frac{1}{2}r \cdot r\, d\phi$

hence, with (III)

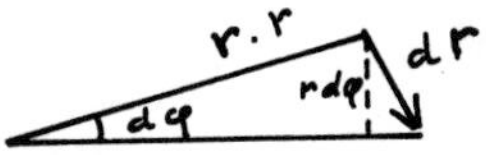

$$\boxed{\frac{dA}{dt} = \frac{1}{2}r^2\ \phi = \frac{1}{2}(\mathbf{r} \times \dot{\mathbf{r}}) = \frac{1}{2}\mathbf{h} = \text{constant}} \qquad \text{(IV)}$$

= law of areas = Kepler's second law

$\mathbf{h}$ = const., furthermore, means that $\mathbf{r}$ and $\mathbf{V}$ always remain in the same plane $\perp$ $\mathbf{h}$.

⟹ The motion takes place in a plane fixed in space.

4.3) *The shape of the orbit*

We multiply the equations of motion (II) vectorially with $\mathbf{h}$

$$\mathbf{h} \times \ddot{\mathbf{r}} = -G\frac{M+m}{r^3}\mathbf{h} \times \mathbf{r}$$

$$= -G\frac{M+m}{r^3}(\mathbf{r} \times \dot{\mathbf{r}}) \times \mathbf{r}$$ ← Using $\mathbf{h} = \mathbf{r} \times \dot{\mathbf{r}}$ from III

$$= -G\frac{M+m}{r^3}r^2\,\dot{\mathbf{r}} - (\dot{r} \cdot r)\mathbf{r}$$

$$= -G\,(M+m)\frac{d}{dt}\left(\frac{\mathbf{r}}{r}\right)$$ ← because: $\frac{d}{dt}\left(\frac{\mathbf{r}}{r}\right) = \frac{r\dot{\mathbf{r}} - \dot{r}\mathbf{r}}{r^2}$.

after integration:

$$\mathbf{h} \times \dot{\mathbf{r}} = -G(M+m)\frac{\mathbf{r}}{r} - \mathbf{C}_1$$

By scalar multiplication with **r**, considering that according to (III)

$$(\mathbf{h} \times \dot{\mathbf{r}})\cdot\mathbf{r} = \mathbf{h}\cdot(\dot{\mathbf{r}} \times \mathbf{r}) = -h^2$$

one obtains

$$h^2 = (M+m)\,r + \mathbf{r}\,\mathbf{C}_1$$

Solve for r using

$$\begin{cases} p = \dfrac{h^2}{G(M+m)} \\ e = \dfrac{|\mathbf{C}_1|}{G(m+m)} \\ \upsilon = \text{angle between } \mathbf{r} \text{ and } \mathbf{C}_1 \end{cases}$$

$$\boxed{r = \frac{p}{1 + e\cos\upsilon}} \qquad \text{(V)}$$

= equation of a <u>conic</u>

= Kepler's 1st law

with the following evident meaning (see 2.2.1)

	circle	ellipse	parabola	hyperbola
e = eccentricity	o	< 1	1	> 1
p = parameter	a	$a(1-e^2)$	p	$a(e^2-1)$
a = semimajor axis	a	a	–	a
b = semiminor axis	a	$a\sqrt{1-e^2}$	–	$a\sqrt{e^2-1}$
r_p = distance at pericenter	a	$a(1-e)$	$p/2$	$a(e-1)$
r_a = distance at apocenter	a	$a(1+e)$	∞	∞

υ = true anomaly

4.4) *Law of conservation of energy*

We put $\mathbf{F}_m = -\,\text{grad}\,\phi$; $\phi = -G\dfrac{Mm}{r}$ according to (I)

Then, we have $\mathbf{F}_m d\mathbf{r} = -\,\text{grad}\,\phi\; d\mathbf{r} = \phi_1 - \phi_2 < 0$

= work performed on by gravitational field when **r** increased by d**r**

$-\mathbf{F}_m d$ = work performed on m <u>against</u> gravitational field when **r** increased by d**r** $= \phi_2 - \phi_1$

= energy gained by m

hence ϕ = potential energy

The value when the unit of mass $m = 1$ is

$$\Phi = -G\frac{M}{r}$$, potential due to M at distance r.

Equation of motion,

$$m\,\ddot{\mathbf{r}} = -\,\mathrm{grad}\,\phi,$$

and scalar multiplication with $\dot{\mathbf{r}}$

yield: $m\,\ddot{\mathbf{r}}\cdot\dot{\mathbf{r}} = -\,\mathrm{grad}\,\phi\cdot\dot{\mathbf{r}}$

or: $\frac{\mathrm{d}}{\mathrm{d}t}\left(\frac{1}{2}m\,\dot{r}^2\right) = \frac{-\mathrm{d}\phi}{\mathrm{d}t}$

or:

$$\frac{1}{2}mv^2 + \phi = \frac{1}{2}mv^2 - G\frac{Mm}{r} = \text{const}$$

$$E_{\text{kin}} + E_{\text{pot}} = \text{total energy } E = \text{const} \qquad \text{(VI)}$$

= law of conservation of energy

Also from this equation one sees that, for instance, the velocity at aphelion (large r) decreases, and vice versa.

For circular orbits: centripetal force = force of attraction

$$-\frac{mv^2}{r} = -G\frac{Mm}{r^2}$$

From this:

$$\frac{mv^2}{2} = \frac{1}{2}G\frac{Mm}{r} = -\frac{1}{2}\phi$$

$$E_{\text{kin}} = -\frac{1}{2}E_{\text{pot}} \qquad \text{(VII)}$$

This law is also valid - in the time average - for elliptical orbits.
It is the virial theorem for the two-body problem.

Circular velocity (from VII): $V_c = \sqrt{\frac{GM}{r}}$

For elliptical orbits it can be shown that $E = -G\frac{Mm}{2a}$;

then from (VI): $V = \sqrt{GM\left(\frac{2}{r} - \frac{1}{a}\right)}$

For parabolic orbits we have at infinity: $E_{\text{kin}} = E_{\text{pot}} = 0$,

i.e., according to (VI): total energy = 0

and $E_{\text{kin}} = -E_{\text{pot}}$ everywhere in the orbit.

Also, from (VI), $\frac{mv^2}{2} = G\frac{Mm}{r}$

which yields for the parabolic or escape velocity:

$$\boxed{v_e = \sqrt{\frac{2\,GM}{r}} = \sqrt{2}\,v_c} \qquad \text{(VIII)}$$

In general we have:

Ellipse (circle) $E_{\text{kin}} = \frac{mv^2}{2} < G\frac{Mm}{r}$

parabola $=$

hyperbola $>$

$G\frac{Mm}{r}$ is the energy which is needed to move mass m to ∞

For the ellipse the kinetic energy is not sufficient for this, for the parabola it is just sufficient, and for the hyperbolic orbit there is kinetic energy left over.

Notice: consequence of this:
single stars cannot capture planets or moons!

4.5) *Kepler's third law*

By means of the equation of the orbit, (V), and with $v = 0$ and $v = \pi$, it follows that

$$a = \tfrac{1}{2}\,(r_{\text{pericenter}} + r_{\text{apocenter}}) = \tfrac{1}{2}\,\left(\frac{p}{1-e} + \frac{p}{1+e}\right) = \frac{p}{1-e^2}$$

$$1 - e^2 = \frac{p}{a} = \frac{h^2}{G(M+m)\,a}$$

Also: period of rotation times areal velocity (IV) yields total area.

$$P\,\frac{\mathbf{h}}{2} = \pi\,ab = \pi\,a^2\sqrt{1-e^2} = \frac{\pi\,a^2\,\mathbf{h}}{\sqrt{G(M+m)\,a}}$$

↳ according to 2.2.1

Take the square: $$\boxed{P^2 = \frac{4\pi^2\,a^3}{G(M+m)}} \qquad \text{(IX)}$$

= Kepler's third law

§ 5 Determination of orbits

According to (2.4.1) 6 integrations are needed to solve the system of differential equations of the two-body problem. This means 6 constants of integration. These are uniquely connected with the 6 orbital elements (2.2.1)

The relation is described in detail by R. Giese, 1966, *Weltraumforschung* I, Bibliographisches Institut, Mannheim, Hochschultaschenbücher 107/107a

[and by S.W. McCuskey,
1963, *Introduction to Celestial Mechanics*, Addison-Wesley.]

Purpose of the determination of orbits:

To derive the 6 orbital elements from the observed positions;

= counterpart of the computing of an ephemeris (2.2.4),

where positions are computed from known elements.

The methods of the determination of orbits are not treated in detail below, but some general viewpoints are compiled. Compare this with a textbook on celestial mechanics.

Observed: planetary positions

Wanted: six orbital elements

i.e., 6 unknowns, hence 3 positions (α and δ) needed

Problem: given three radius vectors at three specified times, to find an ellipse with the sun in the focal point; the ellipse to be intersected by the three radius vectors in such a way that the planet passes the three points of intersection at the given times

Equation so complicated that only an iterative solution is possible

Main difficulty: geocentric distance of the planet

All methods are based on determining this distance.
The rest then is simple.

Laplace method: The rectangular coordinates and the velocity at the time of the middle (2nd) observation as an unknown = initial-value problem

Gauss method: The spatial coordinates at the times t_1 and t_3 as an unknown = boundary-value problem

Scheme:

	1st	2nd	3rd observation
Laplace:		x, y, z $\dot{x}, \dot{y}, \dot{z}$	
Gauss :	x, y, z		x, y, z

[Today, practical calculation only by electronic computers]

At first, from the three observations

the preliminary orbit

is obtained. By means of these provisional elements the ephemeris is computed and compared with further observations.

Corrections to the orbital elements are derived from the deviations.

If the difference, observed minus computed, is smaller than the error of the observations and there is no systematic trend, one has the definitive orbit.

Circular orbits: only 4 orbital elements (eccentricity and longitude of perihelion are omitted).

Parabolic orbits: only 5 orbital elements (eccentricity = 1) e.g. as a first approximation for cometary orbits

§ 6 N - b o d y p r o b l e m; c o m p u t a t i o n o f p e r t u r b a t i o n s

6.1 *General integrals*

Equations of motion for n bodies by addition of all mutual attractions

Equation of motion for mass m_i:

$$m_i \ddot{x}_i = - G\, m_i m_1 \frac{x_i - x_1}{r_{i,1}^3} - G\, m_i m_2 \frac{x_i - x_2}{r_{i,2}^3} - \ldots = - \sum_{k=1}^{n} G\, m_i m_k \frac{x_i - x_k}{r_{i,k}^3}$$

$m_i \ddot{y}_i$ and $m_i \ddot{z}_i$ analogous

i.e., 3n differential equations of the 2nd order, for the solution of which 6n integrations are necessary

E.g., 3-body problem: 9 differential equations, 18 integrations

Of the 6n integrations ten are known:

1st to 6th integration: integrals for the center of mass

Addition of all equations for x (y and z, similarly):

$$m_1 \ddot{x}_1 + m_2 \ddot{x}_2 + \ldots = \sum_i m_i \ddot{x}_i = 0$$

[no external force acting on system]

integrate twice:

$$m_1 x_1 + m_2 x_2 + \ldots = \sum_i m_i x_i = \alpha_x t + \beta_x$$

⟹ Center of mass of the system is at rest or in uniform rectilinear motion (Conservation of linear momentum)

7th to 9th integration: integrals of areas (angular momentum integrals)

As in the case of the two-body problem one gets:

$$\sum_i m_i (x_i \dot{y}_i - y_i \dot{x}_i) = \text{constant, ditto } x,z \text{ and } y,z$$

i.e., sum of the products of the masses and the projections of the areal velocities = constant

⟹ Conservation of angular momentum

<u>10th integration: law of conservation of energy</u>

Potential: $\phi = -G \sum_{i,k} \frac{m_i m_k}{r_{i,k}}$

With this, the differential equations read:

$$m_i \ddot{x}_i = \frac{\partial\phi}{\partial x_i} \quad , \text{ etc.}$$

Hence, after some algebra:

$$\tfrac{1}{2} \sum_i m_i \, (\dot{x}_i^2 + \dot{y}_i^2 + \dot{z}_i^2) + \phi = \tfrac{1}{2} \sum_i m_i v_i^2 + \phi = \text{const}$$

⇒that is, sum of kinetic and potential energy = constant

In the astronomical literature this is sometimes called the "vis viva integral".

$-\phi$ = energy which is necessary to move the bodies to infinity

<u>Total energy</u>:

If $E_{tot} = E_{kin} + E_{pot} < 0$: system has negative total energy

i.e., $E_{kin} < -E_{pot}$, energy is not sufficient to remove all bodies to infinity; the objects are kept together by gravitation.

Contrary to the 2-body case, single bodies can be taken to infinity at the cost of the energy of others. Individual objects can "evaporate".

If $E_{tot} > 0$: Energy is sufficient, i.e., the group of objects is unstable, expands.

Further closed integrals not known. Bruns and Poincaré showed that no further integrals of this type exist, i.e., there are no algebraic solutions. Consequently, even the 3-body problem is not soluble strictly analytically.

a) <u>Mathematics</u>: correct solution: infinite series: in practice poor, because the series converge slowly.

b) In <u>practice</u>: numerical integration (as accurate as you like) Starting from initial position and an initial velocity and with the help of the instantaneous forces, the next position is computed.

In this manner proceed step by step. Each given problem is soluble in this way to any desired accuracy.

von Hoerner, et al., have computed the behaviour of entire star clusters in this manner. (see 8.10.3)

6.2 *The virial theorem*

In mechanics the following can be proved:
(e.g., Landau-Lifschitz I, p. 33)

If n bodies always stay inside a definite volume during their motion, we have for the time average of the kinetic energy and the potential energy

$$\boxed{E_{kin} = -\tfrac{1}{2}E_{pot}} \quad = \text{virial theorem}$$

On the other hand, according to the law of energy:

$$E_{total} = E_{kin} + E_{pot} = \text{const.}$$

Hence $$E_{total} = \tfrac{1}{2}E_{pot} = -E_{kin}$$

(In this context, $E_{tot} < 0$ does not mean that all systems have a negative total energy, because the virial theorem is only valid for systems of negative energy.)

For circular orbits this relation has already been verified in 2.4.4.: the two-body case.

The more negative the total energy, the better the conditions for validity of the virial theorem are fulfilled.

6.3 *Special cases*

There are special cases of the three-body problem, which can be solved analytically.

a) Lagrangian points (libration points)

m_1, m_2: masses in a rotating coordinate system

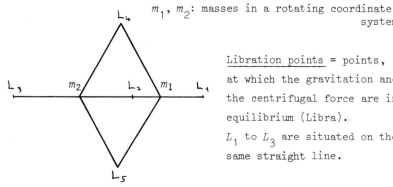

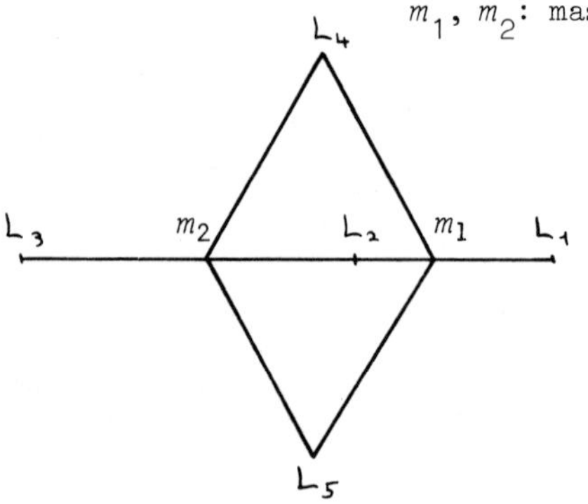

Libration points = points, at which the gravitation and the centrifugal force are in equilibrium (Libra).

L_1 to L_3 are situated on the same straight line.

(At L_2 the effect of the gravitational force of both masses is identical). L_4 and L_5 form an equilateral triangle with m_1 and m_2. If a third mass m_3 is at one of the libration points, a periodic motion is possible, during which the ratio of the mutual distances remains unchanged (e.g., solid rotation, if distance $\overline{m_1 m_2}$ constant).
All bodies describe similar conic section orbits (see figure).

L_1 to L_3: generally unstable. A small perturbation takes m_3 away.

L_4 and L_5 : stable. Under a small perturbation m_3 remains in the neighbourhood of the libration point.

Realized by the "Trojans" = group of asteroids, which on the average form an equilateral triangle with Jupiter and the sun. (orbits, see 2.9.2)

Example: orbits of 3 bodies (libration point L_4)

Figure: three ellipses = three orbits around the common center of gravitation (i.e., center of mass) S.

P = positions at perihelion

A = positions at aphelion

Z = positions at a point between them

--- line of apsides

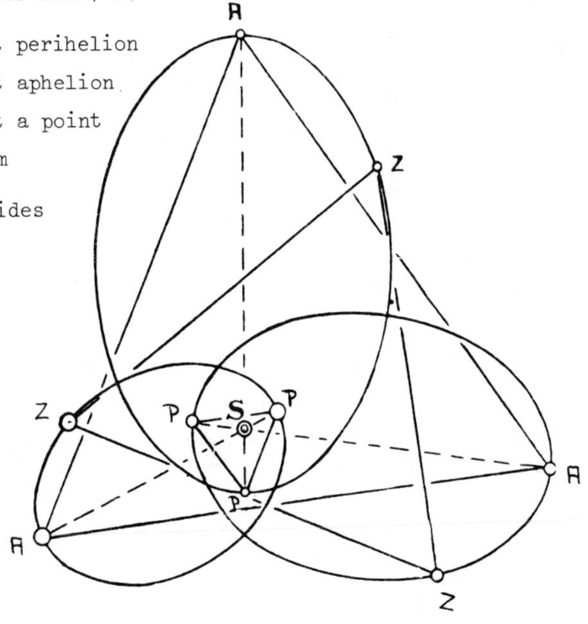

At each moment the bodies form an equilateral triangle. This becomes larger and smaller; it is "pulsating".

b) Restricted three-body problem

Conditions:

1) $m_3 \ll m_1, m_2$, hence no reaction forces
2) motion of the bodies in a plane
3) m_1 and m_2 unperturbed circular orbit around the center of gravitation

Also this problem is not strictly soluble generally, but there are interesting classes of periodic motions (e.g., bean-shaped orbits, ejection orbits, loop orbits, etc.)

6.4 *Perturbations*

Most important special case: m_3 so small or at so great a distance that its influence on m_1 and m_2 is very much smaller than the force between m_1 and m_2

Then, m_3 only "perturbs" the motion of m_1 and m_2

Solar system: many bodies, but $m_\odot \gg m_i$

|| i.e., when dealing with a specified planetary orbit all other bodies act only as perturbations, which can be computed and added individually

Special perturbations: numerical integration from moment to moment
General perturbations: general formulae; perturbation = $f(t)$

computation of the acceleration due to perturbing force: (parallelogram of accelerations)

$\odot$ = position of the sun
P = position of the planet
M = position of the perturbing mass m
R = distance $P\odot$
r = distance PM
ρ = distance $\odot M$

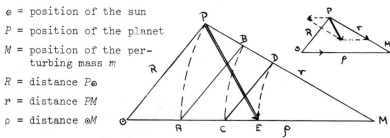

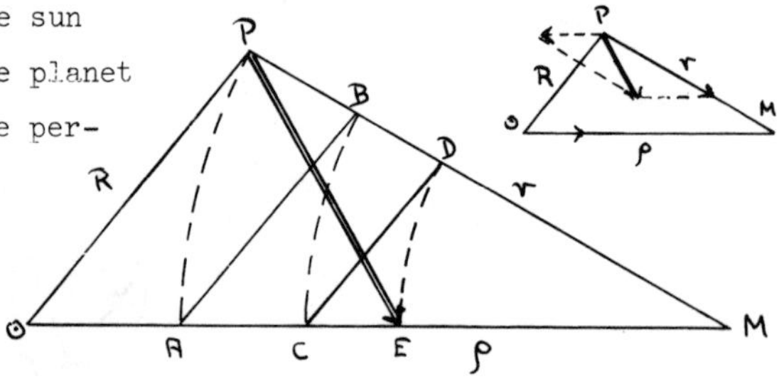

Perturbing acceleration = difference between the accelerations on sun and planet

Let the acceleration by m on P be given by the length of line $\overline{MP}$.

Then, the acceleration upon the sun = $\frac{r^2}{\rho^2}\,\overline{MP}$ in the direction from sun to M

Construction: $\overline{MA} = \overline{MP}$; $\overline{AB}//\overline{\odot P}$; $\overline{MC} = \overline{MB}$; $\overline{CD}//\overline{\odot P}$; $\overline{ME} = \overline{MD}$;

Then: $\overline{MC}:\overline{MP} = \overline{MB}:\overline{MA} = r:\rho \;\rightarrow\; \overline{MC} = \frac{r}{\rho}\,\overline{MP}$

Likewise: $\overline{ME}:\overline{MC} = \overline{MD}:\overline{MC} = r:\rho \;\rightarrow\; \overline{ME} = \frac{r}{\rho}\,\overline{MC} = \frac{r^2}{\rho^2}\,\overline{MP}$

Hence: $\overline{ME}$ = the acceleration upon the sun

and therefore,

$\overline{PE}$ = vector difference ($\overline{MP} - \overline{ME}$)
= perturbing acceleration upon the planet

Maximum influence: if sun-planet-perturbing body lined up.

Acceleration

by m upon P: $a_P = G\frac{m}{r^2}$

by m upon $\odot$: $a_\odot = G\frac{m}{(R+r)^2}$

perturbation: $\Delta a = Gm\left(\frac{1}{r^2} - \frac{1}{(R+r)^2}\right)$

For $R \ll r$: $\frac{1}{(R+r)^2} \simeq \frac{1}{r^2}\left(1 - \frac{2R}{r}\right) = \frac{1}{r^2} - 2\frac{R}{r^3}$

And therefore:

Perturbation $\boxed{\Delta a = 2\,Gm\frac{R}{r^3}}$

First term of the series expansion decreases with the third power of the distance

Numerical data:

Perturbation by Venus upon earth (maximum):	1/37000
Jupiter upon earth (opposition):	1/53000
Jupiter upon Saturn (maximum):	1/360

One can resolve the perturbation into three components:

1. Orthogonal component ⊥ orbital plane

   This component influences only the spatial position of the orbital plane, hence the elements Ω and i

2. Radial component in direction of the radius vector

3. Perpendicular to the radial component, in the orbital plane

   2 and 3 influence shape and orientation of the orbit, hence the elements a, e and $\tilde{\omega}$

Mathematically exact analysis:

a) Equations of motion of the two-body problem plus an additional term with the difference of the accelerations upon sun and planet (perturbation function) (see above figure)

b) Expand the perturbation function into a converging series
First term: $\sim \frac{R}{r^3}$ (see above)

c) Conversion : instead of perturbations of the rectangular coordinates
→ perturbations of the orbital elements

This finally yields six differential equations of the first order in the elements. On the right-hand sides the elements themselves occur too; hence, only an iterative solution. ⟹ Perturbations of the nth order.

One distinguishes:

1) Periodic perturbations: time occuring only in terms like cos t or sin t

2) Secular perturbations: time itself appears as a factor

Stability of the Solar System

/Semi axis a: Essentially only periodic perturbations. Secular perturbations appear only in the third and higher orders (longer than the life time of the sun)

/Eccentricity e and inclination i: only long-period perturbations

/Longitude of the node and of the perihelion, Ω and $\tilde{\omega}$; unlimited variability; unimportant for stability

⟹ the planetary system is practically infinitely stable

The lines of apsides: direct rotation for nearly all planets; for the earth: 11".5 per year

Lines of nodes of all planets have retrograde rotation

Inclinations and eccentricities increase for some planets at present; for others they decrease.

Earth: eccentricity decreases at present; orbit becomes more circular; however, only 4 units in the 7th decimal place annually.

For planets without moons perturbations are the only means for determining the masses.

Jupiter - Saturn Perturbations

Periods of revolution nearly commensurable 2:5

$$\left.\begin{array}{l} P_J = 12 \text{ years} \\ P_S = 30 \text{ years} \end{array}\right\} \quad S = \frac{30 \cdot 12}{30-12} = 20 \text{ years} = 1\tfrac{2}{3}\, P_J = \tfrac{2}{3}\, P_S$$

All conjunctions almost at the same position, about 120° from one another $1 \longrightarrow 2 \longrightarrow 3 \longrightarrow 1$ in figure (———)

i.e., perturbations at the same position in the same direction. But not exactly 120°, because ratio of the periods of revolution not exactly 2:5. Consequence: each successive conjunction shifted by 2°.7

$1 \longrightarrow 2' \longrightarrow 3' \longrightarrow 1'$ (----------)

that is, perturbations have a period of 883 years.

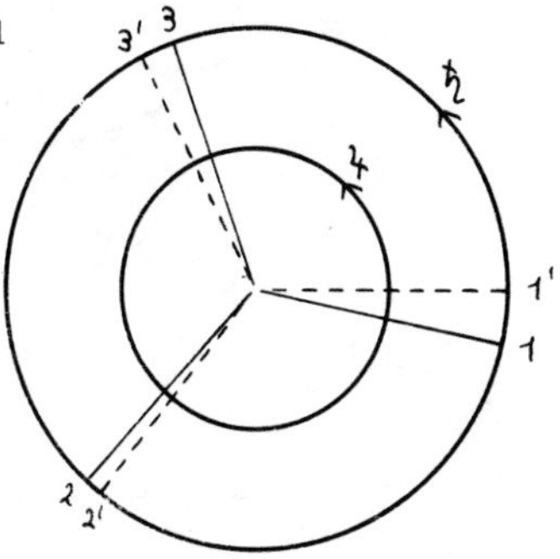

Already in Newton's time knew that Jupiter always is in advance of, Saturn always behind, the computed position. Difference increased then, maximum in 1900, decreasing again at present.

§ 7 The earth-moon system

One of the most difficult problems in celestial mechanics. The moon is exposed to stronger perturbations than any other moon or planet in the solar system.

Mean earth-moon distance:	384 400 km
minimum distance (perigee):	356 410 km
maximum distance (apogee):	406 740 km
mean inclination to ecliptic:	i = 5°9'
mean eccentricity:	e = 0.0549

Analogously to the time equation (1.2), there is a difference between "true" and "mean" moon because the lunar velocity varies on account of the elliptical lunar orbit (so-called: "large inequality of the moon" or "equation of center")

Maximum effect: 6°17'.3

Orbit of the moon always concave to the sun! No waves
(Falling of moon plus earth to sun > falling of moon to earth)

7.1) *Perturbation of the lunar orbit by the sun*

Perturbing acceleration
= acceleration upon the moon minus acceleration upon earth
Construction according to (2.6.4) for various positions

of the moon:

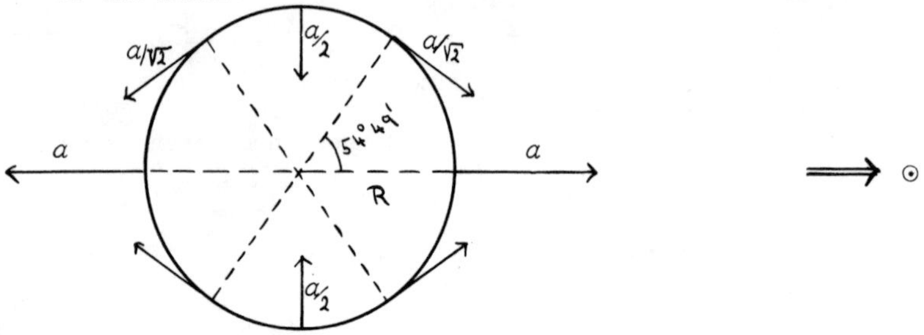

$$a = 2\,GM_\odot \frac{R}{r^3}$$ (series expansion for $R \ll r$, according to 2.6.4)

R : earth-moon distance

r : moon-sun distance

Result:

Full moon and new moon: perturbing acceleration directed away from earth along earth-moon-sun line (= syzygy) of magnitude a

First and last quarter: perturbing acceleration directed toward the earth $\perp$ to the earth-sun line of magnitude $a/2$

At elongation 54°7: perturbing acceleration directed tangential to lunar orbit of magnitude $a/\sqrt{2}$

Normally the direction of the perturbation is inclined and is resolved into:

(1) radial component in the orbital plane

$\longrightarrow$ changes the distance of the moon

As can be seen from the figure, in this case, the effect of the sun is more outward than inwards (as seen from earth).

i.e., ‖ As a whole, distance and period of revolution of the moon are larger than they would be without the sun.

(2) tangential component in the plane of the orbit

$\longrightarrow$ changes the velocity of the moon

(3) component perpendicular to the orbital plane

$\longrightarrow$ tilts the orbit of the moon

The number of perturbations, each considered seperately, amounts to several hundreds; here, only the most important ones:

a) <u>Evection</u>

= perturbation of the difference between "true" and "mean" moon (see above) caused by the variable position of the sun with respect to the line of apsides

Causes an additional effect of $1^{\circ}16\overset{'}{.}4$ at maximum with a period of $31\overset{d}{.}8$

> This largest of all lunar perturbations was already known to Hipparchus.

b) <u>Variation</u> = tangential component

= acceleration and retardation with a semi-monthly period (see figure), i.e., moon sometimes advancing, sometimes lagging

Amplitude 39'30" — discovered by Tycho Brahe, explained by Newton

c) <u>Annual inequality or annual equation</u>

= change of the radial component (see above) on account of the eccentricity of the orbit of the earth

Perihelion (northern winter): sun nearby, retarding effect largest

Aphelion (northern summer): sun more distant, earth's influence stronger, moon approaches and revolves faster

Amplitude: period of revolution ± 10 min; position ± 11'11" (Tycho Brahe)

d) <u>Secular acceleration</u>

= changing of the annual inequality caused by the decrease in the eccentricity of the orbit of the earth.

After one year the annual inequality should return to its starting point and begin again anew. However, because the eccentricity of the orbit of the earth has decreased, no complete compensation is attained

$\Longrightarrow$ Result: shortening of the period of revolution

Discovered by Halley: period of lunar revolution shorter than in antiquity

Explanation by Laplace

Small effect: period of revolution today 1/2 sec shorter than 2000 years ago. Cumulative noticeable effect in position.

Theoretical value:	6" in 100 years
Observed value	8" in 100 years

[Probably the 2" are a result of a change in the rotation period of the earth, hence in the unit of time (see 1.10).]

This effect does not go on for ever, because the eccentricity varies with a long period. Hence, in the future there will again be retardation in the motion of the moon.

e) Rotation of the line of apsides

Line of apsides moves, sometimes direct, sometimes retrograde. Direct motion predominates.

complete rotation in 8.85 years

Connected with this: variation of eccentricity between 0.044 and 0.067, period 1/2 year.

f) Rotation of the line of nodes and variation of inclination

(Perturbation component perpendicular to the lunar orbit)

Sun tends to raise the lunar orbit, the latter reacts as a spinning top

⟹ Result: precession of the lunar orbit

Period of rotation of the line of nodes: 18.6 years, retrograde.
Rotation not uniform (effect = 0, whenever the line of nodes points at the sun; maximum, whenever the line of nodes is perpendicular to earth-sun line)

⟹ Superposed period of 1/2 year

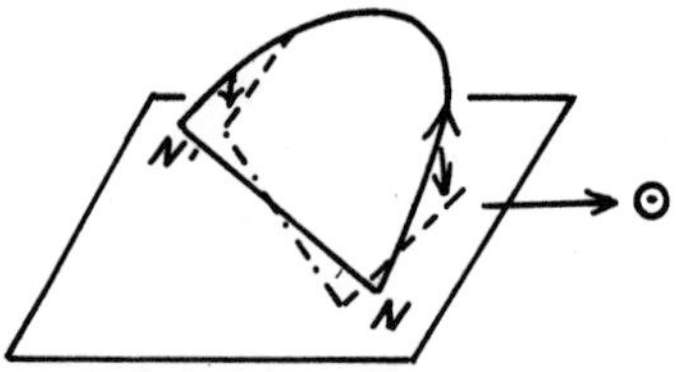

Acceleration of ⊙ perturbs moon toward plane of ecliptic (↓).

---- = perturbed (new) velocity vector of moon.

Tracing perturbed velocity vectors backward or forward to new nodes shows that nodes are shifted retrograde (-·-·- = new line of nodes).

N : After a node, perturbed velocity vector has smaller inclination.

N': Before a node, perturbed velocity vector has greater inclination.

⟹ Change of inclination with semi-monthly period

This variation of i superimposed on semi-annual variation.

$i = 5^\circ 9' \pm 9'$

g) Variation of the distance

Through the combined effects of the perturbations the following extreme values are reached:

Minimum: 55.9 radii of the earth whenever full moon at perigee, moon between the nodes, earth at perihelion

Maximum: 63.8 radii of the earth whenever new moon at apogee, moon between the nodes, earth at perihelion

7.2) *Length of the months* (Average values)

Sidereal (star to star)	: $27^{d}.32166$
synodic (phase to phase)	: 29.53059
draconitic (node to node)	: 27.21222
tropical (equinox to equinox)	: 27.32158
anomalistic (perigee to perigee)	: 27.55455 (variable, 25^{d} to 29^{d})

7.3) *Libration*

More than half of the moon visible

a) Libration in longitude

Period of rotation of the moon = sidereal period of revolution

Rotation: constant angular velocity ω_{rot}

Velocity of revolution ω_R variable (law of areas)

i.e., perigee: $\omega_R > \omega_{rot}$: more visible on the west side

apogee: $\omega_R < \omega_{rot}$: more visible on the east side

Maximum: $\pm 7^{\circ}53'$

b) Libration in latitude

Axis of rotation not perpendicular to orbital plane. In the course of a month one looks at times over the north pole, and at other times under the south pole.

Maximum: $\pm 6^{\circ}40'$

c) Diurnal libration

See slightly different half from various points on the earth, or from a single point at various times because of rotation of the earth

Maximum: $\pm 1^{\circ}$

Sum of the effects: about 60% of the lunar surface is visible from the earth in the long run.

7.4) *Earth-moon interactions*

a) Perturbations of the earth:

earth = sphere + equatorial bulge.

Perturbing effect by sun and moon on this bulge causes the lunisolar precession (see 1.7)

Moon's node makes one revolution in 18.6 years, hence, a superposed perturbation of this period

= nutation (see 1.7)

b) Motion of the earth around the common center of gravity

Earth and moon move around their common center of gravity. It is situated at a distance of about 3/4 of the radius of the earth from the center of the earth, thus still inside the earth.

||This center of gravity defines the ecliptic||

Result:

1) At half moon (1st and 3rd quarters) the earth somewhat fast or slow, therefore apparent inequality in the motion of the sun, $\Delta\lambda = 6''.5$, period 1 month

2) Because lunar orbit inclined, earth sometimes above, sometimes below the ecliptic.
⟶ Change in latitude of the sun: $\Delta\beta = 0''.6$
period 1 month

c) Tides

Perturbing effect of moon (and sun) on the water and air masses of the earth. Effect similar to figure page 58

i.e., bulges (high tides) on the sides turned to and away from the moon:
depression (low tide) on the great circle in between

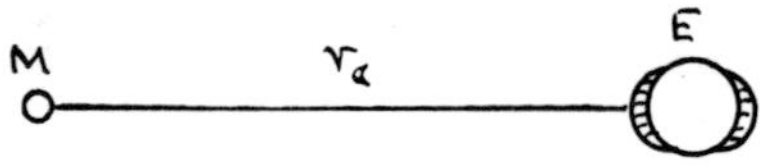

Acceleration caused by lunar perturbation according to 2.6.4

$$\Delta a_{☾} = 2\,Gm_{☾}\,\frac{R}{r^3_{☾}}$$

In the same way, acceleration caused by perturbation by the sun

$$\Delta a_{\odot} = 2\,Gm_{\odot}\,\frac{R}{r^3_{\odot}}$$

$m_{☾}$ = mass of the moon
$m_{\odot}$ = mass of the sun
R = radius of the earth
$r_{☾}$ = earth-moon distance
$r_{\odot}$ = earth-sun distance

Ratio of the effects: $$\frac{\Delta a_{☾}}{\Delta a_{\odot}} = \frac{m_{☾}}{m_{\odot}}\;\frac{r^3_{\odot}}{r^3_{☾}} = 2.18$$

⟶ Effect of the moon about twice as large

Tidal bulge moves around the earth in one lunar day = $24^h 50^m$

i.e., high tide every $12^h 25^m$.

In the ideal case: high tide at upper and lower culmination of the moon. In reality the ocean basins are excited to forced oscillations.

Because of the land masses the arrival of high tide is delayed at particular points, so-called "harbor time".

e.g., Hamburg: harbor time 5^h to 6^h

Effect of sun and moon:

New moon and full moon : additive ⟶ spring-tide

1st and 3rd quarter: subtractive ⟶ neap-tide

Ratio: $\frac{2.18 + 1}{2.18 - 1} = 2.7$

Average height of tides up to 15 m (e.g., Nova Scotia)

in the North Sea: 4 m (consequence of the oceanic tidal flow)

One tidal flow north of England, to Southern Scandinavia, further southwards; another tidal flow along England and the German North Sea coast. Interference of the two tidal flows at the northern Danish coast, no tides here; therefore also hardly any extension of the tides into the Baltic Sea.

Tidal friction:

The motion of the tides uses up rotational energy of the earth - especially in the narrow straits

$$E_{rot} = \frac{1}{2} I\omega^2$$

I = moment of inertia

ω = angular velocity

Effect: $-P = \dot{E}_{rot} = I\omega\dot{\omega}$

(P = power dissipated, >0; ⟹ $\dot{\omega} < 0$)

Rotational angular momentum of the earth:

$L_{♁} = I\omega$ therefore also decreases with time

Conservation of angular momentum of earth-moon system

$$L_{♁} + \Omega\, m_{☾} r^2 = \text{const}$$

neglecting angular momentum of moon's rotation (small).

Ω = angular velocity of the moon around the earth

r = earth-moon distance.

Differentiate, substitute:

$$\frac{d}{dt}(\Omega\, m_{☾} r^2) = -I\dot{\omega} = \frac{P}{\omega}$$

$$\left(\frac{\dot{\Omega}}{\Omega} + 2\frac{\dot{r}}{r}\right)\Omega\, m_{☾} r^2 = \frac{P}{\omega}$$

Kepler's 3rd law: $(\text{Period})^2 \propto \Omega^{-2} = C\, r^3$

differentiated: $-2\,\dfrac{\dot{\Omega}}{\Omega^3} = C \cdot 3\, r^2 \dot{r}$

$$\Rightarrow \frac{\dot{\Omega}}{\Omega} = -\frac{3}{2}\frac{\dot{r}}{r}$$

we get: $\dfrac{1}{2}\dfrac{\dot{r}}{r} = \dfrac{P}{\omega\Omega\, m_{☾} r^2}$

Difficulty: to estimate P

Numerical values:

Lengthening of the day: ~1/1000 sec per century
Increase in the distance to the moon: ~12 cm per year

This will go on till rotation of earth = period of moon (sidereal month) $\approx 50^{d}$

7.5 *Eclipses*

A) Lunar eclipse: moon wholly (= total) or partly (= partial) in the umbra of the earth: or penumbral eclipse: moon wholly or partly in penumbra

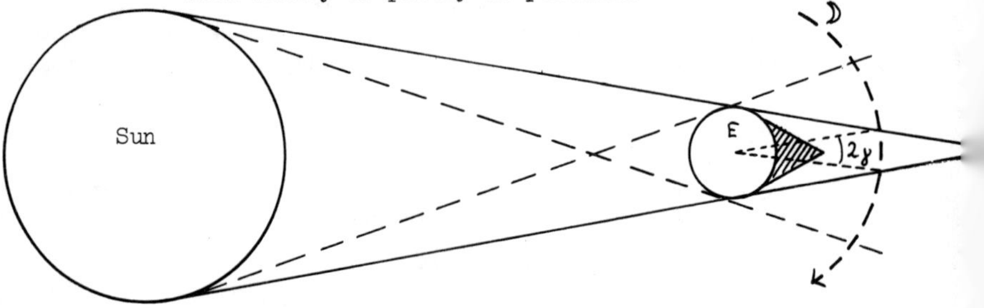

The diameters and lengths of the shadows follow from the distances and the sizes of the bodies concerned:

$R_{♁}$ = radius of the earth

Mean length of the umbra (earth to apex)		= 217 $R_{♁}$
Mean earth-moon distance		= 60 $R_{♁}$
Mean radius of the umbra at the distance of the moon (measured in 'arc)	γ	= 41!2
Mean radius of the moon	$R_{☾}$	= 15!5

From these we obtain:

duration of the whole eclipse up to	$3^{h}.8$
duration of totality up to	1.7

Mean radius of penumbra
duration of whole penumbral eclipse to 6^h

//Effect of refraction

The light which passes the earth at grazing incidence is deflected into the shadow by the double horizontal refraction; 2 times 35' (compare 1.4).
From this length of the absolute shadow = 40 $R_♁$ does not reach to the moon.
The moon always receives light (dark red to purple, because red light is less absorbed). Light conditions are strongly dependent on the existing atmospheric conditions. After the eruption of Krakatoa the eclipses were unusually dark because of the large amount of dust in the air

//Influence of the inclination of the lunar orbit (i = 5°) relative to the ecliptic

Usually the moon passes above or below the shadow of the earth.
Eclipses only if full moon near the node

> Line of nodes, nearly fixed in space, points - because of the revolution of the earth - toward the sun twice a year ⟶ eclipse seasons

Permitted distance from the node (≡ ecliptic limits)

Eclipse, when latitude of the moon (= distance from ecliptic) smaller than radius of shadow.

$$\beta < \gamma = 41'\!.2$$

For the corresponding distance in longitude from the node, we have:

$$\sin \Delta\lambda = \frac{\sin \beta}{\sin i}$$

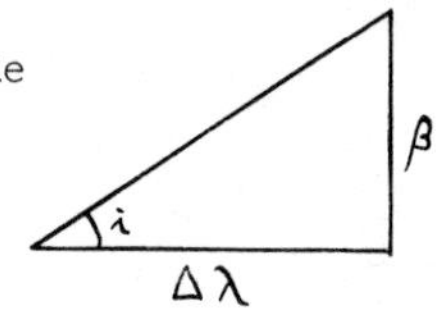

Total eclipse

$$\beta < \gamma - (R_☾) = 25'\!.7 \longrightarrow \Delta\lambda_{max} = \pm\ 4^\circ\!.6$$

Partial eclipse

$$\beta < \gamma + (R_☾) = 56'\!.7 \longrightarrow \Delta\lambda_{max} = \pm\ 10^\circ\!.2$$

($\pm 9^\circ\!.5$ to $\pm 12^\circ\!.1$ since orbit varies)

Motion of the sun ~1°/day = 30° per lunar revolution

> that is, at most one eclipse per eclipse season
> (e.g., at Δλ = - 10°, then next full moon at +20°)
>
> or no eclipse
> (e.g., full moon at Δλ = -12°, then next full moon at +18°)

B) Solar eclipse: (actually lunar occultation of the sun)

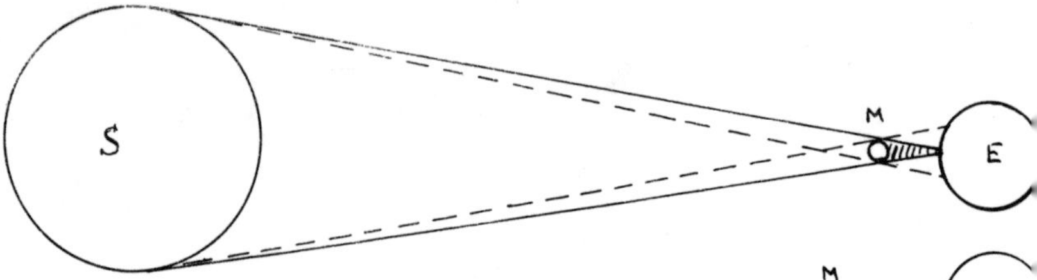

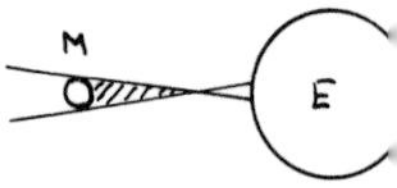

/Umbra of moon reaches the earth in the most favourable cases:

Then in the penumbra: partial eclipse
in the umbra: total eclipse

/At average distance umbra does not completely extend to the surface of the earth,

Then partial and annular eclipse

/Because of the curvature of the earth combination also possible: Annular-total eclipse

/Fortunate coincidence that apparent sizes of sun and moon now nearly equal

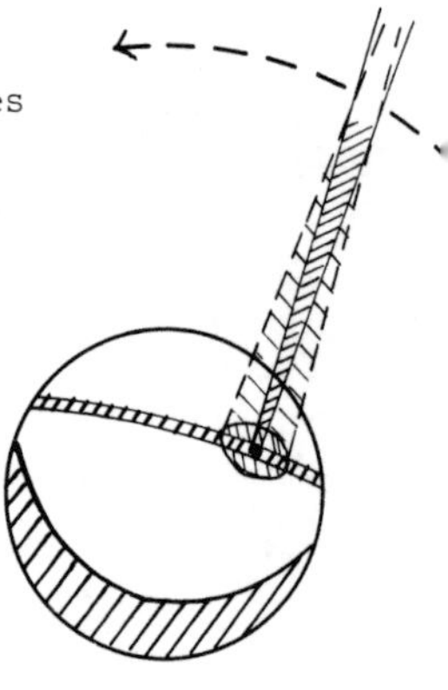

Visibility on the earth:

Only in some regions

Zone of visibility moves on the earth
a) Motion of the moon

$\sim$1 km/sec (W⟶E)

b) Rotation of the earth

$\sim$400 m/sec at equator (following eclipse motion)

The maximum time that the earth can remain in the penumbra is 6^h; maximum time in umbra (central eclipse, moon at node) nearly 4^h

Eclipse paths on maps:

Shadow first touches earth at "eclipse-at-sunrise" lines. Leaves earth at "eclipse-at-sunset" lines.

E.g., positions on the line "end of eclipse at sunrise": at sunrise the last contact just takes place, i.e., no eclipse observable.

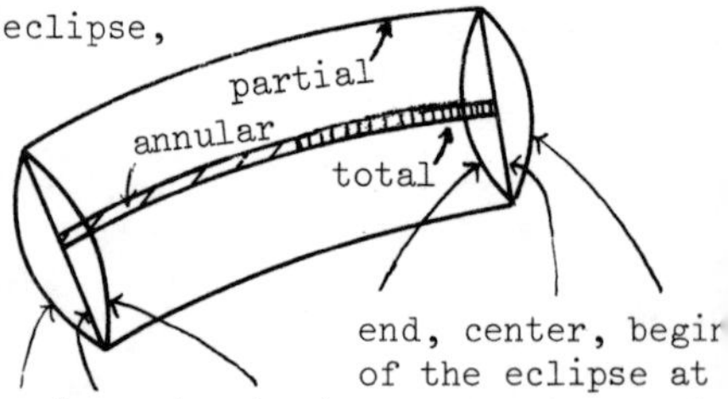

Most favourable eclipse:

Sun at aphelion (as distant as possible)

Moon at perigee (as near as possible)

axis of shadow pointed at the center of the earth (i.e., moon at node);

central zone at the equator, where rotation is the largest.

Then, maximum diameter of umbra: 264 km

Approximate velocity: 0.5 km/sec

Maximum duration at one place: 7 min 34 sec

(very seldom! Even a duration of more than 6 min unusual)

Permitted distance of node

(according to same considerations as for lunar eclipse):

Partial eclipse: $\Delta\lambda = \pm 16.1^{\circ}$

larger than for lunar eclipse, because the diameter of the limiting cone is larger.

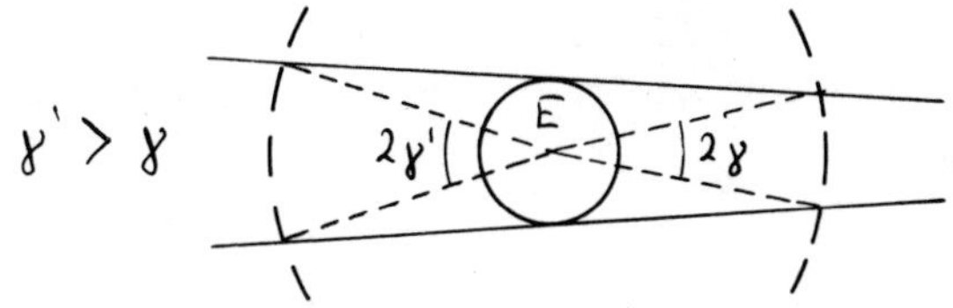

that is, always at least one eclipse per eclipse season (e.g., at $\Delta\lambda = -13^{\circ}$, then next new moon at $\Delta\lambda = +17^{\circ}$)

or two eclipses (e.g., at $\Delta\lambda = -15^{\circ}$, then next new moon at $\Delta\lambda = +15^{\circ}$)
In the case of two eclipses both are partial.

C) Number and cycle of eclipses

Solar eclipses $\sim 1\frac{1}{2}(\sim\frac{13.5}{9.9})$ times more frequent than lunar eclipses.
For a specific place, however, lunar eclipses are more frequent, because lunar eclipse visible from half of the earth, whereas solar eclipse only visible from a narrow strip.

On the average in 1000 years:

1543 lunar eclipses:	716 total	827 partial
2375 solar eclipses:	659 total	773 annular
	838 partial	105 annular-total

Because of the varying distances of the node, there are four possibilities during one eclipse season:

SM, *MS*, *SMS*, *S* | *S* = solar eclipse
M = lunar eclipse

SS does not occur. If both the new moons are symmetrically above and below the node, the intermediate full moon must be very close to the node and, consequently, there will be a lunar eclipse.

Two eclipse seasons per year. Because the node rotates in 18.6 years, the seasons shift in this cycle, hence every year they come about 2/3 month earlier.

E.g., in this manner, one season can occur in January, the next but one partly in December of the same year.

Hence, maximum per year: 7 eclipses

e.g.,	*MS*, *SMS*, *MS*	(4*S*, 3*M*)	e.g. 1917
or	*SMS*, *SMS*, *S*	(5*S*, 2*M*)	e.g. 1805
Minimum per year:	*S*, *S*	(2*S*)	e.g. 1951, 1962

Saros eclipse cycle

A periodicity occurs whenever the conditions repeat, i.e., a whole number of lunar revolutions with respect to the node and with respect to the phase,

that is, an integer multiple of the draconitic (nodical) and of the synodic month.

242 draconitic months = $6585\overset{d}{.}32$
223 synodic months = 6585.36 } 18 years $11\frac{1}{3}$ days

After a period of $18^{y}\,11\frac{1}{3}^{d}$ the cycle of eclipses repeats.

Already known to the Chaldeans, the Babylonians, and the Chinese, before the origin of the eclipses was known; served for forecasting.

The accidental (!) agreement of this Saros cycle with the period of revolution of the node has the result that the eclipses occur nearly at the same season
(every time shifted by about 10 days) (see figure on page 69).

The small difference in the multiples of the draconitic and the synodic months causes the conditions to change slowly. Certain eclipses drop out during the cycle, others join.

A lunar eclipse remains in the cycle, on the average, for 1000 years.
a solar eclipse remains in the cycle, on the average, for 1200 years.

E.g., the total solar eclipse of 22 Sept. 1968 is one of a series that began with a partial eclipse of small phase on March 1049, 51 Saros cycles ago.
From 1067 to 1193: eight more partial eclipses with increasing phase. Since 1211 the eclipses have been total.
The 1968 eclipse is the 43rd and the next-to-last eclipse of the series, the last one to occur on 3 Oct. 1986.
From 2009 to 2149, 9 partial eclipses of decreasing phase follow; thereafter the eclipse disappears from the cycle.

Archeology

Fixing of dates by means of eclipses, especially "zero-points" (for instance "in the 11th year of the emperor...it happened that...)

e.g., Execution of the Chinese astronomers Hi and Ho on 22 Oct. 2137 B.C., because they had not forecasted an eclipse (legend?)

Th. Oppolzer *Canon der Finsternisse* (Vienna 1887; translation O. Gingerich 1962, Dover, New York)
Compilation of all solar and lunar eclipses from -1207 (= 1208 B.C.) to 2161.

○ solar eclipse

● lunar eclipse

according to "Fischer-Lexikon" volume 4.

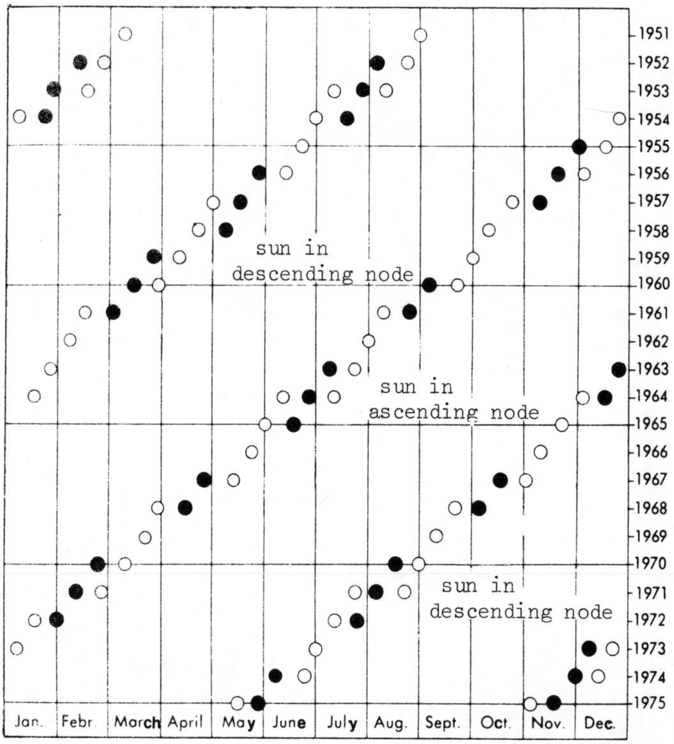

§ 8 Orbits of artificial spacecraft

Reference: R.H. Giese 1966, *Weltraumforschung* I Hochschultaschenbücher, Band 107/107a; Bibliographisches Institut, Mannheim. (Extensive description of rocket propulsion and of the celestial-mechanics foundations, so-called spaceflight mechanics)

8.1 *Rocket propulsion*

a) Fundamental equation for rocket motion

m = instantaneous mass of the rocket

V = instantaneous velocity of the rocket

mV = momentum of the rocket

J = exhaust or jet velocity = velocity of the expelled fuel with respect to the rocket ($J > 0$)

$V-J$ = jet velocity with respect to a coordinate system fixed in space

After elapsed time dt:

change in mass of rocket	$\mathrm{d}m$ (<0)
discharged mass of gas	$-\mathrm{d}m$
momentum of the mass of gas	$-\mathrm{d}m(V-J)$
mass of the rocket	$m + \mathrm{d}m$
velocity of the rocket	$V + \mathrm{d}V$
momentum of the rocket	$(m+\mathrm{d}m)(V+\mathrm{d}V)$

Law of conservation of momentum:

$$mV = (m+\mathrm{d}m)(V+\mathrm{d}V) - \mathrm{d}m(V-J)$$

or

$$\mathrm{d}V = -J\,\frac{\mathrm{d}m}{m}$$

where the term $\mathrm{d}m\mathrm{d}V$ is neglected because small in the 2nd order

Integration:

$$\Delta V = J \,\ln \frac{m_o}{m_B} \quad \text{= rocket formula}$$

where m_o = total mass (rocket+fuel) at time $t = 0$ (ignition

m_B = mass of rocket at end of firing (i.e., at burnout

ΔV = increase of velocity during the duration of firin

If the rocket was launched at the time $t = 0$ with $V = 0$, we have

m_o = mass at launch

and $\Delta V = V_B$ = velocity at end or burnout velocit

Put: m_o/m_B = mass ratio

V_B/J = velocity ratio

Then, the rocket formula is as follows:

Velocity ratio = ln (mass ratio)

$$\frac{V_B}{J} = \ln \frac{m_o}{m_B}$$

b) Efficiency (external efficiency)

{kinetic energy of the rocket at burnout} / {available energy of the fuel}

$$\eta = \frac{m_B V_B^2}{m_F J^2} = \frac{V_B^2/J^2}{(m_o/m_B)-1}$$

| $m_F = m_o - m_B$ = mass of fuel

By means of the rocket formula this can be expressed either as a function of the ratio of velocities only or of the mass ratio:

$$\eta = \frac{(V_B/J)^2}{e^{V_B/J}-1} = \frac{\{\ln (m_o/m_B)\}^2}{(m_o/m_B)-1}$$

V_B/J	m_o/m_B	η
0.001	1.001	0.001
C.01	1.010	0.010
0.1	1.105	0.095
0.5	1.65	0.385
1	2.72	0.582
1.594	4.93	0.647
2	7.39	0.626
4	55	0.299
6	403	0.089
8	2981	0.0215
10	22,000	0.0045

Maximum efficiency at velocity ratio 1.594, corresponding mass ratio 4.93

The efficiency can be increased by adjusting the exhaust velocity to the actual velocity of the rocket.

Optimum, if J is always equal to V

Then $V-J = 0$, i.e. the exhaust at rest with respect to a fixed system

For normal thermal propulsion J is 2 to 4 km/sec.

Because the mass ratio is not arbitrarily large (fuel containers are included in m_B), the escape velocity of 11.2 km/sec can not be achieved in this manner.

c) Multi-stage principle

After the firing of the first stage, the first-stage rocket is jettisoned:

Rocket formula (for constant J):

$$\boxed{V_B = J \ln \frac{M_o}{M_E}}$$

with $\frac{M_o}{M_B} = \Pi_i \left(\frac{m_c}{m_B}\right)_i =$

$=$ total mass ratio

$V_B = \sum_i \Delta V_i$

ΔV_i = velocity gained in stage i

d) Types of propulsion

Thermal propulsion: conversion of thermal energy of hot gases in a combustion chamber into kinetic energy of a gas jet. Thermodynamical considerations yield for the maximum exhaust velocity (full exploitation of total energy):

$$J_{max} = \sqrt{\frac{2\kappa}{\kappa-1} \cdot \frac{RT}{\mu}} = A\sqrt{\frac{T}{\mu}} \quad \{\text{km/sec}\}$$

T = temperature in the combustion chamber

μ = molecúlar weight

$\kappa = c_p/c_v$ — for actual gas mixtures: between 1.1 and 1.6

A = 0.24 to 0.43

Therefore: temperature as high as possible, and molecular weight as low as possible

The present chemical rockets work with liquid or solid fuel.

Future types of propulsion:

Thermo-nuclear fuels:

principle of thermal rockets; however, the energy to heat the gases is taken from a reactor.

Ion fuels:

Ions are accelerated by electric fields. High jet velocity; technical difficulties

Fusion fuels:

conversion of energy by nuclear fusion. Theoretically possible jet velocity at conversion of H to He about 12% of light velocity. Technical realization not yet conceivable.

Photon fuel:

repulsion of photons: jet velocity = light velocity
Accelerations very small. No realization conceivable

Schaifers and von Hoerner have estimated that even with exploitation of all theoretically conceivable possibilities manned space flight to other stars will not be possible.

For further technical details, see Giese (loc. cit.)

8.2 *Orbits of artificial satellites*

Circular orbits: 3rd law of Kepler (2.4.5) with $m_{sat} \ll m_{♁}$

Period of revolution $P = 2\pi \sqrt{\frac{r_c^{\,3}}{G\, m_{♁}}} = 84.491 \left(\frac{r_c}{r_{♁}}\right)^{3/2}$ [min]

$\frac{r_c}{r_{♁}}$ = radius of the circular orbit expressed in units of the earth's radius

Velocity $V_c = \frac{\text{circumference}}{\text{period of revolution}} = \frac{2\pi r_c}{P} = \frac{7.905}{\sqrt{r_c/r_{♁}}}$ [km/sec]

Altitude above surface of earth, $H = r_c - r_{♁}$

H {km}	r_c [km]	P	V_c [km/sec]	ΔV_∞ [km/sec]
0	6 378	$1^h\ 24^m$	7.91	3.27
100	6 478	1 26	7.85	3.24
500	6 878	1 34	7.62	3.15
1 000	7 378	1 45	7.36	3.07
2 000	8 378	2 07	6.91	2.86
10 000	16 378	5 48	4.94	2.04
35 790	42 168	$23^h\ 56^m 4^s$	3.07	1.27
			= synchronous orbit	
378 000	384 400	$27^d.322$	1.02	0.43
			= lunar orbit	

A satellite which rotates around the earth in the equatorial plane in the course of one sidereal day, standing still with respect to the rotating earth

= synchronous satellite

Velocity of escape: $V_e = \sqrt{2} \cdot V_c$ (2.4.4)

= 11.2 km/sec at the surface of the earth

ΔV_∞ = additional velocity necessary for escape

For satellites which are in a circular orbit this quantity becomes smaller with higher orbits.

Transition to other shapes of orbits:

In principle, all kinds of conics are possible orbits (2.4)

The figure shows circular, elliptical, parabolic, and hyperbolic orbits of the same perigee or apogee.

From the law of conservation of energy we have for elliptical orbits:

$$V^2 = Gm_{♁} \left(\frac{2}{r} - \frac{1}{a}\right)$$

(see 2.4.4)

r = radius vector

a = semimajor axis

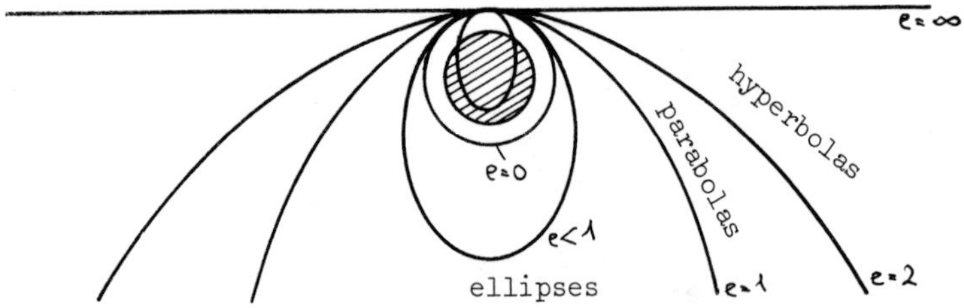

Elliptical orbits whose apogees touch the circular orbit would theoretically pass, in part, through the interior of the earth. The part of their orbit outside the earth represents the ballistic curve of intercontinental rockets or missiles.

Determination of orbits

In principle, same as the case of planetary orbits (2.5). The available initial and observational data are, to some degree, different.

The orbital elements can be determined

(a) from the position and velocity vectors of the space vehicle at a specified time (= initial-value problem)

(b) from the measurements of the topocentric distance (= distance from the observer) as obtained from radar observations, and the change of this distance with time so-called "range and range rate"

(c) from simultaneous measurements of the Doppler effect at three stations

(d) from three measurements of the direction (analogous to the classical determination of planetary orbits)

Detailed description of all these methods by Giese (loc. cit.)

Perturbations

Satellite orbits are subjected to strong perturbations.

a) Oblateness of the earth, mass distribution not spherically symmetric

Consequence: periodic variation of the gravitational force during a revolution (no true central force)

Rapid precession of the satellite orbit, rotation of the line of apsides.

b) Perturbation by sun and moon

Analogous to the perturbations by the sun of the lunar orbit (2.7.1)

c) Air resistance

Satellite is braked, moves lower, orbital velocity becomes higher because of Kepler's 3rd law (paradox). Satellite describes a spiral with increasing velocity.

Elliptical orbits are braked most strongly at perigee, hence apogee brought nearer. Orbit becomes more circular.

d) Radiation pressure of the sun

= 1 mg on 1 m^2 totally reflecting surface

For circular orbits: compensation during the revolution, no net effect.

For elliptical orbits: asymmetric effect, cumulative

Detected first with Vanguard I (1958)
Investigated more precisely with Echo I (1960)

8.3 *Interplanetary orbits*

Hohmann orbits

= elliptical orbits, which are tangent to the circular orbits to be connected (e.g., the orbit of the earth and the orbit of the planet to be reached) at perihelion and at aphelion

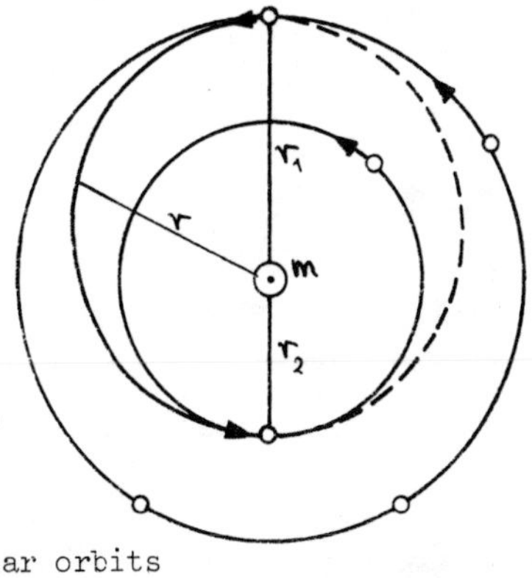

Semimajor axis of the Hohmann orbit

$$a = \frac{1}{2}(r_1 + r_2)$$

r_1 ; r_2 : radii of the circular orbits

Velocity at an arbitrary point of the Hohmann orbit:

$$V^2 = 2\ Gm\ \left(\frac{1}{r} - \frac{1}{r_1 + r_2}\right)$$ (by the law of conservation of energy: 2.4.4)

The spacecraft already has the circular velocity of the planet from which it starts. During flight to an outer planet, it must be accelerated, first to the perihelion velocity of the Hohmann ellipse, and once again at the aphelion, to the circular velocity of the destination orbit.

The necessary increase of velocity

at the starting orbit: $V_1 = V_p - V_{c_1}$

at the destination orbit: $V_2 = V_{c_2} - V_a$

V_p; V_a = perihelion and aphelion velocity of the Hohmann ellipse

V_{c_1}; V_{c_2} = circular velocity of the starting orbit and of the destination orbit

For ratios of the radii $r_1/r_2 < 1/3.4$ the value of $\Delta V_1 + \Delta V_2$ is larger than the increase which is necessary to reach the escape velocity.

During transition to an inner orbit, an analogous braking (deceleration) must take place twice.

Duration of the flight = half the period of revolution for the Hohmann orbit: (according to Kepler's 3rd law)

$$\frac{P}{2} = \frac{P_{c_1}}{2}\sqrt{\left(\frac{1 + r_2/r_1}{2}\right)^3}$$ where P_{c_1} = period of revolution of the starting circular orbit

Resulting earth-planet flight time (in years)

Mercury	0.40	Jupiter	2.73	Neptune	30.6
Venus	0.29	Saturn	6.05	Pluto	45.5
Mars	0.71	Uranus	16.1		

Hohmann orbits are the orbits with lowest energy requirements.

Example: a non-stop round-trip flight to Venus along three Hohmann semi-ellipses (flight time 6 months)

I, II, III: Three semi-ellipses

1 Start on earth

2 Meeting with Venus; change of velocity

3 Change of velocity

4 Return to the earth

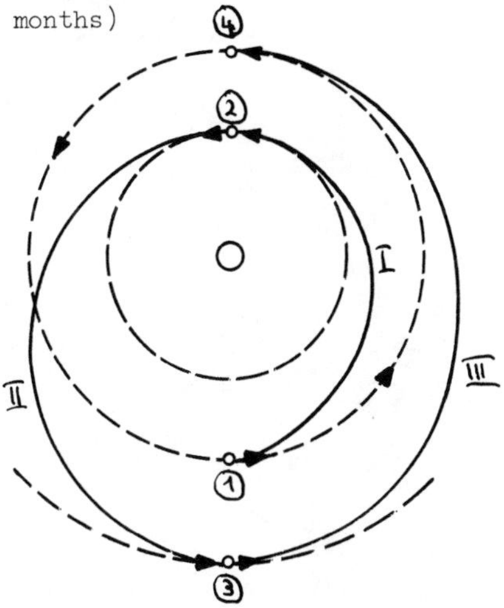

<u>Other (shorter) orbital shapes</u>

Flight times on Hohmann orbits relatively long, because of slow approach to apocenter.

In principle, portions of ellipses, hyperbolas or parabolas, which intersect the orbits of the earth and the planet come into consideration as "fuel-free orbits" (see below).

Examples:

a)

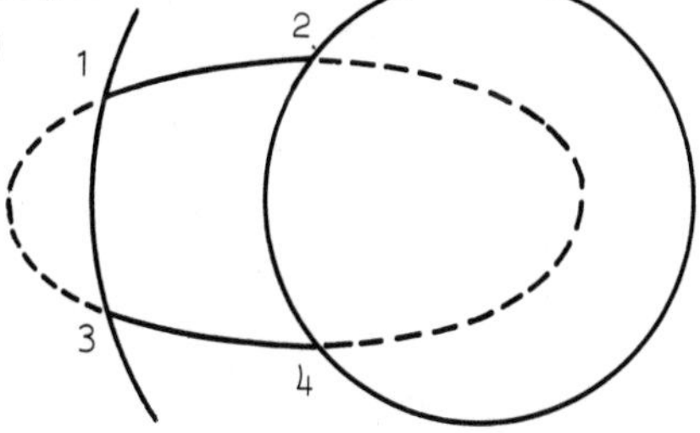

Arcs $\overset{\frown}{12}$ and $\overset{\frown}{34}$ on the ellipse represent <u>rapid-transition orbits</u>

b) <u>Orbital trajectory of one year to Mars</u>

Ellipse which touches the Martian orbit at the apocenter, with a period of revolution of 1 year, so that the spacecraft meets the earth again at the same point of the orbit.

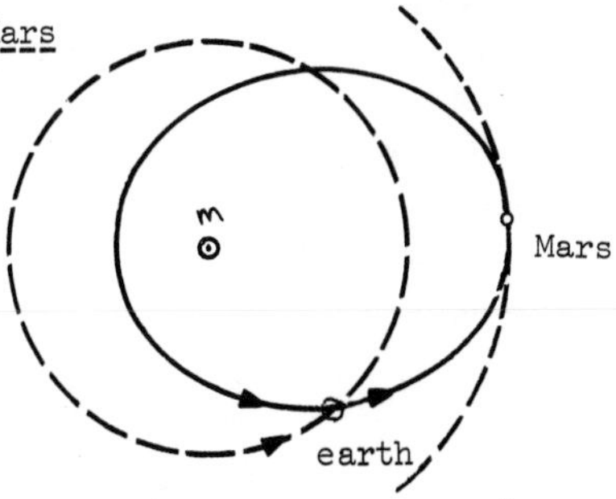

(Analogously for more distant planets, if the period of revolution is a multiple of a year)

c) Equal-time trajectory to Mars

Outward flight = return flight

Start at E_1, return at E_2:

short flight of 142^d

however, much larger consumption of energy than in example b

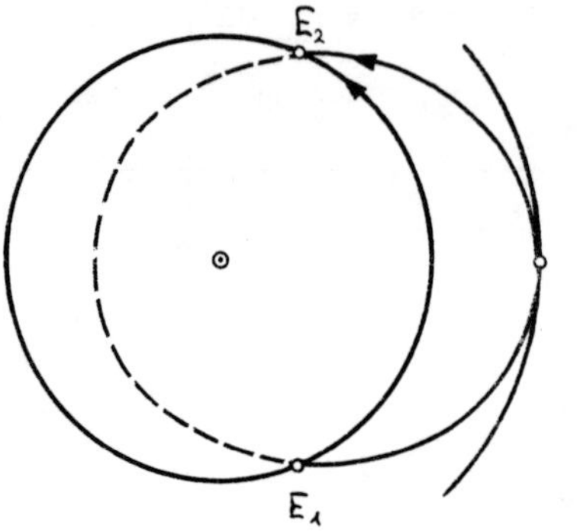

Besides these "fuel-free orbits" (short single acceleration at the start) there are, obviously, many more possibilities with more or fewer long-lasting accelerations during the journey. For instance, ion rockets will work with low but long-lasting thrust. For further details on such space-flight maneuvering reference must be made to the technical literature.

9 The solar system

Introductory remark: the description of the individual members of the solar system has been treated briefly here, because this field is covered very extensively in books on popular astronomy and in all elementary textbooks.

Physics of the sun: see chapters 4 to 6

9.1 *The planets and their satellites*

Reference:

G. Kuiper and B.M. Middlehurst, (editors) 1961, *Planets and Satellites*, Volume 3 of *The Solar System*, Chicago.

General data

1) The most important kinematical data:

Symbol	Name	diameter (equat.) [km]	distance from sun [10^6 km]	period of revolution	mass [$m_♁$]	Number of moons	
☿	Mercury	4 840	57.9	$88^d.0$	0.06	-	Inner Planets
♀	Venus	12 228	108.2	224.7	0.81	-	
♁	Earth	12 756	149.6	$1^y.00$	1.00	1	
♂	Mars	6 800	227.9	1.88	0.11	2	Outer Planets
♃	Jupiter	143 650	778	11.86	317.8	12	
♄	Saturn	120 670	1427	29.46	95.1	10	
♅	Uranus	47 100	2870	84.02	14.5	5	
♆	Neptune	44 600	4496	164.8	17.2	2	
♇	Pluto	6 400?	5940	247.7	0.1	-	

Extensive tables of kinematical and physical data in all reference books and nearly all general astronomy textbooks.

"Inner planets" sometimes refers to Mercury and Venus and sometimes to Mercury through Mars (terrestrial planets, along with Pluto). Hence "outer planets" may mean Mars ⟶ Pluto or Jupiter ⟶ Pluto.
Sometimes also Mercury and Venus are called "inferior planets" and Mars to Pluto "superior planets"

Scale model of the solar system: for visualization of dimensions and distances

Scale 1:10 , i.e., 1000 km ⟶ 1 mm

Object	diameter	distance from sun
Sun	1.40 m	-
Mercury	5 mm	60 m
Venus	12 mm	110 m
Earth	12 mm	150 m
Mars	7 mm	230 m
Jupiter	14 cm	780 m
Saturn	12 cm	1430 m
Uranus	5 cm	3 km
Neptune	5 cm	4.5 km
Pluto	6 mm	6 km
Next star (Proxima Centauri)		

2) Observed Quantities

Radius R: directly, since distance known

Mass m: dynamically; 3rd law of Kepler or from perturbations

(Radius and mass) ⟶ mean density ρ

Rotation: detectable by surface features, Doppler effect, light variation

Reflectivity:

$$\text{Albedo } A = \frac{\text{light scattered in all directions}}{\text{incident solar light}}$$

The rest $(1-A)$ is absorbed and re-emitted as heat.

Polarization, color: directly

Spectrum: reflected solar spectrum; superposed absorption spectrum of the atmosphere; especially in the infrared. H_2O ice is detectable by its diffuse bands in the IR.

3) Phases Especially in the case of Mercury and Venus

In the case of the moon the picture is somewhat different; the formulae, however, are valid for the phases of the moon, too.

View from the earth

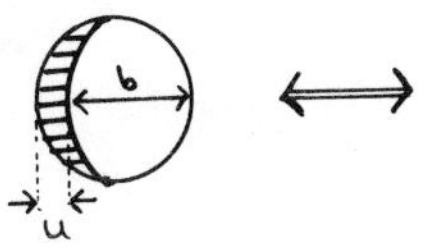

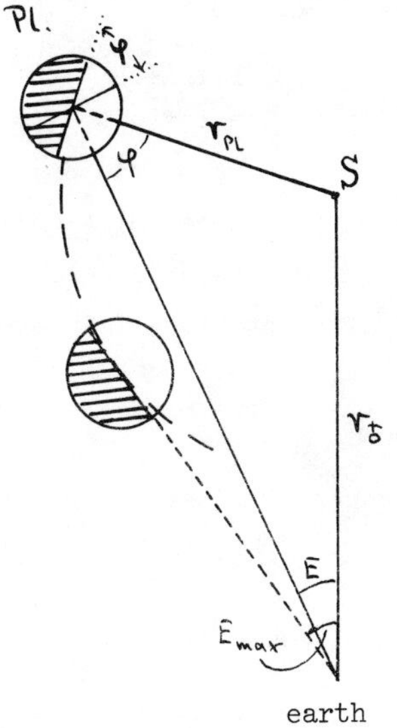

$r_{♁}$ = earth-sun distance

r_{pl} = planet-sun distance

ϕ = phase angle
= angle formed by earth-planet-sun

E = elongation
= angular distance of the planet from the sun;
angle formed by planet-earth-sun

d = angular diameter of the planet

One derives from the figure:

$$\sin \phi = \left(\frac{r_{♁}}{r_{pl}}\right) \sin E$$

Illuminated (light) part of the planet: $l = \frac{d}{2} + \frac{d}{2} \cos \phi = d \cos^2\left(\frac{\phi}{2}\right)$

dark (shaded) part of the planet: $s = d - l = d \sin^2\left(\frac{\phi}{2}\right)$

At greatest elongation E_{max} (for the inner planets)

we have $\phi = 90^\circ \Longrightarrow$ "Half-Venus"

For Mercury and Venus:

"Full planet" at $\phi = 0^\circ$, $E=0$ superior conjunction
"New planet" at $\phi = 180^\circ$, $E=0$ inferior "

For moon: Full moon: $\phi = 0^\circ$, $E = 180^\circ$
New moon: $\phi = 180^\circ$, $E = 0^\circ$

For the outer planets the maximum phase angle decreases:

Mars	45°	Saturn	6°
Jupiter	11	Uranus	3

Variations in brightness with phase

For Mercury and moon (no atmosphere):

Steep phase curve, i.e., bright at full phase
rapid decrease of brightness with decreasing phase.

For Venus (thick atmosphere): broad maximum

4) Temperature

Direct observation: comparison of the thermal infrared radiation with the reflected solar radiation in IR. Absolute intensity of the radio radiation.

Theoretical calculation: the planets (perhaps with the exception of Jupiter) have no significant heat sources.

T adapts itself in such a manner, that - taking account of the albedo -

emitted radiation ($\sim T^4_{eff}$) = incoming radiation from the sun

Hence: brightness temperature T_S at the subsolar point of a slowly or synchronously rotating planet:

$$\varepsilon_{pl}\ (T_s)^4_{pl} = (1-A)\ (T_{eff})^4_{\odot} \left(\frac{R_{\odot}}{r}\right)^2$$

where ε = infrared emissivity
for a black body = 1
for planetary material $\leqslant 1$, but usually ≈ 1

r = distance from the sun

R = radius

subscript $\odot$: sun

subscript pl: planet

A = albedo

For rapid rotation (adjustment between day and night):

surface exposed to solar radiation = $4\pi R^2_{pl}$

However, cross section of the beam of radiation only = πR^2_{pl}

Hence, average temperature:

$$\overline{T}_{pl} = \frac{T_s}{\sqrt[4]{4}} = 0.7\ T_s$$

Influence of the atmosphere:

The computed brightness temperature refers to an average emission level in the atmosphere, at which the optical depth for IR radiation ≈ 1.

$||$ Surface temperature T_o > theoretical brightness temperature T_s

Difference: $T_o - T_s$ = "greenhouse effect"

5) Atmosphere

Essential in determining the stability: mass, radius, temperature

a) Molecules (of velocity v) escape (according to 2.4.3)

if $E_{kin} > E_{pot}$

or $v^2 > v_e^2 = \frac{2Gm}{R}$

| m = mass of the planet
| R = radius of the planet
| v_e = velocity of escape

b) Probable velocity of the molecules according to the laws of thermodynamics:

$$\bar{v} = \sqrt{\frac{2\mathcal{R}T}{\mu}} = \sqrt{\frac{3kT}{m_A}}$$

| T = absolute temperature
| $\mathcal{R}$ = gas constant $= 8.3 \cdot 10^7$ erg deg^{-1} mol^{-1}
| μ = molecular weight
| m_A = atomic mass in grams
| $k = 1.38 \times 10^{-16}$ erg/deg = Boltzmann's constant

Hence, favourable: Large mass at small radius, low temperature

According to this, we have the following sequence of stability:

Jupiter, Saturn, Neptune, Uranus, Earth, Venus, Pluto, Mars, Neptune's satellite Triton, Saturn's satellite Titan --- Satellites of Jupiter JIII, JI, JII, JIV --- Mercury, the Moon Saturn's satellite Rhea ...

Result: up to Titan: atmosphere detected

From Mercury on: no atmosphere

Satellites of Jupiter: intermediate position; no gaseous atmosphere detectable, but ice and snow on the surface

6) General composition Two groups

a) "Terrestrial planets": Mercury to Mars (maybe Pluto)

= solid bodies; mass$\leq m_♁$; mean density $\bar{\rho}$ = 3.8 to 5.5 g/cm^3

Oxidizing atmosphere (O_2, CO_2, H_2O, N_2...)

b) "Jovian" planets: Jupiter to Neptune

Mass 13 to 320 $m_♁$; mean density $\bar{\rho}$ = 0.7 to 2.2 g/cm^3

Reducing atmosphere (H_2, CH_4, NH_3...)

More similar to solar composition; predominantly H and He

| E.g., Jupiter 78% H; Saturn 63% H

Reason: in the case of the planets near the sun H and He were volatized at the time of formation of the planets.

7) The individual planets

P = sidereal period of revolution
S = synodic period of revolution

(same position relative to the earth)

Mercury $P = 88^d$, $S = 116$ | 2 or 3 superior and 2 or 3 inferior conjunctions annually

Greatest elongation 28°, therefore difficult to observe

Transit of Mercury (= passage in front of the disk of the sun as seen from earth)

if Mercury close to the node at inferior conjunction.

Passages through the nodes around 8th of May and 10th of November.

Transits repeat with a period of 217 years. During this time: 20 transits in November and 9 in May.

Future transits: Nov. 10, 1973 (central)
Nov. 13, 1986
Nov. 6, 1993
Nov. 15, 1999 (grazing)

Rotation: according to radar measurements $58^d.64 = \frac{2}{3}P$, hence not synchronous

It can be shown that not only $t_{rot} = P$ (synchronous) but also $t_{rot} = \frac{1}{2}P$, $= \frac{2}{3}P$ etc are stable ratios if shape or density of the planet is asymmetrical.

Atmosphere: < 0.001 atm.

Surface: presumably very similar to the moon.

Albedo and polarization similar to those of the moon temperature between + 400° and -200°C approximately.

Venus $P = 225^d$, $S = 1$ yr 219^d | $5\,S = 8$ years: i.e., every 8 years Venus returns at the same time to th same position with respect to the su

Greatest elongation: 48° (morning and evening star)

Transits of Venus: beginning of June and beginning of December: in 8-year pairs, approximately every 120 yrs

1631, Dec. 6	1761 June 6	1874 Dec. 8	2004 June 7
1639, Dec. 4	1769 June 3	1882 Dec. 6	2012 June 5

Rotation: according to radar measurements 243^d

One Venus day corresponds to about 120 earth days hence, longer than a Venusian year and retrograde!

Atmosphere: thick envelope of clouds:
$97\%\ CO_2$, $0.6\%\ H_2O$, $<0.1\%\ O_2$, $<2\%\ N_2$ (Venera 4,5,6)

Also small amounts of HCl, HF, CO.

Pressure at surface = 95 ± 20 atm

Temperatures: theoretical brightness temperature, 230° C

Surface temperature: 430° C (Mariner 2)
$500 \pm 25^\circ$ C (Venera 4,5,6, Mariner 5)
700° C (radio obs., 3.2 cm)

At a height 70 to 100 km: -15° to -38° (Mariner 2)

Probability of organic life on Venus is very low.

Magnetic field: $< 10^{-4}$ Gauss

Reference: Handbook of the Physical Properties of the Planet Venus 1967, (NASA SP-3029, Washington);

Planetary Atmospheres 1971, I.A.U. Symposium no. 40 (edited by C. Sagan, T.C. Owen, H.J. Smith).

Earth Orbit of earth, see 2.2.3; earth-moon system, see 2.7

Reference: G. Kuiper and B. Middlehurst 1954, *The Earth as a Planet*, Vol.II of *The Solar System*, Chicago

Equatorial radius R_E = 6 378 388 m conventional value
= 6 378 165 m proposed new system of astronomical constants (see 1.8)

Polar radius R_P = 6 356 912 m

Oblateness $\frac{R_E - R_P}{R_E} = \frac{1}{298} = .0034$

Atmosphere: 78% N_2; 21% O_2 (by volume)

Average temperature: $+14^\circ$ C; magnetic field: 0.5 Gauss

Surface: 71% water; 29% land masses

Internal composition: earth mantle of 2900 km thickness (silicates), then iron-nickel core.

Moon Radius = 1740 km = 0.27 $R_♁$

Synchronous rotation (because of libration (2.7.3) about 59% of the surface visible)

No appreciable atmosphere: $\lessdot 10^{-9}$ atm.

Surface Solid; less dust than presumed; structure probably similar to the outer layers of the earth.

Low thermal conductivity (the thermal radio radiation which originates below the surface, shows a considerable phase lag with respect to the infrared radiation from the surface.)

Temperature: $+110^\circ$ to -150° C

Formations on the surface

Maria (singular: Mare): extended dark stone deserts, covered with basaltic lava (some are circular and probably originated by the impact of large meteors or comets); only a few craters

Terrae (highlands): bright regions, specially outstanding near the south pole, over all covered with craters

Craters: on good lunar maps about 40 000 with diameters from 200 to 2 km. According to recent explorations, pits down to <1 m. Origin: Very probably both, impact of meteorites and vulcanism (the relative proportion is still controversial)

Mountains: up to 8 000 m in height

Rills: grooves up to 100 km long

Rays: rectilinear, radiating from the large craters, several hundred km long: line composed of many very small craters

Domes: like blisters, diameters of some km; height up to 100 m

More results from recent Apollo flights, see, for instance:

Mason and Melson 1970, *The Lunar Rocks* (Interscience, N.Y. and reports in *Science*

The earth-moon system has a mass ratio of 81.3:1.

It resembles a double planet more than it does the other planet-satellite systems.

Mars

P = 687 days

S = 2 yrs 48 days

Minimum distance from earth (every 15 years) = 0.37 AU

Atmosphere: at the surface density $\leqslant 0.01\ \rho_{♁}$; pressure at surface ~ 5 mb

Main constituent CO_2

Detected: H_2O, possibly CO ($\leqslant$ 0,1 vol -%), in the upper atmosphere (Mariner 6): CO_2^+, CO, H_2 (L_α), O

Polar caps: at the end of winter extend up to 10^7 km^2

Very probably CO_2-snow ("dry ice") and not H_2O-snow or hoarfrost

Surface: yellowish-red, presumably iron compounds; variations in intensity and contrast (haze) point on meteorological phenomena (fog, dust storms)

Dark areas show seasonal color changes; mosses and lichens?

For more details see *Handbook of the Physical Properties of the Planet Mars* 1967, (NASA SP-3030, Washington);

I.A.U. Symposium no. 40 (*Planetary Atmospheres*), 1971.

Temperatures:

maximum temperature at equator	~300 °K
night-side temperature at equator (estimated)	~200
day-side temperature at poles	~220
mean temperature of day side	~260
mean temperature of whole planet	~230
lowest temperature at polar cap (Mariner 6)	~150

Pictures by Mariner 4, 6 and 7 show great similarity to the moon; hundreds of craters with diameter ~700 m (limit of resolution) to 200 km.

Magnetic field (according to Mariner 4): $<10^{-3}$ to 10^{-4} Gauss

Two satellites diameters about 10 to 15 km (estimated)

Phobos: Only 2.8 Mars-radii distant. Period of revolution $7^h.7$, i.e., shorter than Martian rotation ($24^h.6$); consequently Phobos rises in the west and sets in the east!

Deimos: 7 Mars-radii distant; $P = 30^h.3$, thus somewhat longer than Martian rotation. Deimos moves from east to west, but very slowly; remains above the horizon for almost 3 Martian days and passes at that time through all its phases several times

Jupiter P = 11.86 yrs, S = 1 yr 34 days | fast rotation: $9^h 50^m$ (at equator) i.e., 10 000 days per Jovian year, oblateness: $\frac{1}{15}$

Largest planet, mass = 0.001 $M_\odot$

Differential rotation: at intermediate latitudes, about 1% slower than at equator

Atmosphere: CH_4 (methane); NH_3 (ammonia); H_2

Temperature: -130° C

Jupiter has "cloud" belts parallel to its equator, which are readily visible. Near south temperate belt is the elliptical Great Red Spot, ~10 000 km x 40 000 km, (size and color variable). Its rotation period varies slowly ($\pm$ 12 sec), result: spot drifts completely around planet in longitude.

Radio radiation:

cm region: thermal radiation

dm region: non-thermal radiation, $T_s \approx 50\,000^{\circ}$

presumably synchrotron radiation

m region: short-period radiation bursts

$\Longrightarrow$ Jupiter has an ionosphere and radiation belts

Reference: *Handbook of the Physical Properties of the Planet Jupiter* 1967, NASA SP-3031, Washington

Satellites: 12 known up to now

The four large ones (Io, Europa, Ganymede, Callisto) with diameters of 3100 to 5600 km have been known since Galilec Masses 0.6 to 2.1 m . No noticeable gaseous atmosphere, but presumably partly covered by H_2O snow. The inner satellites move so fast that viewed from Jupiter they have loop and retrograde orbits.

Eclipses in the Jovian system are readily observable.

O. Roemer, 1675, determined the velocity of light using them. Before the invention of the radio, the shadow ingresses and egresses, the beginnings and ends of the transits, etc., serv as time indicators for longitude determinations (see 1.10.2).

The other 8 satellites are small (10-60 km) and difficult to observe

The 12 satellites can be divided into three groups according to their orbits.

Distances to scale:

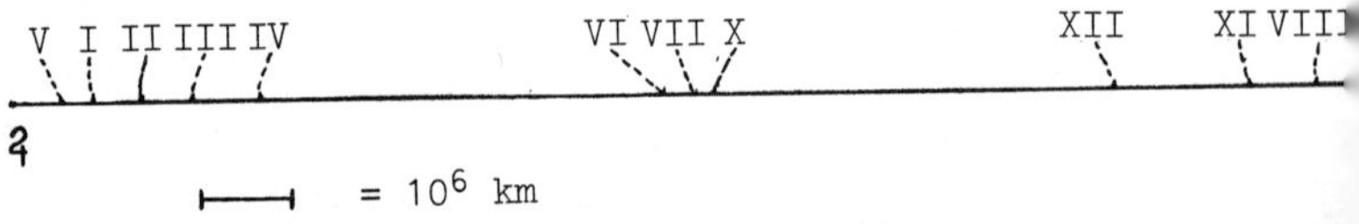

	Inner group	Central group	Outer group
Satellites	I through V	VI, VII, X	XII,XI,VIII,IX
Distance in R_{Jup}	2 to 26	160 to 165	290 to 336
Period of revolution	$0\overset{d}{.}5$ to 16^d	250^d to 260^d	617^d to 758^d
Orbital inclination i	3°	28°	147° to 155°
Eccentricity e	< 0.01	0.13 to 0.21	0.17 to 0.38
	circular orbit	high ellipticity	

The satellites of the outer group have retrograde orbits ($i > 90°$). Presumably they may be captured asteroids.

Saturn

P = 29.46 yrs Rotation 10^h14^m

S = 1 yr 13 days Oblateness $\frac{1}{10.2}$

Differential rotation: at intermediate latitude about 4% slower than at the equator

Atmosphere: like Jupiter: CH_4, NH_3, H_2
Helium not observed, but certainly present
Faint belts visible, similar to Jupiter's

Ring system:

Small particles (probably ice crystals), which revolve individually according to Kepler's law

The ring is inside the Roche limit (see 8.6.1).

A large body (satellite) cannot exist here; it would be broken up by the differential effect of the gravitation of Saturn

Total mass of ring estimated to ≈ 1/2500 $m_♄$

Ring system inclined by 28° to the orbit of the earth; from the earth it appears sometimes as a line, sometimes as an ellipse with $b \approx 0.5a$.
Ring's aspect has a period of $P_{Sat}/2$ = 15 years.

Description and dimensions:

			width
Outer ring (A) bright	outer diameter inner diameter	278 000 km 240 000 km	19 000 km
Cassini's division			3 000 km
Central ring (B) very bright	outer " inner "	234 000 km 178 000 km	28 000 km
Inner (crepe) ring (C) faint	outer " inner "	178 000 km 144 000 km	18 500 km

Distance inner border ring C from surface of Saturn: 12 000 km

Equatorial diameter of Saturn 120 700 km

Maximum thickness of the rings: 20 km

> "Cassini's division" is swept empty by perturbations; the period of revolution at the distance of this gap has a ratio 1:2 to the period of revolution of the inner satellite Mimas, and 1:3 to the period of Enceladus. The boundary between the central ring and the crepe ring corresponds to a period 1:3 that of Mimas.

Satellites of Saturn: 10 known

Observation of a small gap in ring led to prediction of existence of No. 10, Janus, discovered 1966, very close to Saturn

> An additional satellite Themis was observed only once, 1905. Presumably a mistake

Titan, the largest, has nearly the dimensions of Mercury; it has its own atmosphere (CH_4; $T = -180°$ C)

Diameters of the satellites: 300 to 5000 km

Four groups, according to distance from Saturn

3 - 9 R_s:	Janus, Mimas, Enceladus, Tethys, Dione, Rhea
20 - 24 R_s:	Titan, Hyperion
50 R_s:	Iapetus
216 R_s:	Phoebe (retrograde; presumably a captured asteroid)

Uranus P = 84 yrs; S = 1 yr 5 d

> Rotation 10^h49^m retrograde
>
> Axis of rotation is almost in the orbital plane
>
> Oblateness 1/18

Discovered 1781 (F.W. Herschel)

Atmosphere: CH_4, H_2 (ammonia will be frozen, therefore not visible in spectra)

5 Satellites Miranda, Ariel, Umbriel, Titania, Oberon

Inclination to ecliptic 98° (!), hence retrograde rotation

Diameters: 400 to 1000 km; distances evenly distributed between 5 and 24 $R_♅$

Periods of revolution: $1 - 13^d$

Neptune P = 165 yr | Rotation $15^{h}.8 \pm 1^{h}$

S = 1 yr 2 days

Existence computed from perturbations on the orbit of Uranus (Adams, Leverrier); discovered by Galle 1846.

Atmosphere: CH_4, H_2

2 satellites: Triton, Nereid (very dissimilar pair)

Triton: (discovered 1846), diameter 4000 km, own atmosphere
Density ~ 5 g/cm^3 (Neptune only 1.3)
Very similar to the planet Pluto

Nereid: 16 times more distant and about 1/10 diameter of Triton. Cometary orbit with = 0.76. Discovered 1949.

From the distance of Neptune the sun appears as a disk of 1' diameter (almost starlike) but its brightness would still be 4000 times the brightness of the full moon.

Pluto P = 248 years | Rotation $6^{h}.4$ (photometric value)

S = 1 yr $1^{d}.5$

Discovered by Tombaugh (1930), during search for planet (with $m = 6.6\ m_{\oplus}$); predicted by Lowell (1916) to explain supposed further Uranus residuals. Residuals actually insignificant; discovery near predictal position coincidental!

Orbit very eccentric, extends within the orbit of Neptune; perihelion will be reached in 1989

No detectable atmosphere; composition similar to the inner planets
Maybe a former satellite of Neptune

> Possibly Neptune's orbit was perturbed during Pluto's escape from it, causing deviation from Titius-Bode law. (see 2.2.1) (?)

In summary: at the extreme borders of the planetary system unusual conditions may prevail. (Perturbations by a passing star, cosmogonic causes??)

9.2 *The asteroids* (= minor planets = planetoids)

Kepler predicted another celestial body between Mars and Jupiter. Discovery of the first asteroid Ceres, 1801. Today about 5000 have been found, about 1700 with known orbits.

> No current computation of ephemerides of all orbits; hence it is often difficult to decide whether a newly discovered asteroid is really "new".

A name and number are assigned to objects with known orbits.

Orbits: mainly between Mars and Jupiter, concentrated to the ecliptic, often high eccentricities

e.g.,	Adonis	e = 0.78	almost to the orbit of Mercury
	Hidalgo	e = 0.65	to the orbit of Saturn, largest a (= 5.8 AU)
	Icarus	e = 0.83	closest to sun (.08 AU) at perihelion (inside the orbit of Mercury)

Highest inclinations: Betulia i = 52°
Hidalgo i = 43

Minimum distance from the earth:

Eros:	0.15 AU	
Amor:	0.1 AU	
Hermes:	0.004 AU	(accurate orbital elements unknown

Perturbations: gaps, known as Kirkwood gaps, at those distances at which the period of revolution has a commensurable ratio to the orbital period of Jupiter

e.g., 1:2 (Hecuba-gap), 1:3 (Hestia-gap), 2:5, 3:7.

In contrast to this, there is a still unexplained clustering at 2:3 (Hilda-group)

Special case of the "Trojans": 14 asteroids at the libration points L_4 and L_5 of Jupiter (see 2.6.3). Names of heroes of the Trojan War. They describe - in a simultaneously rotating coordinate system - kidney-shaped orbits around these libration points:

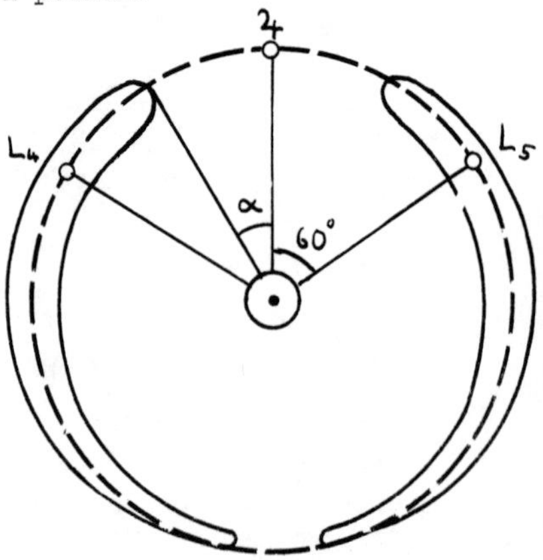

$\alpha_{min} = 23\overset{\circ}{.}9$

Total number of asteroids: about 2000 asteroids were discovered in a field of 12° by 18° on plates taken with the Palomar-Schmidt telescope. From this

magnitude	estimated number
up to 15^m:	1 000 asteroids
up to 19 :	30 000 "
up to 20 :	75 000 "

Total estimated mass: lower limit: 0.001 mass of the earth ($m_♁$)
upper limit: 0.4 to 0.6 $m_♁$ (would be detectable by their perturbations)

Diameter:

Micrometric measurements only for the four largest (Ceres, Pallas, Juno, Vesta): 770 to 200 km

Photometric estimates:

200 asteroids with diameters above 100 km
500 " " " between 100 and 50 km
the rest below 50 km

Possibly a continuous progression in size down to the interplanetary dust (?)

9.3 *Comets*

Designation: year of discovery with lower case letter in order of discovery. After determining the definitive orbit: year of perihelion passage and Roman numeral in order of the time of perihelion passage. In addition the name of the discoverer, and, eventually, the number of his discovery.

e.g., 1930 I (= 1930 d) Schwassmann-Wachmann 3

Orbits: nearly parabolic orbits, $e \approx 1$

16% of the comets $e < 0.96$
84% of the comets $0.96 < e < 1.004$

The hyperbolic orbits are presumably all caused by perturbations of elliptical orbits. No comets known with $e > 1.004$

⟹ Comets belong to the solar system. A "cloud of comets" accompanies the sun.

(a) Long-period comets: planes of orbits nearly isotropically distributed. Aphelia up to 1 parsec (interstellar space). Periods of revolution 10^2 to more than 10^7yrs.

(b) Short-period comets: captured by the planets

Orbital inclinations up to 15°, direct, aphelia cluster around the large planets, so-called "families"

e.g., Jupiter family: 68 members

Periods of revolution 2 to 200 years

famous example: Comet Halley, since 239 B.C. in 29 perihelion passages observed

Because the comets break up in the course of time, apparently these families are replenished by new captures.

Number of comets:

About 1600 known (record of comet observations back to the 3rd millenium B.C.) about 600 with well known orbital elements (~100 short-period comets)

Total number: only rough estimates

Bobrovnikoff (1921, Publ. Astr. Soc. Pacific, **41**, 98)
About 10^6 comets with perihelion inside Neptune's orbit

Oort (1950, Bull. Astr. Inst. Netherlands, **11**, 91)
About 10^{11} comets within a radius of 150 000 AU (= 0.75 pc) around the sun

Masses: upper limits from kinematical data for 5 comets:

10^{16} to 10^{23} g (mass of earth: 6×10^{27} g)

Composition and dimensions

Nucleus 1 - 100 km diameter

Meteoric material + compounds of the elements H, C, N, O (frozen radicals, ice, hydrides)

Similar to the outer planets

Structure of the matter unknown (cloud of small particles or few large fragments or a single body), probably single object

Spectrum: reflected solar light.

Coma (or head): 10^4 to 10^5 km diameter

As the sun is approached, H_2O and other molecules evaporate from the nucleus, streaming outwards at about 1 km/sec, are further broken down by photochemical processes and excited by solar radiation to fluorescence and resonance emission.

At first dust and ions (it is doubtful that this mechanism governs neutral molecules) evaporate predominantly in the direction of the sun, often forming jets and parabolic shells. Then they are pushed outward by the radiation pressure, and, a diffuse nebulous halo develops around the nucleus,

⟶ coma

Spectrum:

1) Reflected solar light (scattered by the particles)
2) Molecular bands, radicals, ions of radicals:

   CH, NH, OH, CH_2, NH_2, CN, C_2, C_3, OH^+, CH^+, ...

   Occasionally atomic lines: Na, Fe, Ni, O, ...

Brightness: (reduced to the distance comet-sun = comet-earth = 1 AU)

varies with the activity of the comet.
Occasionally eruptive phenomena, explosions.

Tail = Material "blown away" from the sun

Lenghts of tails 10^6 to 10^8 km, width up to 10^6 km

Velocity 100 to ~300 km/sec

Formation of tail occurs approximately as the comet enters within the orbit of Mars.

//Type I tail: elongated, narrow, points almost directly away from sun

spectrum: ions of molecules and radicals (low density inhibits recombination):

N_2^+, CO^+, OH^+, CO_2^+, CH^+, ...

Resonance radiation ends where the dissociations begin. This determines the length of the tail. The most long-lived ions:

N_2^+, CO^+ (10^6 sec)

The radiation pressure is not sufficient to form the tail.

Material is blown away by the solar wind (see 2.9.5). This explains the variations with solar activity that are occasionally observed.

//Type II tail: broad, diffuse, often curved

Predominantly colloidal particles

Spectrum: scattered solar light

Solar wind has only little effect (neutral particles); the solar radiation pressure and the solar gravitation are of the same order, therefore almost force-free motion; material stays behind the nucleus, formation of a tail.

Dissipation: short-period comets dissipate because of phenomena in the cometary interior, because of perturbations from planets and because of the differential effect of the solar attraction. Observed decrease in brightness up to a factor of 100 in 50 years.

Matter is spread out over the orbit; when earth crosses orbit ⟶ meteor showers (see 2.9.4)

Famous example: comet Biëla. Before 1845 several normal appearances; 1845 two nuclei, 1852 distance of the nuclei $2.5 \cdot 10^6$ km; After 1852 not anymore observed, but from this time meteor shower "Biëlides"

Extensive descriptions of individual comet appearances in the literature

9.4 *Meteors and meteorites*

Definition (International Astronomical Union terminology,'61)

Meteor: A streak of light produced by an extraterrestrial particle as it penetrates, and burns up in, the earth's atmosphere

Small meteors = shooting stars

Large meteors = fire balls, bolides

Meteorite: the extraterrestrial object itself after it has fallen to the surface of the earth.

Meteoroid: the object itself in space or in the atmosphere Frequently still referred to as meteors

Penetration into the atmosphere:

Parabolic heliocentric velocity of the meteoroid at the position of the earth:	42 km/sec
Velocity of the earth:	30 km/sec
Hence, relative velocity:	up to 72 km/sec

In the morning, high; observer in front } with respect to the motion of the earth
In the evening, low; observer in back } with respect to the motion of the earth

Notice: it is a question of a collision between the meteoroid and the earth, not an attraction by the earth. The latter only changes the orbit somewhat.

During penetration into the atmosphere: compression of the air, excitation of shock waves; matter from the meteoroid evaporates from the surface; slowly a long, cylindrical tube of ionized air (a trail or train) is formed.

Begins to glow at 130...100 km height

Fades out at 90...20 km height (depending on the size)

The ionized trail reflects microwaves and thus makes possible the observation of meteors using radar echos (even during the day and through clouds!)

In the case of meteor showers the ionized regions make a noticeable contribution to the ionosphere, the so-called anomalous E-layer.

Mass-luminosity relation uncertain

For meteors of the 1st magnitude (like the brightest stars) masses between 0.006 and 1.6 g are given (depending on the theoretical assumptions applied).

Spectrum: emissions of the evaporated material; occasionally emissions of the atmospheric gases

Orbits, meteor showers (meteor streams)

According to origin and shape of the orbit one distinguishes:

a) Planetary meteoroids (sporadic) (about 50%)

= small bodies belonging to the planetary system

intermediate between the asteroids and the substratum of zodiacal light.

Heliocentric orbits: ellipses with short periods of revolution

b) Cometary meteoroids (shower) (about 20%)

= small particles from dissipated cometary nuclei

Ellipses with short to medium periods of revolution (several years to several centuries)

c) Meteoroids with nearly-parabolic orbits (sporadic)(about30%)

= small bodies of unknown origin,

but members of the solar system, probably perturbed by the planets.

Occasionally (1-3%) hyperbolic orbits observed, the reality of which, however, is doubtful

Development of cometary showers

Cometary meteoroids appear if original orbit of the comet and orbit of the earth cross each other. The small bodies from a dissipated comet first stay together and revolve around the sun according to the original nucleus;

thus only in periodic intervalls they meet the earth, causing a so-called periodic shower (period of the original comet). After a while the bodies spread out over the whole orbit, showers appear every year, the stream has become a permanent stream. On account of the perturbations by the planets the orbit is changed or the stream is dissipated completely, thus the observed showers become fainter and fainter and finally vanish.

About 50 showers are known - some recurring over many decades, some short-lived or irregular.

e.g., Perseids:
beginning of August, remnant of Comet 1862 III

Leonids:
beginning of December, remnant of Comet 1866 I

Designated according to the constellation, which the "radiant" is in

= point on the sphere, from which the meteors appear to come

In several cases a night- and a day-meteor shower (evidence from radar) originate from the same former comet, the orbit of which intersects the orbit of the earth at two points.

This only can happen if the orbit of the shower has a small inclination towards the ecliptic, therefore called:

ecliptical showers or ecliptical streams

Meteorites

In the case of large fragments the heat does not penetrate quickly enough into the interior; remnant, pitted by melting, falls to the earth as a meteorite.

About 1600 finds; for about half of them the descent was observed (among those: 1/10 iron- and 9/10 stony meteorites), for the other half descent not observed (2/3 iron meteorites).

List of falls of meteorites:

F. Heide 1957, *Kleine Meteoritenkunde* 2nd ed., Springer

Summary:

Stony meteorites 93%: chondrites 86%, achondrites 7%

density ≈ 3.4 g/cm^3: similar to terrestrial silicate rocks.

Most contain 'chondrules' - glass-like globules formed from hot droplets of melted rock.

Iron meteorites 6%: density 7.8 g/cm³.

Mainly Fe-Ni crystals (> 99% Fe, Ni), internal structure resulting in the 'Widmanstätten' pattern of lines seen if the meteorite is sliced, polished and etched with acid.

Stony-iron meteorites 1.5% (~60% Fe)

> More details in J.A. Wood 1968, *Meteorites and the Origin of Planets* (McGraw-Hill, New York)

Micrometeorites: diameter D smaller than a few μ

Air resistance $\propto D^2$ Gravitation ~mass $\propto D^3$	For micrometeorites air resistance so strong that they do not become luminous. Meteorite floats to the ground intact.

Micrometeorites, collected by rocket, when examined under a microscope are seen to consist of

a) loose, soft, fluffy particles

b) compact particles - not molten - of irregular shape

c) globules: small spherical particles

Analysis: (especially of the radioactive isotopes, etc.)

(a) Nearly all chemical elements found (except Kr, Pm, At, Fr)

(b) Age of the elements $\approx 10^{10}$ years

(c) Age of stony meteorites (solidification and formation of larger bodies) 4 or 5 x 10^9 years

(d) Radiation age (= time since the body was first exposed to cosmic rays)

for iron meteorites: 10^8 - 10^9 years
for stony meteorites: 10^7 - 10^8 years

(Presumably the moment at which the meteorite is knocked off a larger body by a collision)

(e) Cosmic radiation constant within a factor of 2 during the last 10^9 years

Masses: stony meteorites known up to 1 ton
iron meteorites known up to 60 tons (Hoba, South-West Africa)

Meteorites of more than 100 tons must vaporize on impact, so that only small quantities of meteoric matter remain. Indeed, in the case of large craters scarcely any meteoric material, much less a massive body, is found.

e.g., Arizona Meteor Crater (also known as Canyon Diablo or Barringer Crater) diameter 1200 m, depth 175 m. The meteorite (impact about 20,000 years ago) must have had a weight of ≈60 thousand tons. Its kinetic energy was approximately that of a 30 megaton H-bomb.

Only large falls known in historical times:

1908 Tunguska, Siberia

Compression wave in the atmosphere traveled at least once around the world; destruction to 65 km radius. No meteoritic fragments found. Probably the core of a comet (Krinov) or a meteorite with such great kinetic energy that it vaporized not only the meteorite but a large mass of soil and rock as well. In either case, probably exploded while still in the air.

and 1947: eastern Siberia in the Sikhotay-Alin mountains near Vladivostok; a "rain of iron" over several square km, more than 100 craters. Not nearly as powerful as the 1908 event, however.

Daily influx of meteorites

Daily accumulation from falls of meteorites (particles $>10^{-2}$ cm):

Almost 10^8 meteors brighter than 5^m appear daily over the whole earth.

Daily total mass (predominantly micrometeorites) very difficult to estimate:

between 20 and 6500 tons (values given in the literature)

Figure: number of meteorites per km^2 per year with mass > m

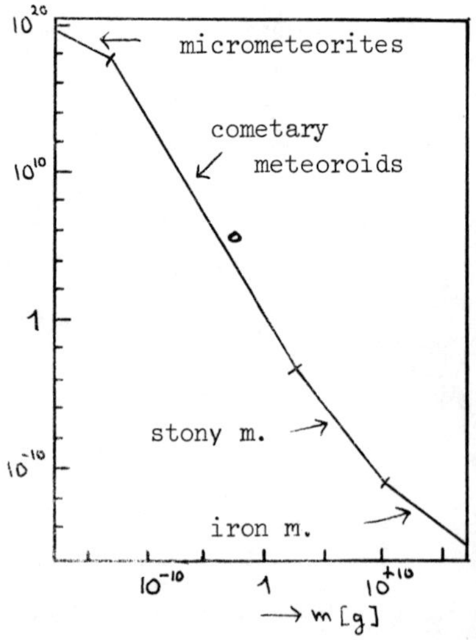

Data on cometary meteoroids come from radar measurements, since these particles are too small to reach ground.
So far, a meteorite from a cometary shower has never been found.

Taken from Unsöld 1969, *The New Cosmos*, Springer-Verlag (transl. by W.H. McCrea).

9.5 *Interplanetary matter*

The existing observational material does not yet yield a coherent, consistent picture.

A) Interplanetary dust

Zodiacal light - gegenschein - F-corona

/Zodiacal light = cloud of dust (and, to a small extent, free electrons) around the sun, a lens-shaped disk, approximately in the plane of the ecliptic

Observable as a cone-shaped band of light in the region of the zodiac after sunset and before sunrise.

Tip of the cone at about 90° to 100° elongation

Origin of the light: scattering of the light from the sun

Visual brightness at 40° elongation: equivalent to:

1000 stars of $10^{m}/\square^{\circ}$

10^{-12} to 10^{-13} the solar intensity averaged over the disk

Color same as sun

Density very low: at 1 AU from the sun only a few particles per km^3

/Gegenschein (or counterglow) = diffuse faintly luminous patch at the point on the ecliptic nearly opposite to the sun

Angular extent $\approx 40^{\circ}$ (visual $\approx 10^{\circ}$)

Max. visual brightness ≈ 200 stars of $10^{m}/\square^{\circ}$

Narrow light-bridge from the zodiacal light to the gegenschein (= zodiacal band) difficult to observe; washed out by light of the night sky

Origin: probably normal continuation of the zodiacal light; brightening by backscattering

Possibly also: gas- and dust-tail of the earth, caused by solar wind or concentration of matter at the libration point of the earth. (distance 0.01 AU (see 2.6.3))

/F-corona = outer corona with solar Fraunhofer spectrum (only observable during eclipses: extends to $\approx 9^{\circ}$ from sun)

= continuation of the zodiacal light; particles between sun and earth. Essentially the F-corona (false corona) does not belong to the sun (see 5.6).

Light arises from Tyndall scattering

= predominantly forward scattering by small particles (little larger than wavelength)

Dust-free zone around the sun: $\sim 4\ R_{\odot}$

Data on the interplanetary dust very uncertain, only estimates

Sources of information:

direct measurement from satellites and space probes; trapping of particles as collected on the earth; visual, photographic, radar measurements of meteors; photometry of the F-corona, of the zodiacal light and of the gegenschein.

Mean density at a distance of 1 AU from the sun:

given values $10^{-19} - 10^{-25}$ g/cm^3

(predominantly particles between 0.1 and 0.001 mm)

Mass loss of the interplanetary dust: 10^6 g/sec

(by Poynting-Robertson effect: small particles, too large to be repelled by radiation pressure, gradually spiral into the sun. Energy is lost as a result of absorption and isotropic re-emission of solar radiation.)

Replaced by disintegrating comets and asteroids.

Isotropic flow of particles in the neighborhood of the earth:

$$F(>m_p) = 10^{-17}\ m_p \quad \text{for } 10^{-10} < m_p < 10^{-6}$$

where F = number of particles/m^{2}sec

m_p = mass of a single particle in g

B) Interplanetary gas -- solar wind

Hydrodynamic expansion of the corona. Heating of the corona (see 5.6) causes acceleration of the coronal plasma. Up to several solar radii the acceleration is to supersonic velocity. Plasma is streaming into space

$\Longrightarrow$ solar wind (95% protons and electrons)

Near to the earth:

1 to 10 particles cm^{-3}, $V_{pl} \approx 400$ km/sec

corresponding to a flux: F = several $\times\ 10^8$ cm^{-2}sec^{-1}

(directly measured by Mariner 2 and other space probes)

Variation with solar activity; inhomogenities and variations with time. E.g., correlation between V_{pl} and geomagnetic activity (K_p = index of activity)

$V_{pl} = 330 + 8.4\ K_p$ [km/sec] > velocity of sound
$\pm 17 \pm 0.7$

Temperature about 10^5 °K

Plasma time scales: (disturbances on the sun and corresponding geomagnetic disturbances)

1 - 6 days ⟶ $v \sim 1700 - 300$ km/sec

Kinetic pressure on the magnetosphere of the earth:

$\frac{1}{2}\rho V^2$	$3.5 \cdot 10^{-3} r_o^{-6}$	r_o = radius of the magnetosphere [units of R_+] = 10 to 11 on magnetically quiet days = 8 to 9 on fairly disturbed days

The solar wind deforms the magnetosphere, causing a shock front in direction to the sun (radius r_o) and a tail on the backside (longer than distance to the moon).

Table: mass loss of the corona computed for various temperatures (Parker's model)

T[°K]	loss [g/sec]	time to blow away the whole corona	flux in the vicinity of the earth
0.65 10^6	3 10^8	10 years	$6 \cdot 10^4$ $cm^{-2}sec^{-1}$
1 10^6	2 10^{10}	2 months	$4 \cdot 10^6$ "
2 10^6	2 10^{14}	7 min	$6 \cdot 10^{10}$ " ←
4 10^6	9 10^{15}	8 sec	$2 \cdot 10^{12}$ "

Observed: $10^7 \ldots 10^8$

Extension: until kinetic pressure = interstellar total pressure probably at a distance of 50 - 100 AU so-called heliosphere (similar to the behaviour of a "Strömgren sphere", see 9.1.4)

Like the magnetosphere of the earth in the solar wind also the heliosphere of the sun stays in the interstellar wind of neutral hydrogen (peculiar motion of the sun, see 9.4.2), causing again a shock front anda tail of perhaps 1000 AU.

C) Interplanetary magnetic field

The solar wind takes a "frozen-in" magnetic field with it.

Shape of the magnetic field: archimedic spiral (because of solar rotation; analogous to a lawn sprinkler)

Field strength in the vicinity of the orbit of the earth: 2 to 10 x 10^{-5} gauss

during magnetic storms: 20 to 40 x 10^{-5} gauss

9.6 *Cosmogony (origin) of the solar system*

The pecularities of the solar system which do not follow from the laws of celestial mechanics:

a) All planets approximately in a plane

b) Orbits nearly circular; revolutions and rotations almost all in the same sense (direct)

c) Rotational axes (angular-momentum vectors) of planets and satellite systems nearly parallel to the total angular momentum ($\perp$ to the "invariant plane")

d) Law of distances of the planets (Titius-Bode sequence, see 2.2.1)

Exceptions to a) through d) mainly at the edge of the system

e) Sun has 99.87% of the total mass, but only 0.54% of the total angular momentum

f) Physical conditions

Terrestrial (Inner) planets	Jovian (Outer) planets
High density	low density
low mass	high mass
metals, rocks	composition like sun
slow rotation	fast rotation
few or no satellites	many satellites

Young stars have extended gaseous shells or nebulae and fast rotation (50 to 500 km/sec). Because magnetic fields are frozen into the plasma of the shell, angular momentum can be transferred hydrodynamically from the central star to the slower rotating nebula (3rd law of Kepler)

Qualitatively reasonable: transferring the angular momentum of the planets back to the sun would yield $V_{rot} \approx 30$ km/sec.

Because of the rotation the shell flattens to a thin disk.

From the above, the facts a) through c) and e) are understandable.

Law of distances not so simple to explain. According to von Weizsäcker regularly spaced vortices were formed in the original disk. Planets were formed at the boundary regions of the vortices, which move in opposite directions.
Some astronomers now consider the Titius-Bode distance relation to be largely coincidental or accidental, having little physical significance.

Origin of the planets by condensation of matter in the nebula in a "cold way" (Whipple).

Duration of origin of sun and planets $\sim 10^7$ years.

Physical conditions: in the outer regions the temperature was low; water, ammonia and methane remained in a liquid state. In solar vicinity the temperature was high; hydrides volatized

(about 1% of original mass condensed to planets)

Origin of the sun: see the origin of stars, chapter 6.5.

Atmosphere of the earth: present atmosphere is not the original atmosphere. It has developped secondarily from volcanic outgassing (H_2O, CO_2, N_2, SO_2 ...).
Helium by alpha decay of the radio-active elements.
Original atmosphere had no oxygen, 4.5×10^9 years ago!

(totally bound up in oxides and silicates)

Formation of O_2 and O_3, at first, by photo-dissociation of H_2O by means of UV radiation of the sun, until the UV-absorbing ozone layer had been formed.

Further formation of oxygen by photosynthesis in living organisms. Hence, most oxygen was formed simultaneously with the development of life, plant-life at present produces so much, that all the atmospheric oxygen goes through the process of photosynthesis once every 2000 years.

3

ELECTROMAGNETIC RADIATION AND INSTRUMENTS

§ 1 Electromagnetic spectrum

Electromagnetic (e-m) radiation of various wavelengths is virtually our only source of information about celestial objects.

We investigate: Direction (positions and motion of the objects)
Quantity (brightness)
Quality (color, spectrum, polarization)

E-m spectrum and transmission by the terrestrial atmosphere

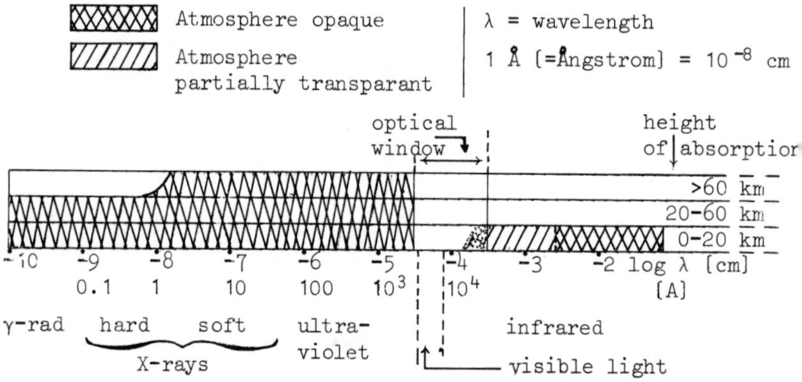

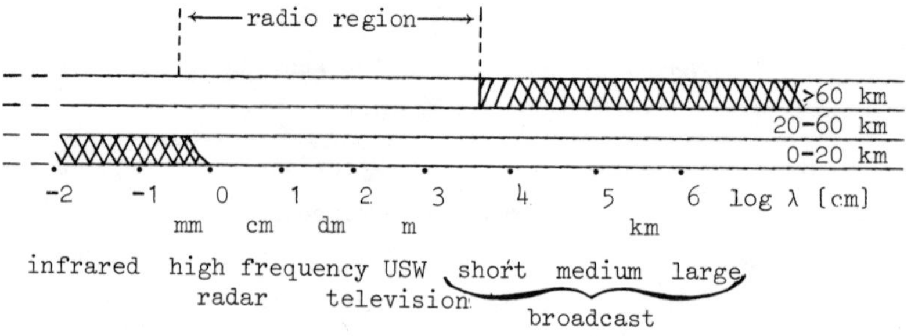

γ rays, X rays, UV radiation: < 3000 Å

Absorption predominantly by ozone O_3 (also N_2, O_1, ...)

Observed only from rockets and satellites

Subdivisions:

Near UV	>	~1700 Å	processes in the electron shell
Far UV	>	100 Å	
Soft X rays	>	1 Å	
Hard X rays		< 1 Å	
γ radiation		< 0.1 Å	nuclear origin

Optical window: ~3000 to ~20 000 Å, less than one power of ten.

Extends somewhat shortward and longward of visual light (~3800 to ~7500 Å)

3000 - 3800	ultraviolet		
3800 - 4200	violet	5500 - 5700	yellow green
4200 - 4500	blue violet	5700 - 5900	yellow
4500 - 4800	blue	5900 - 6000	orange
4800 - 5100	blue green	6000 - 6300	red orange
5100 - 5500	green	6300 - 7500	red

(Properties of the eye, see 3.5)

Infrared: ~7500 Å (=.75μ) to ~1 mm (= 1000μ)

Absorption by bands of H_2O (water vapor), CO_2, O_3 and others.

From .75μ to 10μ, absorption bands alternate with several transmission windows.

Radio region: a few mm to about 20 m (~3.3 powers of ten)

1893 First idea of "radio radiation by the sun" (Ebert), but technique still too primitive for detection

1920 Technique sufficient, but idea forgotten

1932 Discovery by chance of extraterrestrial radio radiation by Jansky

After 1945: rapid rise of radio astronomy (largely a result of the development of radar during the war).

In the radio region often the frequency ν is used instead of the wavelength

$$\boxed{\nu\lambda = c} \qquad c = 3 \times 10^{10} \text{ cm/sec}$$

λ:	10 m	1 m	10 cm	1 cm	
ν:	30	300	3000	30000	Mhz

1 Mhz = 10^6 Hz = 10^6 oscillations/sec, [sec^{-1}]

For $\lambda > 20$ m: radio radiation cut off by ionosphere

Energy: for each photon (light quantum) there is a corresponding energy, inversely proportional to the wavelength:

$$\chi \propto \frac{1}{\lambda} \propto \nu$$

$\boxed{\chi = h\nu}$, h = Planck's constant = 6.6×10^{-27} erg sec

short waves: high energy

long waves: low energy

Units: 1 eV = 1.6×10^{-12} erg = energy gained by an electron accelerated by a potential difference of 1 volt.

Hence:

$$\boxed{\lambda\,[\text{A}] = \frac{12\,400}{\chi\,[\text{eV}]}}$$

e.g.,	X rays	1 Å = 10^4	eV
	visible light	5000 Å = 2.5	eV
	infrared	12 400 Å = 1.0	eV
	radio region	21 cm = $6 \cdot 10^{-6}$	eV

as a comparison: 1 Watt-second = 10^7 erg $\approx 10^{19}$ eV

Doppler effect:

= Shifting of the wavelength because of relative motion between light source and observer

In general (relativistic):

$$\frac{\lambda - \lambda_o}{\lambda_o} = \frac{\Delta\lambda}{\lambda_o} = \frac{\sqrt{1 - \frac{v_r^2}{c^2}}}{1 - \frac{v_r}{c}} - 1 = \frac{1 + \frac{v_r}{c}}{\sqrt{1 - \frac{v_r^2}{c^2}}} - 1$$

where λ_o = emitted wavelength

λ = observed wavelength

v_r = velocity component in line of sight,

+ for recession, red shift
- for approach, blue shift

As long as $v_r \ll c$: $\frac{\Delta\lambda}{\lambda_o} = \frac{v_r}{c}$; $\lambda = \lambda_o(1 + \frac{v_r}{c})$

e.g., at 5000 Å and v_r = 1 km/sec: $\Delta\lambda$ = 0.02 Å

For treatment when v_r not small relative to c, see 10.6.1.

§ 2 Origin of radiation

Literature: all astrophysics and stellar atmosphere textbooks (see introduction and chapter 5)

Further: all appropriate textbooks on physics

2.1 *Thermal radiation*

Every object emits radiation corresponding to its temperature.

Ideal case conditions of thermodynamical equilibrium (TDE) state in which all atomic processes are balanced by their inverse processes. We then refer to the radiation of a "black body" (perfect absorber and hence perfect emitter):

Distribution of energy with wavelength then obeys

Planck's law:

$$B_\nu(T) = \frac{2h\nu^3}{c^2} \cdot \frac{1}{e^{h\nu/kT} - 1} \quad [\text{erg cm}^{-2}\ \text{sec}^{-1}\ \text{sterad}^{-1}\ \text{Hz}^{-1}]$$

band width ≡ sec^{+1}

h = Planck constant = 6.6×10^{-27} erg sec

c = velocity of light = 3×10^{10} cm/sec

k = Boltzmann constant = 1.4×10^{-16} erg/degree

$$B_\lambda(T) = \frac{2hc^2}{\lambda^5} \cdot \frac{1}{e^{c_2/\lambda T} - 1} \quad [\text{erg cm}^{-2}\ \text{sec}^{-1}\ \text{sterad}^{-1}\ \text{cm}^{-1}]$$

band width

$$c_2 = \frac{hc}{k} = \text{second radiation constant} = 1.44\ \text{cm degree}$$

For the conversion from frequency to wavelength:

$$\lambda = \frac{c}{\nu} \qquad B_\nu d\nu = B_\lambda |d\lambda|$$

$$|d\lambda| = \frac{c}{\nu^2} d\nu \qquad B_\nu = \frac{c}{\nu^2} B_\lambda = \frac{\lambda^2}{c} B_\lambda$$

Limiting cases

1) Short wavelengths or low temperatures:

$$h\nu/kt \gg 1; \quad e^{h\nu/kT} \gg 1$$

Wien approximation

$$B_\nu(T) \approx \frac{2h\nu^3}{c^2} e^{-h\nu/kT}$$

2) Long wavelengths or high temperatures:

$$\frac{h\nu}{kT} << 1; \; e^{h\nu/kT} \approx 1 + \frac{h\nu}{kT}$$

Rayleigh-Jeans approximation

$$B_\nu(T) = \frac{2\nu^2}{c^2}\,kT \qquad (h \text{ vanishes})$$

This approximation is valid in essentially the whole radio region

For λ = 1 m and T = 1 °K the error is only about 1%

Because of this proportionality of B and T, in radio astronomy T is generally used as a measure of the radiation intensity, even though the radiation may not be thermal.

The "brightness temperature" T_s, in that case, is only a (formal) measure of the energy.

(= temperature of the "black-body" radiation source, which in thermal equilibrium would emit the same observed intensity at the specified wavelength)

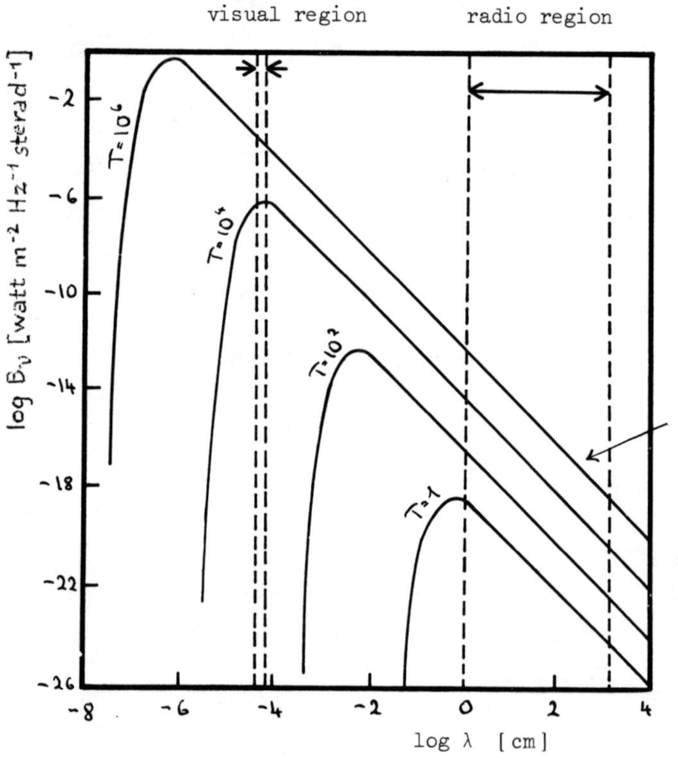

Stefan-Boltzmann law

Integration over direction and frequency yields:

$$\boxed{E = \frac{\sigma}{\pi} T^4}$$ erg $cm^{-2} sec^{-1}$

σ = Stefan-Boltzmann constant
= $5.67 \cdot 10^{-5}$ erg cm^{-2} sec^{-1} $degree^{-4}$

Wien's displacement law:

$\lambda_{max} T$ = const = 0.2898 cm degree

λ_{max} = wavelength of the maximum of Planck's curve B_λ ($\neq \lambda$ of $B_{\nu\ max}$)

2.2 *Atomic processes* (Predominantly in the region below 10 μ; ultimately of thermal origin)

References: L.H. Aller 1963, *Astrophysics, the Atmospheres of the Sun and the Stars*, 2nd edition, (The Ronald Press, New York)

G. Herzberg 1944, *Atomic Spectra and Atomic Structure*, (Dover Publications, New York)

A) Emission and absorption lines

1) Radiative transitions

Electron transitions in the shell. Energy difference between two orbits (Bohr's model of the atom) or between two discrete eigenfunctions (quantum mechanics), respectively, correspond to the energy of emitted or absorbed radiation:

$$\boxed{h\nu = \Delta E}$$

If the energy is measured in *eV*, we have according to (3.1)

$$\lambda [\text{Å}] = \frac{12,400}{\chi\ [eV]}$$

Usual representation of the discrete states by the energy-level diagram or term diagram (or Grotrian diagram after W. Grotrian 1928). Energy level of an electron is characterized by "quantum numbers":

n principal quantum number (related to major axis of the orbital ellipse). $n = 1, 2, 3, \ldots$

l orbital angular momentum or (reduced) azimuthal quantum number (originally Bohr introduced the quantum number $k \equiv l+1$ which is related to the minor axis of the orbital ellipse); $l = 0, 1, 2, \ldots, (n - 1)$

- s spin angular momentum (related to rotation (spin) of electron). $s = \pm\frac{1}{2}$
- m magnetic quantum number (orientation in the magnetic field). $m = 0, \pm 1, \pm 2, \ldots, \pm l$.
- j total angular momentum
  $\mathbf{j} = \mathbf{l} + \mathbf{s}$ (e.g., l=1, s=1 → j=2, 1 or 0)

Absorption: photon is absorbed, electron is "excited" (raised to a higher orbit)

Spontaneous emission: electron jumps spontaneously to a lower level, photon (= light quantum) is emitted.

> Transition probability of spontaneous emission covers an extremely wide range:
>
> normal lines: life time $\sim 10^{-8}$ sec
>
> forbidden lines: life time sec, min, ..., years,...

Induced emission: Incident photon of wavelength λ may induce an electron to make a permitted downward transition, emitting a photon of same λ, in same direction as incident photon (principle of laser and maser action)

Types of spectra

a) Line spectrum (atomic spectra)

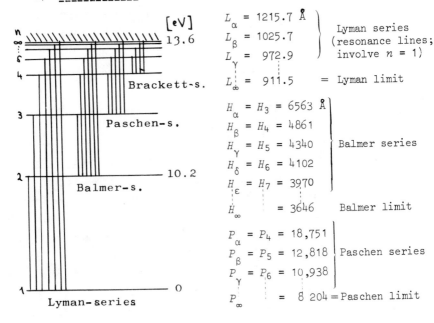

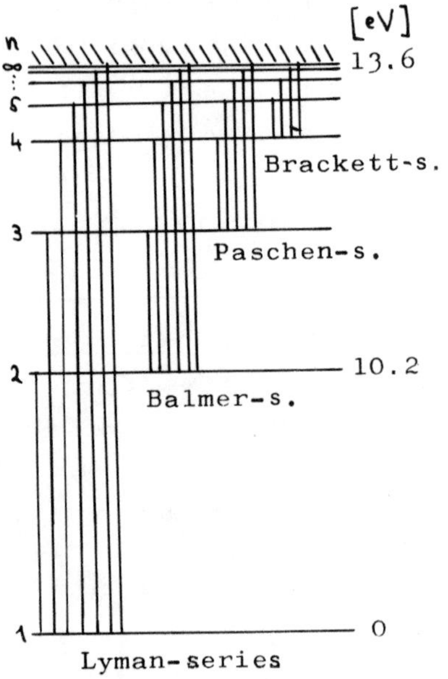

L_α = 1215.7 Å
L_β = 1025.7
L_γ = 972.9
} Lyman series (resonance lines; involve n = 1)

L_∞ = 911.5 = Lyman limit

$H_\alpha = H_3$ = 6563 Å
$H_\beta = H_4$ = 4861
$H_\gamma = H_5$ = 4340
$H_\delta = H_6$ = 4102
$H_\varepsilon = H_7$ = 3970
} Balmer series

H_∞ = 3646 Balmer limit

$P_\alpha = P_4$ = 18,751
$P_\beta = P_5$ = 12,818
$P_\gamma = P_6$ = 10,938
} Paschen series

P_∞ = 8 204 = Paschen limit

One speaks of a "spectral series" if transitions from a single level to numerous successive levels corresponding to increasing principal quantum numbers, e.g., hydrogen:
(see figure opposite page)

In the radio region several lines from transitions between two high levels have been observed recently. Such radio recombination lines involve enormous atoms, which can exist only in very low-density regions.

e.g., $H137_\beta$ = transition $(n=139) \rightarrow (n=137)$ at 5005 MHz
$H166_\alpha$ = transition $(n=167) \rightarrow (n=166)$ at 1424.7 MHz

For complex atoms with several valence (outer) electrons the energy-level diagram gets complicated; the upper, lower, or both terms are split; several lines (multiplets) arise from one transition. ⟶ "multiplet spectra"

Notation

Upper or lower level in a transition designated by

nl,	$^{2S+1}L^{\circ}_{J}$
configuration	term

where n = principal quantum number

l = angular momentum quantum number, designated by letters:

	s	p	d	f	g	...
l =	0	1	2	3	4	...

$2S+1$ = multiplicity: 1 = singlet, 2 = doublet, 3 = triplet,...

S = vector sum of s_i for all valence electrons N
= 0, 1/2, 1, 3/2, ... $N/2$

L = vector sum of l_i for all valence electrons N
= 0, 1, 2, ...

Designated by letters:

	S(sharp)	P(principal)	D(diffuse)	F(fundamental)	G...
L =	0	1	2	3	4...

J = total angular momentum vector = vector sum
= $L+S$ or $L+S-1$ or ... $|L-S|$ (LS coupling - for for most light atoms)
or
= vector sum of j_i for all valence electrons (jj coupling - for most heavy atoms)

$^{\circ}$ indicates Σl (parity) is odd; omitted if parity even

Examples:

Sodium doublet	D_1 line	$3s^2S_{1/2} - 3p^2P^o_{1/2}$	:	5896 Å
	D_2 line	$3s^2S_{1/2} - 3p^2P^o_{3/2}$	:	5890 Å
Ca II doublet	K line	$4s^2S_{1/2} - 4p^2P^o_{3/2}$	:	3934 Å
	H line	$4s^2S_{1/2} - 4p^2P^o_{3/2}$	:	3969 Å

For catalog of wavelengths and multiplet identifications by element and by λ see C. Moore 1959, *Multiplet Table of Astrophysical Interest*, Rev. Ed. National Bureau of Standards.

Selection rules

For "permitted" transitions (transition probabilities not very small),

$\Delta\Sigma l$ must = ± 1 (parity must change)

ΔJ must = 0 or ± 1, except that $J=0 \rightarrow J=0$ is forbidden

ΔL must = 0 or ± 1 } for strict LS coupling

ΔS must = 0 }

Transitions which disobey the selection rules for ΔJ and parity are called "forbidden" transitions and have very low probabilities of occurring. Forbidden lines can occur if no competitive transitions occur, for example, in emission at extremely low pressures where de-exciting collisions are rare.

b) Band spectra (molecular spectra)

For molecules rotational and vibrational states are also quantized. A whole system of lines arises from a single electron jump $\longrightarrow$ a band

2) Transitions not involving radiation (collisional processes):

When two particles collide, kinetic energy can be converted to excitation energy and vice versa. Population of various excitation levels is dependent on collision rates, hence on temperature.

Boltzmann equation: gives distribution of electrons among the the various energy levels, under condition of thermodynamic equilibrium

$$\frac{N_s}{N_o} = \frac{g_s}{g_o} \cdot e^{\left(\frac{-\chi_s}{kT}\right)}$$ (subscript o = ground state)

or more generally

$$\frac{N_a}{N_b} = \frac{g_a}{g_b} \cdot e^{-\chi_{ab}/kT} \qquad \text{(subscript } b = \text{lower level; } a = \text{upper level)}$$

which, if χ is expressed in electron volts (eV), can be written as

$$\log \frac{N_a}{N_b} = \frac{-5040}{T} \cdot \chi_{ab} + \log \frac{g_a}{g_b}$$

In the above equations:

g = statistical weight (Hydrogen: $g = n^2$; multiplets: $g = 2j + 1$)

k = 8.6×10^{-5} eV degree^{-1} = Boltzmann constant

χ_s = excitation energy in [eV]
= $E_s - 0$ = difference in energy between the considered level and the lowest one

$\chi_{ab} = E_a - E_b$ = energy difference between the upper and lower levels

$\frac{5040}{T}$ is often designated by Θ.
$T = T_{exc}$ = excitation temperature (see 4.6)

Example: hydrogen in solar photosphere:

$n = 2$; $T = 5000°$, $\chi_s = 10$ eV; $\chi/kT \approx 24$; $e^{-24} \approx 10^{-10}$
i.e., for about 10 billion atoms in the ground state there is a single excited one!

B) Continuum

Ionization: the energy received by absorption or collision is higher than the energy binding the electron to the nucleus, $\longrightarrow$ electron is detached (elliptical $\rightarrow$ hyperbolic orbit), atom is ionized. The excess over the ionization energy χ_{ion} (analogous to the escape velocity) is converted into kinetic energy of the electron. Because this is not quantized $\Longrightarrow$ continuous absorption, which sets in at the series limit.

E.g., ionization of hydrogen from the 2nd quantum state:

$\chi_{ion} - \chi_2 = 13.6 - 10.2 = 3.4$ eV $\rightarrow$ 3646 Å
= Balmer limit or Balmer jump

Designation: Roman numerals
e.g., neutral hydrogen H I
singly ionized hydrogen H II (or H^+)
21 times ionized iron: Fe XXII

The energy needed to ionize inner electrons always greater ("nuclear excess" gets stronger)

e.g., Li I → II: 5.4 eV
Li II → III: 75.6 eV
Li III → IV: 122.4 eV

Saha equation or ionization equation = distribution of atoms between two neighboring ionization states r and $(r + 1)$

$$\frac{N_{r+1}}{N_r} = \frac{2\,u_{r+1}}{u_r} \cdot \frac{1}{P_e} \cdot \frac{(2\pi m)^{3/2}\,(kT)^{5/2}}{h^3}\, e^{-\chi_r/kT} = f(P_e, T)$$

In logarithmic form after substituting the atomic constants:

$$\log \frac{N_{r+1}}{N_r} = \log \frac{2\,u_{r+1}}{u_r} - 0.48 - \log P_e + \frac{5}{2} \log T - \Theta\chi_r$$

where: $u_r(T)$ = partition function = $\sum_{i=0}^{\infty} g_{r,i}\, e^{-\chi_{r,i}/kT}$

$g_{r,i}$ = statistical weight, $\chi_{r,i}$ = excitation energy — of the individual levels

P_e = electron pressure in [dyn/cm^2]
$T = T_{io}$ = ionization temperature (see 4.6)
χ_r = ionization potential

upper formula in [erg]
lower formula in [eV]

$\Theta = \frac{5040}{T}$

If one replaces the partition function by $g_{r+1,0}$ and $g_{r,0}$, respectively, one obtains the ratio of the number of atoms in the ground state of $(r + 1)$ times and r times ionized atoms, respectively

Recombination = inverse process. Free electron is captured, photon is emitted.

⟹ Continuous emission at the limit of a series

For ionization and recombination we have for the photon energy (analogously to line transitions):

$h\nu$ = energy difference (ionization potential minus lower level) + kinetic energy of the electron

$h\nu = \Delta E + \frac{1}{2}mv^2$

Free-free transitions: an electron which passes by a positive ion is perturbed in its orbit; loss (or gain) of kinetic energy is emitted (or absorbed, respectively) as radiation

C) Summary

In the energy-level diagram one can imagine the eV scale extended (addition of kinetic energy). Then, formally, to every value of the kinetic energy there corresponds a state in the continuum, the so-called "free states", corresponding to hyperbolic orbits.

Hence:

Bound-bound transitions = discrete-discrete " = elliptical-elliptical "	lines	↑absorption ↓emission	
bound-free " = discrete-continuous " = elliptical-hyperbolic "	ionization		continuum
free-bound " = continuous-discrete " = hyperbolic-elliptical "	recombination		continuum
free-free " = continuous-continuous " = hyperbolic-hyperbolic "	bremsstrahlung		continuum

Remark: physically, in the discrete states, conditions of negative energy ($E < 0$) are involved; in the free states, conditions of positive energy. $E = 0$ (parabolic orbit) corresponds to the ionization limit. In spectroscopy, however, it is normal to compute the energy from the ground state (lowest bound level).

The continuous spectrum of the stars is produced predominantly by bound-free and free-free transitions.

2.3 *Plasma oscillations*

The radiation considered up to now (mostly in the optical and short-wave range) is caused by microscopic motions (single quanta in individual atoms). In the long-wavelength region (radio astronomy) more and more macroscopic organized motions of many electrons play a role (analogous to an oscillating circuit).

Plasma = highly ionized, but, taken as a whole, neutral gas (i.e., contains ≈equal numbers of positive ions and electrons)

Process of plasma oscillations:

Exterior force, which acts differently on electrons and ions, because of their different mass

$\Longrightarrow$ separation of charges $\Longrightarrow$ space charges

$\Longrightarrow$ electric fields $\Longrightarrow$ repulsive force

$\Longrightarrow$ oscillations

Detailed calculations yield the plasma frequency

$$\nu_{Pl} = \sqrt{\frac{e^2}{\pi \cdot m} N_e} = 9 \times 10^{-3} \sqrt{N_e} \text{ [M z]}$$

$$N_e = \text{electron density [cm}^{-3}]$$

Electromagnetic radiation with $\nu < \nu_{Pl}$ can not escape from a plasma, because then refractive index < 0.

2.4 *Synchroton radiation* (magneto-bremsstrahlung)

Fast charged particles (high-energetic electrons) move in an external magnetic field **H** in circular orbits ⊥ **H** around the field lines (or helical orbits, in the case of an additional component in the direction of **H**). Relativistic (with $v \sim c$) revolving electrons emit in a narrow cone of angle

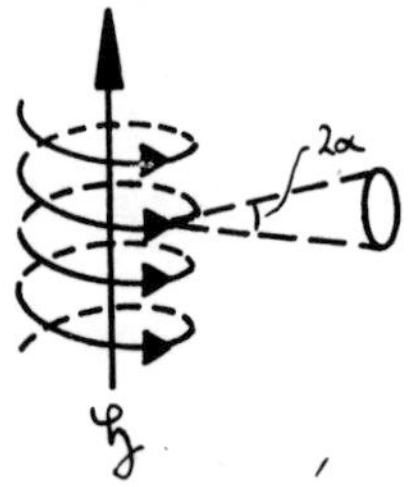

$$\alpha \simeq m_o c^2/E$$

$m_o c^2$ = rest energy = 0.511 MeV

E = energy of the electron

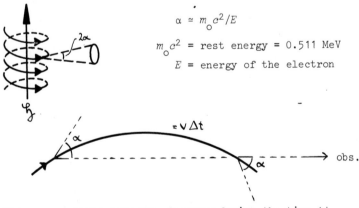

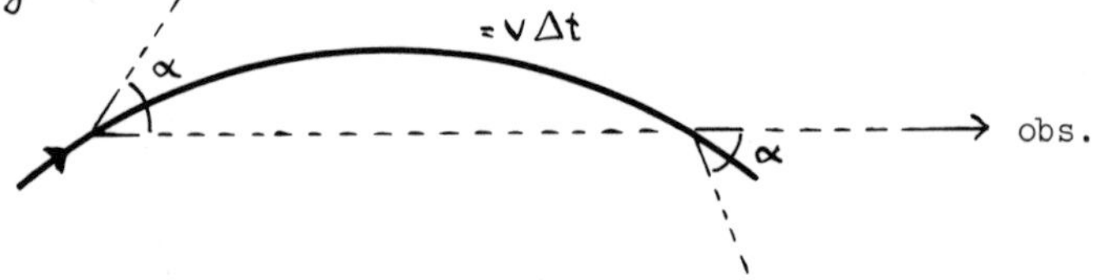

This cone sweeps over the observer during the time Δt.

Spectral resolution of this sequence of "flashes" (Fourier analysis) yields a continuous spectrum;

maximum at about $\sim 1/\Delta t$.

Exact calculation yields:

$$\nu_{max} \approx 4.6 \times 10^{-6} H_{\perp} E^2_{eV} \quad [Hz]$$

[$H_{\perp}$ = component of magnetic field perpendicular to the direction of motion [Gauss]

If E and H are large enough, the synchroton radiation can extend into the visible region

e.g., optical synchroton radiation of Crab Nebula, *dMe* star flares, solar flares, ...

Intensity: if the energy distribution of the electron is given by $N(E)\, dE \propto E^{-\gamma}\, dE$, we have for the intensity

$$I_{\nu} \propto \sqrt{H^{\gamma+1} \quad \nu^{-(\gamma-1)}}$$

§ 3 Telescopes (optical)

Literature: *Telescopes* Vol. I of *Stars and Stellar Systems*, G.P. Kuiper, B.M. Middlehurst, editors, Chicago 1960

Bahner, K. 1967, *Teleskope*, in: Hdb. d. Physik, 29, p. 227, Springer

"Processing" of the incoming radiation:

Telescopes (optical, radio)
↓
Analyzers (filters, spectrographs, polarizers)
↓
Receivers (eye, photographic plate, photoelectric cell)
↓
Reduction apparatus (micrometers, photometers, measuring engines for positions, etc.)

3.1 *Basic concepts*

1) Principle: objective lens (or concave mirror) projects an image of the object, which is, for practical purposes, at infinity, onto the focal plane; the image is then photographed, measured photoelectrically or examined through an eye piece. (see figures next page)

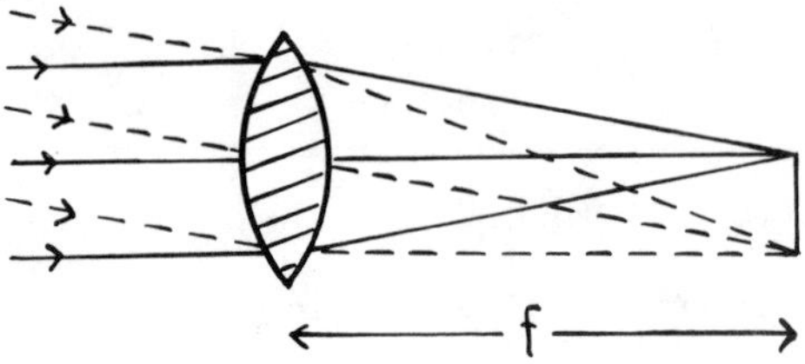

D = diameter (aperture of the objective lens (or mirror)

f = focal length

f/D = focal ratio (sometime written f/–; e.g., /8")

=(f-stop in the case of a camera)

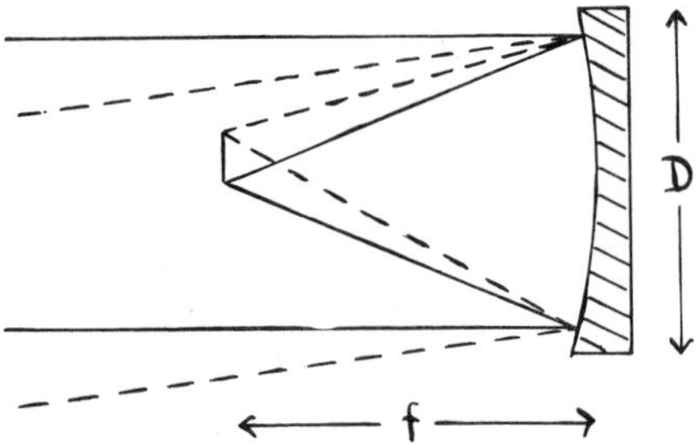

2) Scale of the image:

Image of an infinitely far distant object subtending angle ω:

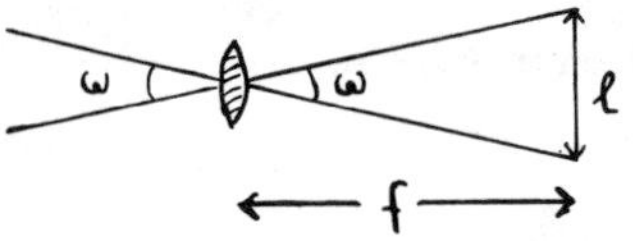

$\tan\omega \approx \omega \approx l/f$ (for small ω)

Diameter of the image

$\boxed{l = 0.0175\ \omega\ f}$ (ω in $^{\circ}$)

$$\text{Plate scale } [''/\text{mm}] = \frac{20626.5}{f\,[\text{cm}]} = \frac{8120.5}{f\ [\text{in}]}$$

Angular diameter of the sun $\sim 0^{\circ}\!.5$

Rule of thumb:

$\Longrightarrow$: image of the sun in [cm] $\approx$ focal length in [m]

Scale of the image, hence, resolution, important for double stars, etc.

3) Magnification: visual magnification at the eye piece

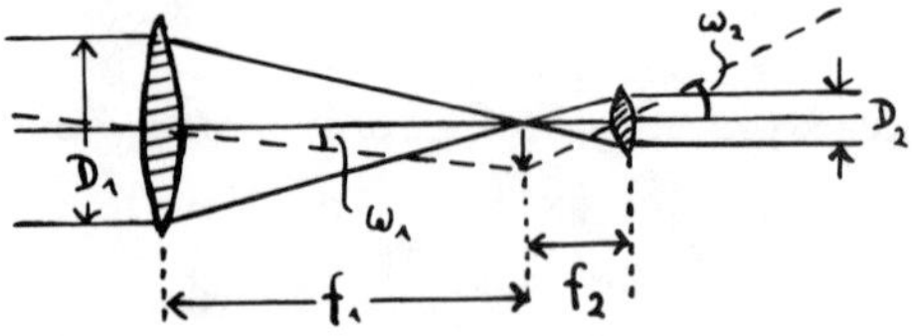

f_1 focal length of objective

f_2 focal length of eyepiece

D_1 diameter of objective

D_2 beam width at the eyepiece = exit pupil

$$\text{Magnification} \quad m = \frac{f_1}{f_2} = \frac{D_1}{D_2} = \frac{\omega_2}{\omega_1}$$

Aperture of the pupil of the eye adapted to the dark: 6 mm; hence sensible to put D_2 = 6 mm. The so-called "normal magnification" corresponding to this is

$$m_n = \frac{D_1[\text{mm}]}{6}$$

(For $m < m_n$ light is wasted because D_2 > pupil)

Kepler's telescope: (upper figure)

Real image at the focal plane. Possible to place a micrometer wire here. Inverted image.

Galileo's telescope: (opera glass)

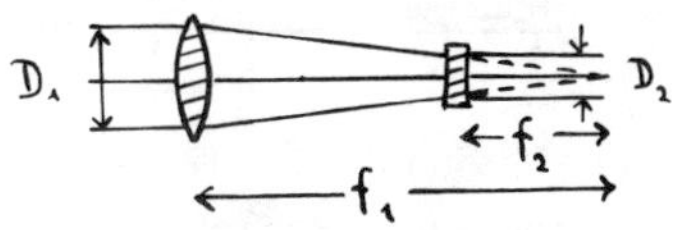

Image erect: but no real image (it is virtual)

No micrometer possible

4) Image brightness: Telescope should direct to receiver the maximum possible energy flux [erg $cm^{-2} sec^{-1}$].

Important: /size of collecting surface (mirror or lens); energy $\propto D^2$

/Area of the receiver, on which the light is distributed

a) Extended objects (comets, sky background, etc.)

/Dimension of image $\propto f$, area of image $\propto f^2$

hence

$$\boxed{\text{intensity} \propto (D/f)^2}$$

only dependent on the focal ratio

b) Point sources (e.g., stars)

/As long as the image is a "point" with respect to the receiver (i.e., < plate grain, photo cathode, or eye resolving power):

$$\boxed{\text{intensity} \propto D^2}$$

/If the image is no longer a "point": area of the image in the diffraction disk $\propto (\lambda \cdot \frac{f}{D})^2$ (see below),

hence

$$\boxed{\text{intensity} \propto \frac{D^2}{(f/D)^2}}$$

at a constant value of the focal ratio, $\propto D^2$

If, for a large aperture, the diffraction disk becomes smaller than the "seeing disk" caused by the air turbulence, we have, as in the case of extended objects: intensity $\propto (D/f)^2$.

5) Resolving power (point sources)

Objective produces a diffraction pattern: central disk concentric rings

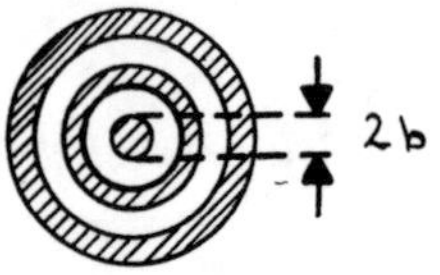

(visible when seeing is very goood)

Cross section of intensity distribution:

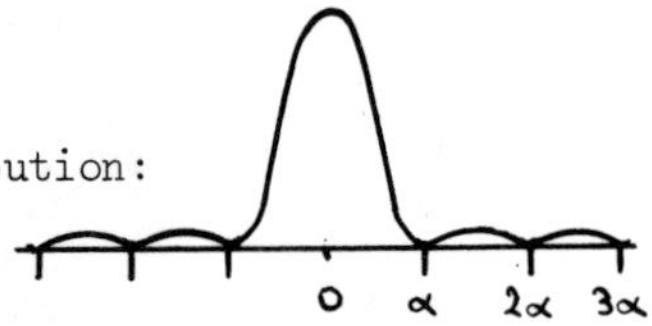

For good objectives
84% of the light in the central image, 7% in the first ring

Angular radius of the central image as seen from the objective (diffraction theory):

$\alpha = 1.22 \frac{\lambda}{D}$ [radians]

For λ = 5500 Å and using 1 rad = 206265":

$\alpha'' = \frac{13.8}{D[\mathrm{cm}]} = \frac{5.4}{D[\mathrm{in}]}$

Linear radius:

$b = \alpha \cdot f = 1.22 \frac{\lambda \cdot f}{D}$

$b = 6.67 \frac{f}{D}$ [μ]

Separation of two images (double stars) if angular distance d is sufficiently large

$d = \alpha = 1{,}22 \frac{\lambda}{D}$ clear separation (Rayleigh's criterion)

$d = 0{,}95 \frac{\lambda}{D}$ saddle between the central peaks just disappear (theoretical resolving power according to Strehl)

Use resolving power $\boxed{d_o = \frac{\lambda}{D}}$ for practical purposes

For λ = 5500 Å: $d''_o = \frac{11}{D[\mathrm{cm}]} = \frac{4.5}{D[\mathrm{inch}]}$

e.g., D = 11 cm → resolution ≈ 1"

Rayleigh-Strehl-criterion: tolerance for the focus

Maximum tolerable focus error = $|\Delta| = 2\left(\frac{f}{D}\right)^2 \lambda$

e.g., λ = 5000 Å, $\frac{f}{D} = 3.2 \rightarrow |\Delta| = 20\,\lambda = 0.01$ mm

$\frac{f}{D} = 32 \rightarrow |\Delta| = 2000\,\lambda = 1$ mm

Visual observation: resolving power of the eye: 1'

i.e., angle must be magnified to about $\delta_o = 60''$;

"useful magnification" $m_o = \frac{\delta_o}{d_o} = \frac{60''}{11''} D_{[cm]} \approx 5D[cm]$ or $\frac{D[mm]}{2}$

At higher magnification more detail can not be seen; only see larger diffraction disks. At lower magnification the resolving power of the instrument is not fully utilized.

Photographic observation

In practice, the limit is nearly always determined by the resolving power of the photographic plate (~25 μ). The full resolving power of the instrument is usually not utilized.

E.g., $f/D = 10 \longrightarrow b =$ 6.7 μ
$= 40$ 25 μ only reached by solar telescopes (or in long coudé systems)

For large instruments the resolving power is determined by the air turbulence (seeing) with good seeing ~1"

3.2 *Image aberrations*

1) Chromatic aberration

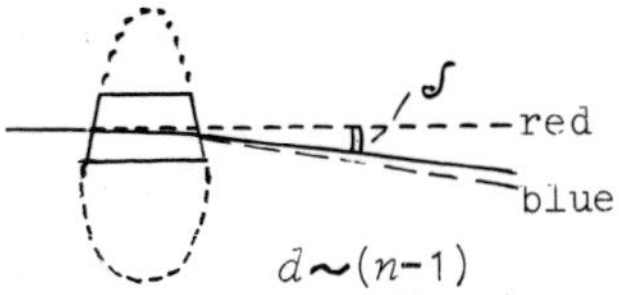

Focal length $f = f(n)$
refractive index $f = n(\lambda)$ } $f = f(\lambda)$

$d \sim (n-1)$
$f \sim 1/(n-1)$

Hence: a) $f_{blue} < f_{red}$: images in different planes
b) diameter of blue image < diameter of red image

Correction: achromatic lens = lens composed of two kinds of glass (flint and crown) of different n and $n(\lambda)$. Thus one gets, at a single wavelength, $\frac{df}{d\lambda} = 0$.

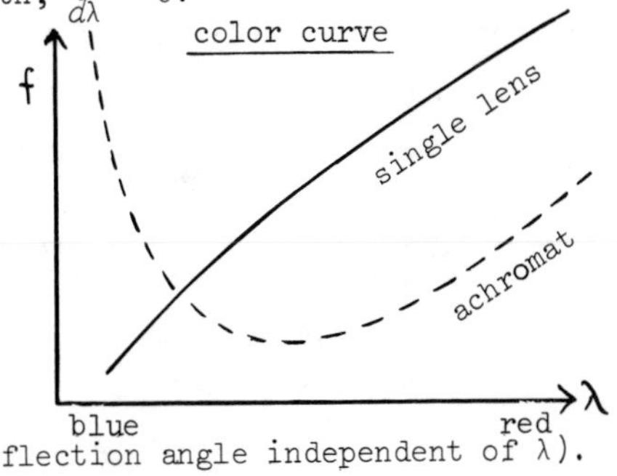

According to the wavelength of this minimum, one speaks of photographically, visually, etc., corrected objectives.

For astronomical telescopes (thin lenses), both errors (a and b) are thereby corrected.

→ Mirror systems have no chromatic aberration (reflection angle independent of λ).

2) Spherical aberration (aperture error)

Outer region of a spherical lens or of a spherical mirror has a shorter focal length than the central zone.

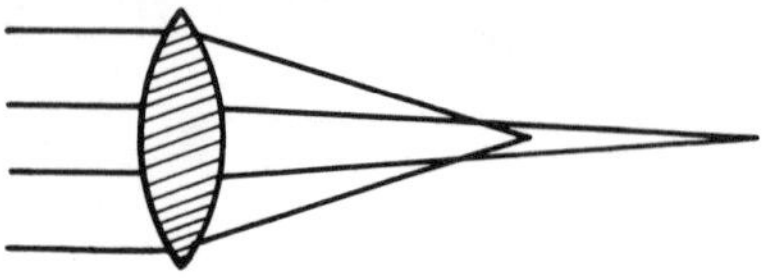

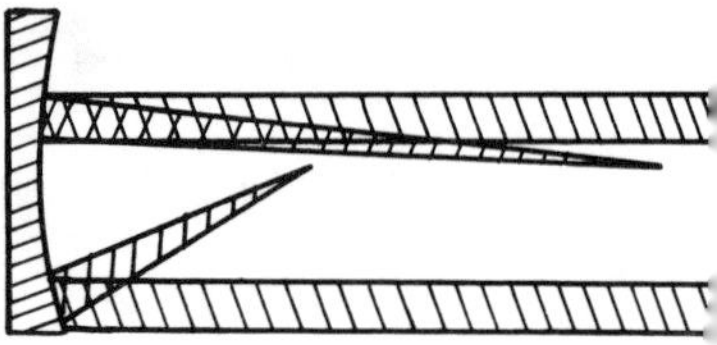

Correction:

Lens: aplanatic = compound lens system

Mirror: mirror surface = paraboloid (exact focus for all rays parallel to the axis)

Chromatic and spherical aberration occur even with rays parallel to the optical axis. In addition the following errors occur for off-axis rays:

3) Astigmatism

For off-axis rays the objective is no longer a circle, but an ellipse → two planes of symmetry → image not at one point, but in two focal lines:

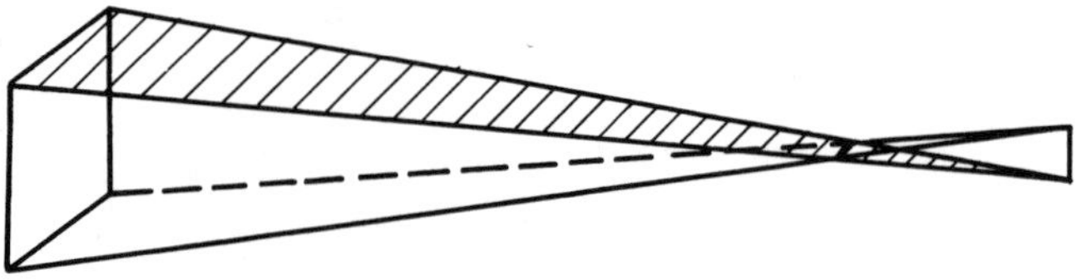

4) Curvature of field

Image not in a plane

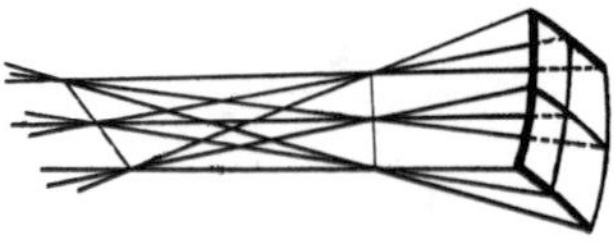

To correct astigmatism and curvature of field a system of 3 or more lenses with elements separated may be used (called anastigmats)

5) Coma

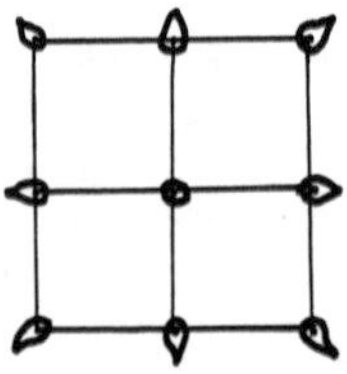

Off-axis stars have a cometary shape.

Correctable by a doublet aplanatic lens or a correcting plate (= lens of zero power)

6) Distortion

a) object

b) barrel distortion

c) pincushion distortion

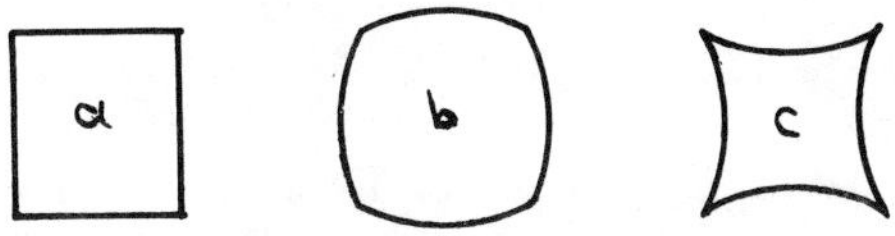

Usually not corrected in astronomical instruments. To correct use a symmetrical lens combination, one lens reversed. If optical system is free from distortion, it is orthoscopic.

3.3 *Refracting telescopes*

a) Refractors Usually achromatic with two lenses having focal ratios 1:12 to 1:20; small field of view

// Visual refractor: chromatic correction for the eye, minimum of color curve (see 3.3.2) at ~5600 Å

// photographic refractor: corrected for ~4300 Å

Largest refractors

visual	: D = 40 in (102 cm);	f = 19.4 m;	f/19 Yerkes
photographic:	32 in (80 cm);	12 m;	f/15 Potsdam

Main applications: positional astronomy, measuring of angles, double stars, planets

b) Astrographs: refractors with a large field (5° and more); most have three or four lenses; small focal length; focal ratio 4 to 7

e.g., Lick: double astrograph D = 20 in (51 cm), f ratio = 7.4, $6^\circ \times 6^\circ$ field

"Carte du Ciel" astrograph: f = 3.44 m

1' on the sky = 1 mm on the plate

Application: star clusters, proper motion surveys: used for Astrographic Catalogue (Carte du Ciel)

3.4 *Reflecting telescopes*

a) Parabolic mirrors (primary mirror = paraboloid of revolution)

Free from chromatic aberration

free from spherical aberration

however, only a small coma-free field [e.g., Palomar 200" (5m) mirror field ~5' diameter

Ideal instrument for single objects (high-resolution spectra; photoelectric measurements, etc.)

Primary focus main mirror only, plate holder inside the tube -"F_P"

Newtonian focus with 45° plane mirror, focus close to the side of the tube -"F_N"

Focal ratios mainly 3 to 5

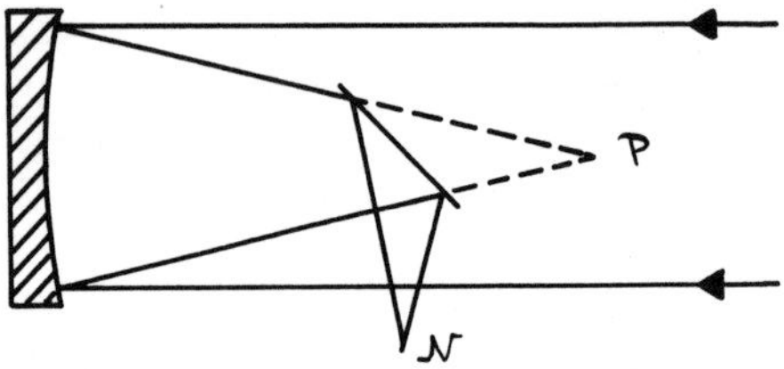

Cassegrain system

Hyperbolic secondary mirror "C", ahead of the primary focus "F_P" diminishes the convergence of the beam and thus increases the focal length. Focal ratios 10 to 20

/Original Cassegrain: observation through a hole in the primary mirror -"F_C"

/Nasmyth focus: observation at the side by means of an additional plane mirror -"F_{Na}"

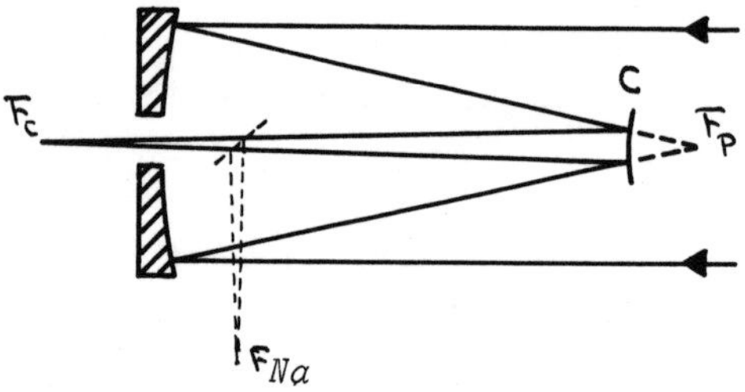

F_P = primary focus
F_C = Cassegrain focus
F_{Na} = Nasmyth focus
C = Cassegrain secondary mirror

Coudé system

= extremely extended Cassegrain

Path of rays deflected by flat mirror into the polar axis, and down to separate stationary observing room: position of focus fixed in space; large, fixed spectrographs.

Focal ratios 30 to 40

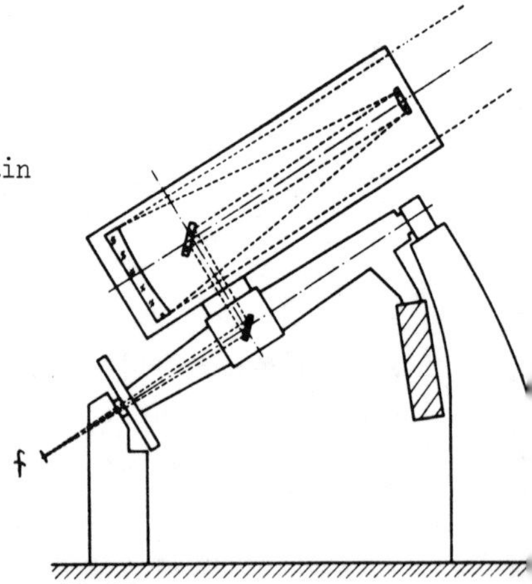

The large reflectors generally have all three arrangements,

e.g.,:	Palomar		Tautenburg		ESO (under construction)	
D	200 in		200 cm		360 cm	
Primary focus:	17 m	$f/3.3$	4 m	$f/2$	11 m	$f/3$
Cassegrain focus:	81 m	$f/16$	21 m	$f/10.5$	29 m	$f/8$
Coudé focus:	152 m	$f/30$	92 m	$f/46$	108 m	$f/30$

b) Variations of the Cassegrain system

One can distribute the deformations needed for the elimination of the spherical aberration arbitrarly over the mirrors, rather than using a paraboloid mirror.

E.g., quasi-Cassegrain: spherical primary mirror, over-corrected secondary mirror (e.g., Tautenburg).

Advantage: can be used also as Schmidt mirror

Dall-Kirkham system: elliptical primary mirror
spherical secondary mirror

Ritchey-Chrétien: hyperbolic primary mirror, and (in contrast to the Cassegrain) more strongly hyperbolic secondary mirror.
With the Ritchey-Chrétien the coma can be corrected for a large field (up to $\sim 1^{\circ}$). The 3.6 m mirror of ESO is a quasi-Ritchey-Chrétien.

Gregorian system: instead of hyperbolic secondary mirror in front of the primary focus, an ellipsoidal mirror beyond the primary focus.
(e.g., Mt. Stromlo Obs., 50 in.; solar telescope Locarno-Orselina)

c) Schmidt system (developed by Bernhard Schmidt, Hamburg)

Large field and small focal ratio by combination of refracting and reflecting surfaces.

Trick 1: spherical primary mirror, and a light stop (diaphragm) in the center of curvature.

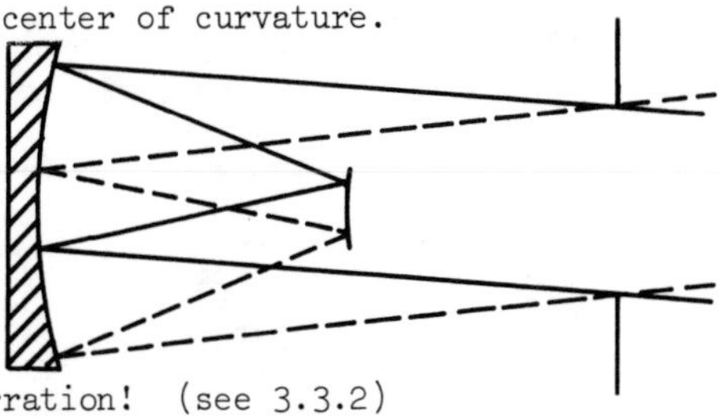

The special position of the axis is removed thereby;
all beams are axial,

no astigmatism

no coma

however: spherical aberration! (see 3.3.2)

Trick 2: an aspherical correcting plate (i.e., lens of zero power) within the diaphragm has effect of correcting sphere to parabola

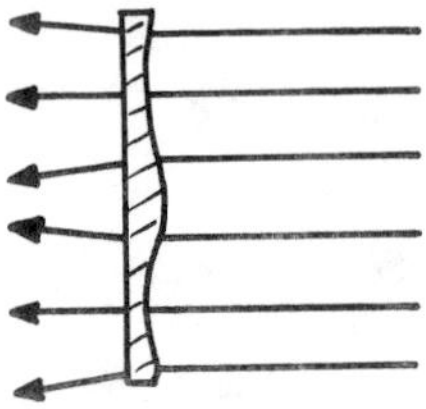

Increases f for rays far from the axis decreases f for rays close to the axis,

→ common focus

Focal ratios mainly 2.5 to 4

The aperture is given by the diameter of the correcting plate. The mirror is larger than the correcting plate in order to avoid vignetting (i.e., a decrease of the effective aperture away from the center of the plate).

Disadvantages: curved focal plane (concentric to the mirror), double telescope length
Plate holder inside the beam (therefore light lost,

Data on some Schmidt telescopes:

	Diameter: correcting plate = D	Diameter: mirror	f	f/D	field	photograph plate
Palomar	122 cm / 48 in	183 cm / 72 in	307 cm / 10 ft	2.5	6.5×6.5	35×35 cm^2
Hamburg	80 cm	120 cm	240 cm	3.0	5.5×5.5	24×24
Tautenburg	134 cm	200 cm	400 cm	3.0	3.4×3.4	24×24

In preparation similar telescopes at European Southern Observatory and at Siding Springs (Science Research Council, U.K.).

Further developments of the classical Schmidt e.g.,:

Maksutov (thick meniscus lens instead of correcting plate
Baker-Schmidt; super-Schmidt (fields of more than 50°, et

3.5 *Mountings*

Goal: free mobility to all points of the sky, motion around two axes.

a) Altitude-azimuth: vertical and horizontal axes. Unsuitable for the compensation of the earth's daily motion (rotation around two axes required). Only for expeditionary instruments and large radio telescopes.

b) Equatorial: polar axis (α) parallel to the axis of the earth, declination axis (δ) perpendicular to it. Rotation of earth compensated by rotation around a single axis.

Asymmetrical equatorial mountings (with counterweight)

1) Polar-axis mounting   One-point support of the polar axis

a) German mounting

short polar axis on a vertical pier

Disadvantage: tube must be reversed at high declinations when crossing the meridian. → see figure

b) bent-column mounting

column bent (or polar axis extended) so that the tube can pass underneath. → see figure

(ex.: Kitt Peak National Obs. 36-inch telescope)

2) English or cross-axis mounting

The long polar axis rests on two piers. Figure on page 126

(ex. 82-inch telescope at McDonald Obs., Texas)

Symmetrical equatorial mountings (without counterweight!)

3) Fork mounting (see figure next page)

Polar axis is forked, the tube hanging between the two arms. for reflectors, because, in that case, center of gravity is close to the mirror. (ex.: 120-inch of Lick Observatory).

4) English yoke mounting

Fork extended and closed, forming a frame, the upper end of which rests on a second pier (ex.: Mt. Wilson 100-inch)

Schematic diagrams:
(see also next page)

According to Bahner (1965) in
Landolt-Börnstein, H.-H. Voigt, ed.,
New Series Vol. VI/I
Springer Verlag

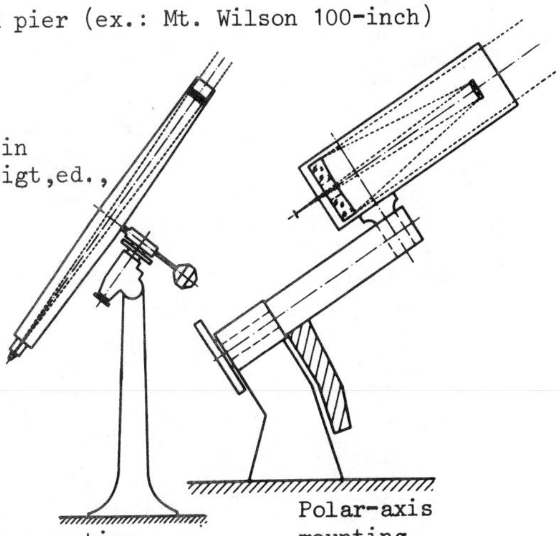

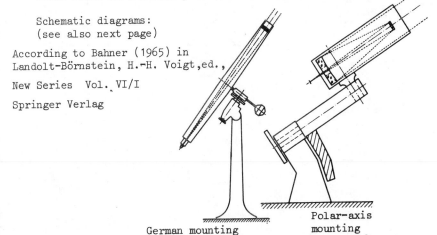

German mounting   Polar-axis mounting

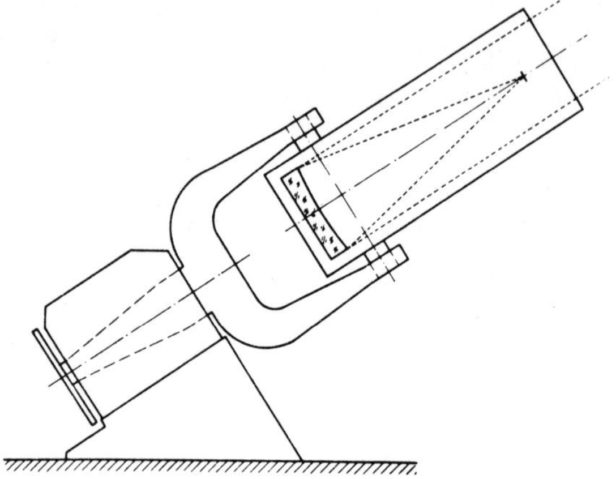

Fork mounting

5) <u>Modified yoke mounting</u>

For supporting great mass of the Hale 200" telescope, with access to polar bearing in large horseshoe.

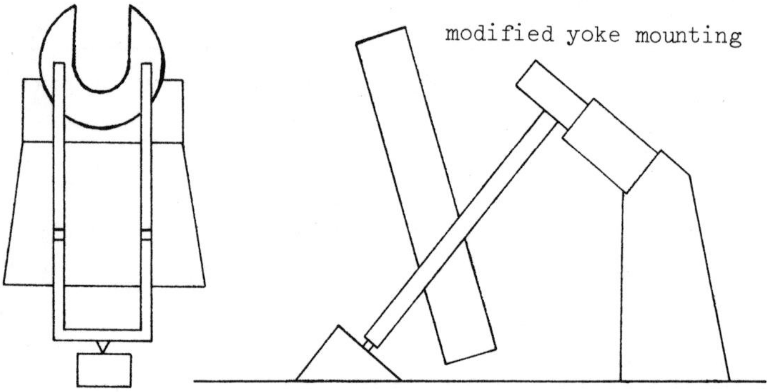

view from south
(telescope tube omitted
to simplify the diagram)

view from east

Several variations and combinations of these basic types exist.

<u>Coelostat</u>: predominantly for large solar telescopes
Telescope mounted fixed; light is deflected into the telescope by two moving mirrors. ⟶

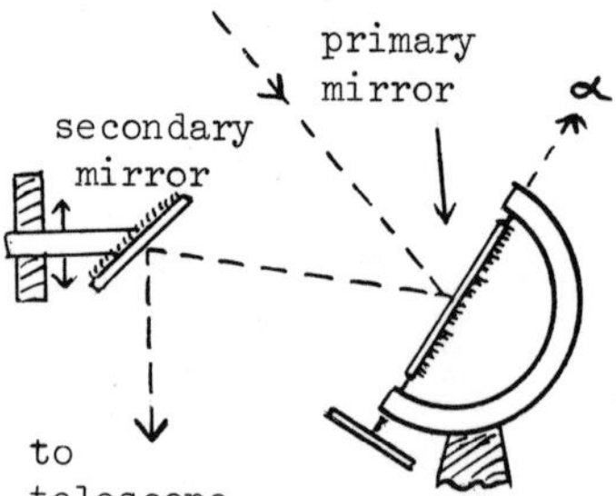

§ 4 Spectrographic instruments

Literature: I.S. Bowen 1962, *Spectrographs*, in *Stars and Stellar Systems*, vol. II (Astronomical Techniques). p. 34, Chicago

4.1 *Methods of spectral dispersion*

1) Prism

deviation ϕ due to two refractions is given by Snell's law (1.4) as a function of index of refraction n

$n = f(\lambda) \longrightarrow$ different wavelengths deviate by different amounts $\longrightarrow$ dispersion

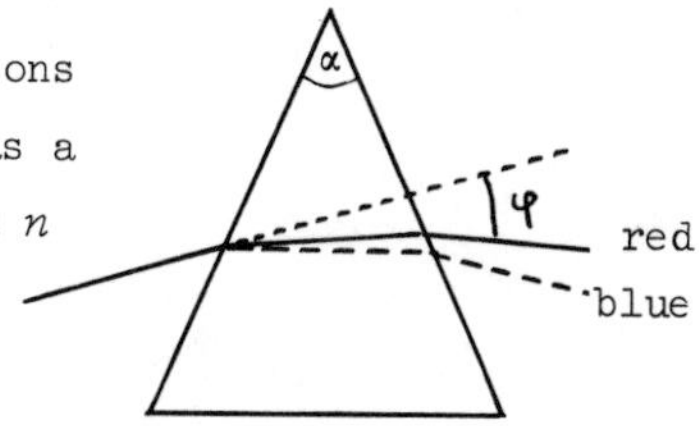

angular dispersion (for symmetrical passing)
$$\frac{d\phi}{d\lambda} = \frac{d\phi}{dn} \cdot \frac{dn}{d\lambda}$$
$$= \frac{2\sin(\frac{\alpha}{2})}{\sqrt{1-n^2\sin^2(\frac{\alpha}{2})}} \cdot \frac{dn}{d\lambda}$$

where α = prism angle

To a first approximation: $n \propto 1/\lambda^2$

hence angular deviation
$$\frac{d\phi}{d\lambda} \propto \frac{dn}{d\lambda} \propto \frac{1}{\lambda^3}$$

i.e., decreasing dispersion with increasing wavelength

2) Diffraction grating

Basic equation

Reflecting grating

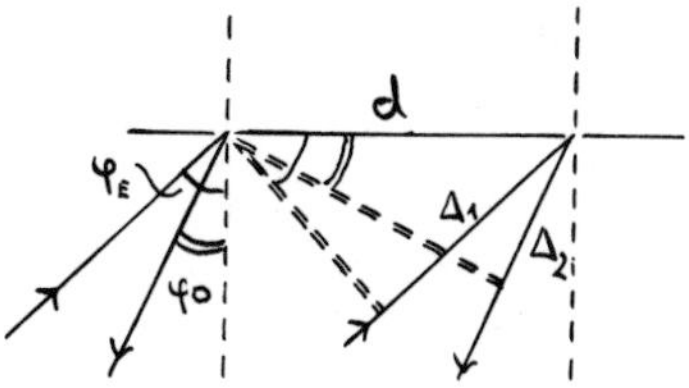

Transmission grating

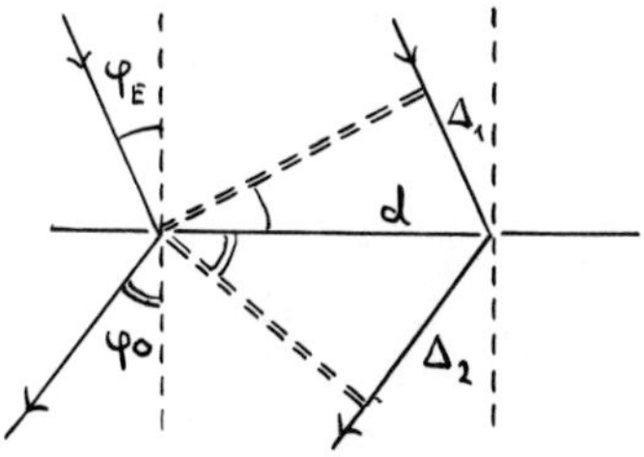

Each groove or opening is the starting point of a spherical wave (Huygens' principle).

= = = = = = = = = = : wave front

d = grating constant = distance between two lines (grooves)

ϕ_e = entrance angle (fixed initially)

ϕ_o = exit angle (arbitrarily chosen beam)

|| positive if at the same side of the normal

Difference in phase between the arriving and departing wave front: $\Delta = \Delta_1 + \Delta_2 = d \sin \phi_o + d \sin \phi_e$

Amplification occurs, if this is an integral multiple of the wavelength; hence the following basic equation holds for intensity maxima:

$$\boxed{d(\sin \phi_e + \sin \phi_o) = m \cdot \lambda} \quad m = 0, \pm 1, \pm 2, \ldots = \text{order}$$

Construction: directions of the orders (for a given ϕ_e)

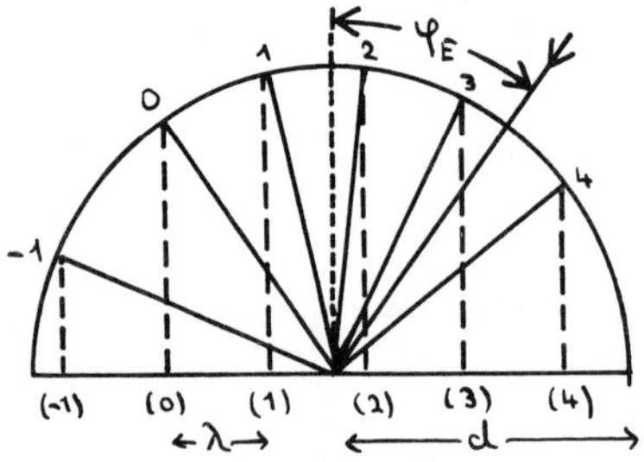

Semicircle with radius d, entrance direction ϕ_e given;

Reflection = zero order, 0

From 0, drop a perpendicular to the diameter, → (0); mark off λ to the right and to the left, → (-1) to (4).
There construct ⊥'s upwards; intersections with circle yield directions of the orders -1 to 4.

Maximum number of orders: $m_{\text{total}} = \frac{2d}{\lambda}$

e.g., grating with 500 lines/mm → $d = 2 \cdot 10^{-3}$ mm, $\lambda = 5000$ Å $= 5 \cdot 10^{-4}$ mm $\Big\}$ $m_{\text{total}} = 8$

Overlapping of the orders:

For a given direction we get, from the basic equation $\Big\}$ $m_i \lambda_i = m_k \lambda_k$

e.g.,	λ_1 in the 1st order	↔	$\lambda_{1/2}$	in the 2nd order
	6000 Å, 2nd order	↔	4000 Å,	3rd order
	5000 Å, 40th order	↔	5128 Å,	39th order

Angular dispersion:

Differentiate the basic equation (ϕ_e = const):

$d \cos \phi_o \, d\phi_o = m d\lambda$ or

$$\boxed{\frac{\phi_o}{\lambda} = \frac{m}{d \cdot \cos \phi_o}}$$

Except for the small change in $\cos \phi_o(\lambda)$ independent of the wavelength $\Big\}$ → so-called normal spectrum

Linear dispersion on the plate = $f \cdot \frac{d\phi_o}{d\lambda}$, f = focal length of the camera

Blazed grating:

Suitable shape of the grooves or lines allows most of the light to fall into one chosen order.

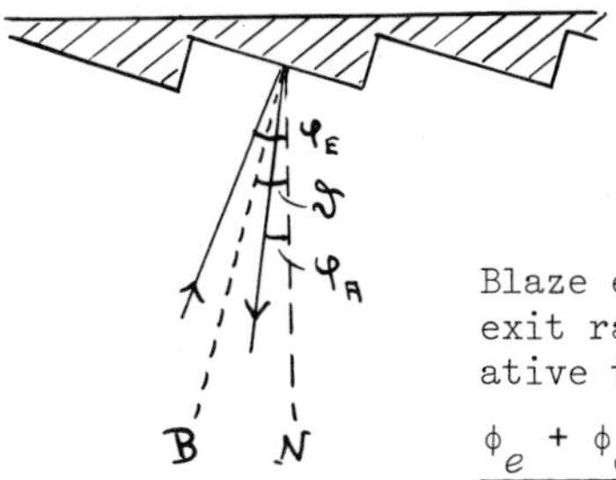

N = Normal (perpendicular) to the grating
B = normal to the "reflecting surface" of the blaze (blaze normal)
θ = blaze angle

Blaze effect occurs if the incident and exit rays satisfy the reflection law relative to B, i.e.,

$$\frac{\phi_e + \phi_o}{2} = \theta$$

Echelle grating: $\theta > 45^\circ$, i.e., the "narrow" side of the grooves operates as a mirror.

Littrow mounting: light is incident in direction B, i.e., $\phi_e = \phi_o = \theta$.

Here, one obtains, from the basic formula for the relation between wavelength and order in the region of the blaze:

$$m\lambda = 2\, d \sin\theta$$

Example: grating with 73 lines/mm = $1/d$; $\theta = 64\overset{\circ}{.}5$

λ = 5000 Å: $m = \frac{2 \sin\theta}{(1/d)\cdot\lambda} = 49.3 \rightarrow$ blaze in the 49th order
λ = 4900 Å: m = " $= 50.3 \rightarrow$ " in the 50th order

Principal and secondary maxima

Superposition of the effects of all grooves

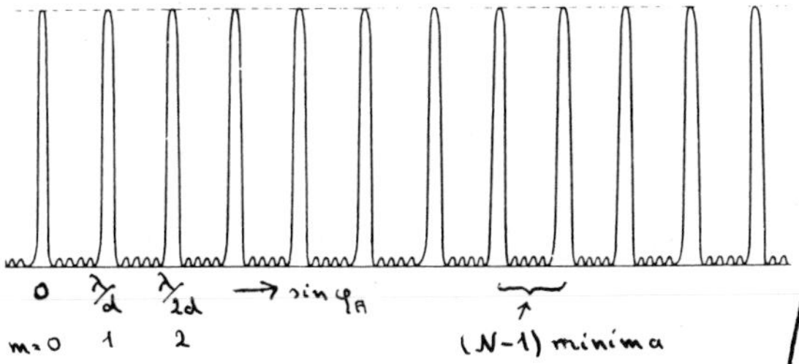

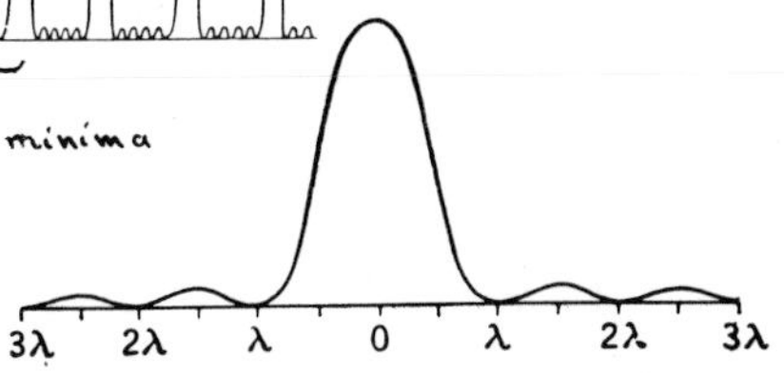

diffraction image of a rectangular slit

Consider monochromatic light, D = total width

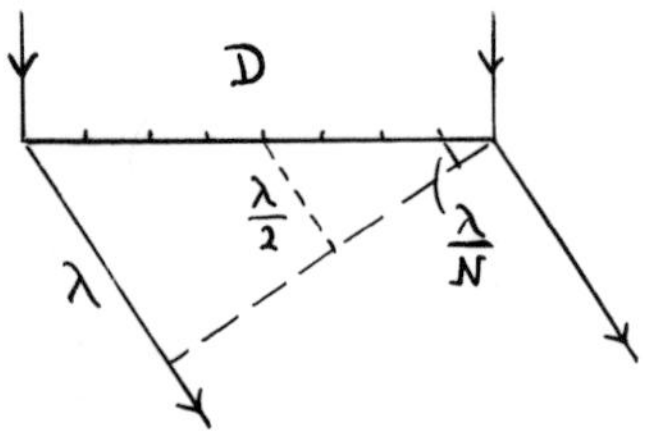

First minimum, adjacent to (zero order) principal maximum occurs if path difference (Δp) between rays at edges of grating = λ, since the two halves of the beam then interfere destructively. (For each ray, there is a corresponding one with Δp of $\lambda/2$.)

Analogously further minima for Δp (between extreme rays) = $n\lambda$ (with $n = 2,3,4...$). Secondary maxima between such minima are small since some rays always interfere destructively, see fig.p.133(similar to single-slit diffraction image).

Note that Δp between two rays from adjacent slits then = $\frac{n\lambda}{N}$, where N = total number of lines = $\frac{D}{d}$; N usually very large.

Principal maxima occur if Δp between adjacent rays = $m\lambda$ (basic equation m = order). For N lines, this yields total Δp across grating of $Nm\lambda$, see fig.p.133. (N-1) secondary minima between two principal maxima.

N determines the sharpness of the principal maxima

d determines the separation of the principal maxima (i.e. of the orders

Resolving power

Consider the principal maximum for which Δp_{max} across grating = $Nm\lambda$; constructive interference. If Δp across grating now is increased by λ, get destructive interference of beam halves as in the figure above,

and hence 1st minimum, i.e., Δp_{min} acroos grating = $N\,m\lambda + \lambda$.

Rayleigh's criterion states that two spectral lines at λ and $\lambda_1 = \lambda + \Delta\lambda$ are resolved in order m if principal maximum for λ_1 falls on first minimum of λ;

$$\text{i.e., } \Delta p_{max} \text{ for } \lambda_1 = \Delta p_{min} \text{ for } \lambda$$

$$Nm\lambda_1 = Nm(\lambda + \Delta\lambda) = Nm\lambda + \lambda$$

$$Nm\,\Delta\lambda = \lambda$$

Hence, resolving power $\boxed{R \equiv \frac{\lambda}{\Delta\lambda} = mN}$

Example: grating with 500 lines/mm; D = 100 mm, 4th order

$R = 500 \cdot 100 \cdot 4 = 200\ 000$

For 5000 Å: separation $\Delta\lambda = \frac{\lambda}{R} = \frac{5000}{200\ 000} = 0.025$ Å

Supplementary effects decrease this "theoretical resolving power":

1) finite width of the slit (compromise between light loss and resolution)
2) Errors of the grating
3) Errors in the optics

Together these effects produce the "instrumental profile", which must be determined empirically and applied later as a correction to observations.

4.2 *Instrumental setups*

1) Objective prisms and gratings

/Prism in front of objective of the telescope yields a small spectrum of every star on the plate.

Dispersions: 100 to 1000 Å/mm; for classification.

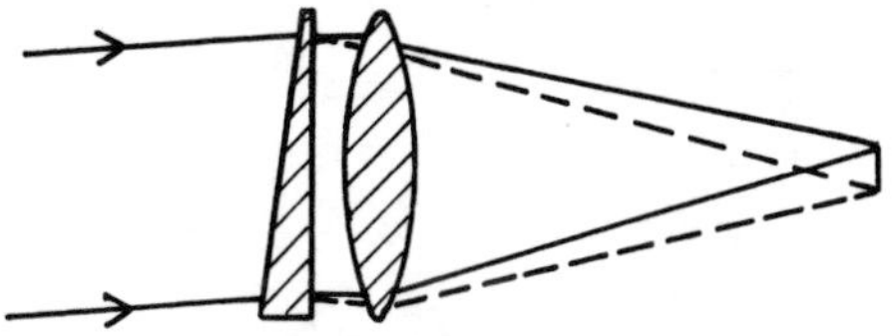

/Grating in front of the objective: for each star get central, undispersed, image and secondary, tertiary, ... spectral images.

"Normal grating": thickness of rods = space between rods; unblazed

Δm (without grating - central image) = $1\overset{m}{.}5$

Δm (central image - 1st order image) = $1\overset{m}{.}0$

suitable as "photometric scale"; if very low dispersion used

2) Slit spectrographs (see figure next page)

The slit isolates a star from most of sky background and nearby stars, to prevent overlapping spectra; also gives fixed resolution, independent of variable stellar image size and position (atmospheric seeing). Spectral lines are images of slit; star trailed along slit to widen spectrum.

The collimating lens insures that the light falling on the grating consists of parallel rays.

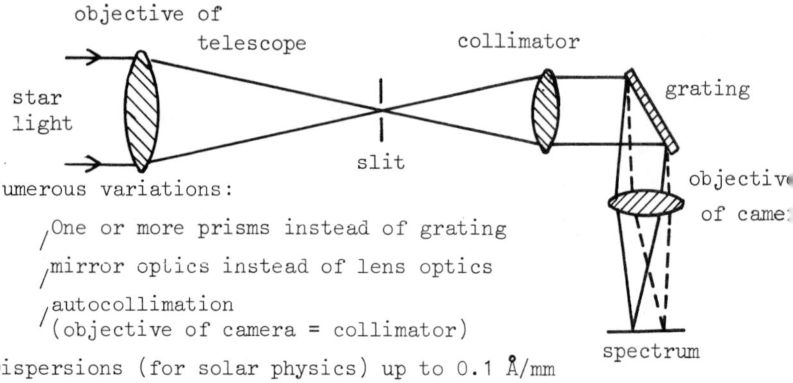

Numerous variations:

- One or more prisms instead of grating
- mirror optics instead of lens optics
- autocollimation (objective of camera = collimator)

Dispersions (for solar physics) up to 0.1 Å/mm

3) Concave gratings

Grating lines on a spherical surface. The grating itself assumes the function of image formation.

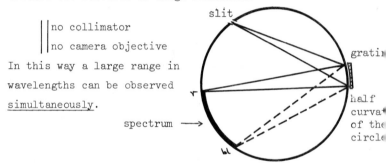

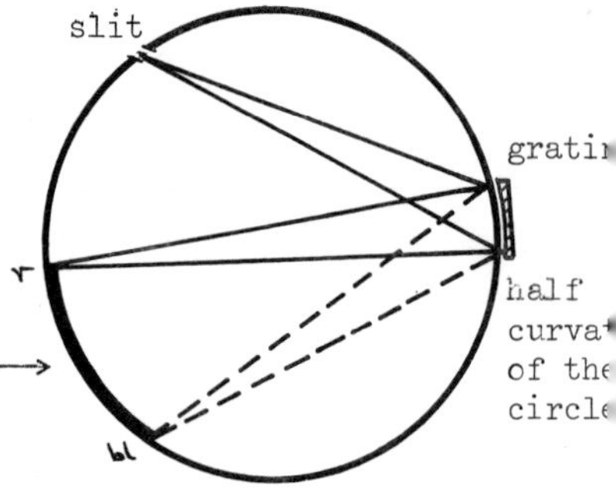

- no collimator
- no camera objective

In this way a large range in wavelengths can be observed simultaneously.

Several possibilities for mountings:

e.g., slit, grating, and spectrum on a single circle (= Rowland circle). Diameter of the circle = radius of curvature of the grating.

Strong astigmatism of concave gratings can be reduced by use of a cylindrical lens.

§ 5 Light detectors; filters

Literature: *Astronomical Techniques*, 1962 (W.A. Hiltner, editor) vol. II of *Stars and Stellar Systems*, Chicago.

5.1 *Detectors*

1) The eye   Two kinds of radiation-sensitive elements

Cones: color sensitive, slightly light sensitive
Rods: very light sensitive, not color sensitive ("At night all cats are grey!")

The cones are located predominantly in the fovea (= central position of the retina, upon which an image of an object "stared at" is formed), the rods predominantly extrafoveal. Hence, very faint objects often detected only outside the fovea (i.e., with averted vision)

Dark adaption (= becoming accustomed to darkness)

a) Diameter of the pupil increases in a few seconds.

b) Increase in sensitivity of the rods with regeneration of the visual purple takes up to 30 minutes.

Spectral sensitivity curve (separate relative ordinates for rods and cones):

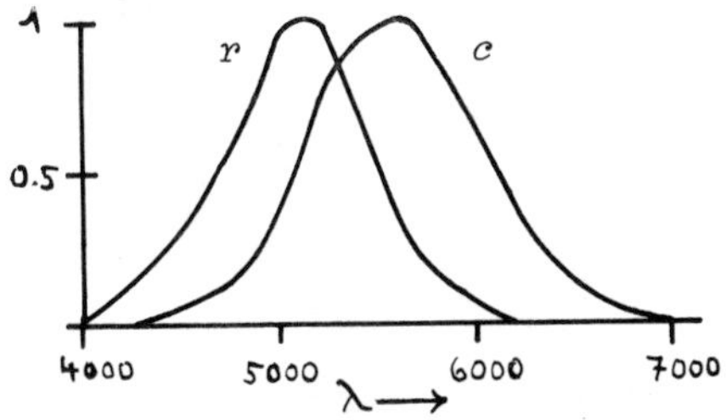

λ	cones	rods
4000	0.00	0.02
4400	.02	.21
4800	.14	.66
5200	.71	.98
5600	1.00	.36
6000	0.63	.05
6400	.18	.01
6800	.02	.00

Cones (eye adapted to bright light), maximum at 5600 Å

Rods (eye adapted to the dark), maximum at 5100 Å

Sensitivity threshold for detection of light under most favorable conditions:

Absorption of 4 quanta in 0.15 seconds
(requires 60 incident quanta in $0\overset{s}{.}15$

Limit of resolution: ~1', corresponds on the retina to ~5 μm

2) Photographic plate

References: J. Stock and A.D. Williams 1962, *Photographic Photometry* in *Astronomical Techniques*, p. 374, vol. II of *Stars and Stellar Systems*, Chicago.

Eastman Kodak 1964, *Plates and Films for Science and Industry*, Rochester, N.J.

Principle: Unexposed plate: silver bromide, *AgBr*

Effect of light: photochemical separation of *Ag* and *Br*

Developing: enhancement of the separation; amplification of 100 million or more

Fixing: elimination of *Br* and *AgBr* by rinsing in a thiosulfate solution

The processed emulsion exhibits a permanent image, presumably built up from *Ag*-colloids.

Process in detail complicated and obscure

<u>Opacity</u>: at the place where light has impinged, the developed plate shows a blackening. This opacity causes the weakening of a beam of light passing through the plate.

I_o = intensity of the incident light

I = " " " transmitted "

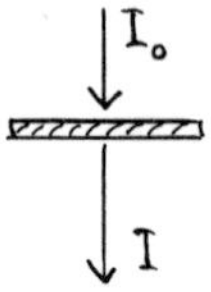

Definitions:

Transparency $T = I/I_o$

Opacity $O = I/T = I_o/I$

Density $D = \log_{10} (I_o/I)$

Disadvantage: D not linearly proportional to the exposure (= intensity of incident light × time). The relation is given by the "characteristic curve", which must always be determined empirically. It allows conversion of D into intensity.

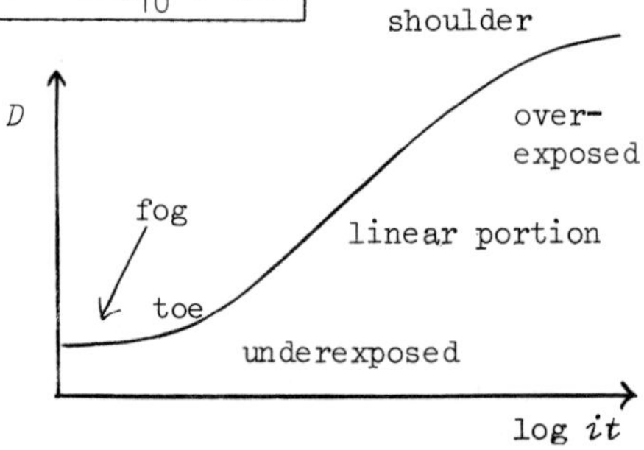

For long exposures the reciprocity law is <u>not</u> valid for the photographic plate, i.e., half intensity and double exposure time do not yield the same density D, but a lower D:

"reciprocity failure".

Reduction of the photographic plate:

For direct photographs: iris photometer to measure D and diameter of images.

For spectral: microdensitometer to measure $D(\lambda)$

Various different types:

See sketch for principles.

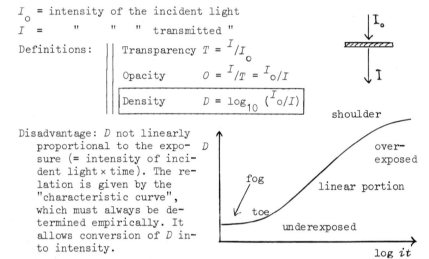

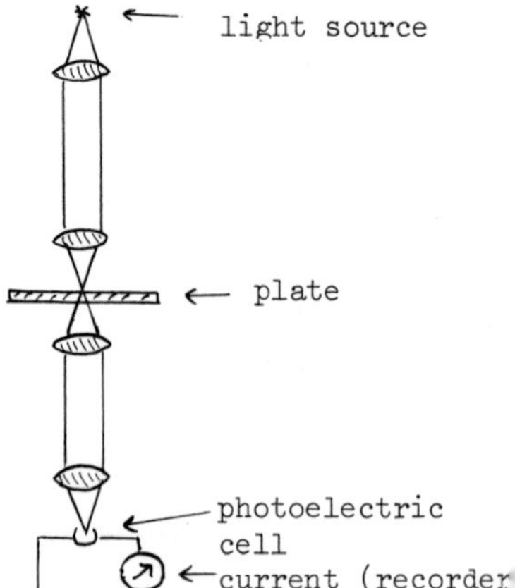

Modern photometers simultaneously perform the conversion of densities to intensities, or give digital output for subsequent conversion to intensities by means of an electric computer.

Sensitivity:

Normal emulsion sensitive only in the blue, λ < 4600 Å. By adding dyes one can extend sensitivity to other spectral regions. (See Eastman Kodak, op. cit.)

3) Photoelectric Measurement

Photomultiplier tube (or, formerly, photoelectric cell - Stebbins, 1910) used directly at the telescope. Used now for most high-precision photometry, especially of standards.

Photo cathode (Cs-Sb, (cesium-antimony), PbS (lead sulfide), Ga-As (gallium-arsenic) ...) emits electrons when struck by photons; electron flux multiplied by series of dynodes and collected by anode. Output signal amplified and observed:

/d.c.: measure voltage drop across resistance through which output current passes

/charge integrating: measure time required for current to charge capacitor

or (usually preferred now)

/pulse counting: count the current pulses due to each incident photon, using high speed electronics.

Record measure with strip-chart recorder, paper tape or punch, on-line computer....

Observe standard stars to transform measures to magnitudes on standard color systems (see 4.1.2) and extinction stars (stars observed over sizable range of zenith distances) to permit extrapolation of observations to outside the atmosphere.

Advantages relative to the photographic plate:

//more sensitive (quantum efficiency - fraction of incident photons recorded - now approaching 50% contrasting with .1 - 1% for photography)

//more accurate (with care, possible accuracy of ±0.01 mag = ± 1% error in brightness)

//linear response

Disadvantage: only a single star recorded at a time

4) Image tubes

Reference: W.K. Ford, Jr. 1968, *Electronic Image Intensification*, Ann. Rev. Astron. and Astrophys. 6, 1.

Photocathode used to increase quantum efficiency by ~100 times over classical photography. Final picture displayed on a phosphor screen.

5.2 *Filters*

1) Normal color filters using color dyes for broad spectral bands, for instance to establish color systems such as *UBV* (see 4.1.2), and

   neutral filters to reduce the intensity;

   e.g., extensive series of Schott filters

   NG = neutral glass filters, *RG* = red glass filters, *BG* = blue glass filters, etc.

2) Interference filters for narrow-band photometry (see 4.2.4)

   Band widths ~10 to several hundred Å

   Operate on principle of the Fabry-Perot interferometer:

   Utilizes interference produced by multiple reflections between 2 plane glass plates with facing surfaces half-silvered in thin homogeneous layer. Normal color filter used to select a single maximum.

   Tunable: the above with continuous change possible in the wavelength range transmitted

red	green	blue

   Also suitable for the elimination of neighboring orders in large spectrographs.

3) Polarizing interference filters (Lyot filters)

   Band widths < 5 Å

   used to observe the sun in the light of individual spectral lines: H_α filter, etc.

   Basic component: a plane-parallel doubly refracting crystal plate, with optical axis parallel to its face, sandwiched between 2 || polarizers whose directions of polarization are 45° from the optical axis of the birefringent crystal.

   Plane-polarized light entering crystal is split into 2 polarized beams (ordinary and extraordinary) || and ⊥ to optical axis (hence circular polarization). *O* and *E* beams travel at different speeds through crystal and hence emerge out of phase. 2nd polarizer transmits || polarization components of these beams, which then interfere with each other, producing dark interference fringes at the wavelengths

$$\lambda \quad \frac{d \cdot \Delta n}{m - \frac{1}{2}}$$

   d = thickness of the crystal plate
   Δn = difference between the indices of refraction for the ordinary and the extraordinary ray
   m = 1,2,3,... = order of interference

If combine crystal plates whose thickness have ratios 1:2:4:8 ...(alternating with polarizers), each plate suppresses alternate maxima of the next thicker plate, hence narrow transmission ranges can be achieved, as illustrated in the figure. Ordinary color filters isolate the individual narrow transmission bands.

Schematic cross-section of a Lyot filter, and the effects of the individual crystal plates

(According to A. Behr 1951, *Sterne* 27, 195)

P_n = polarizers

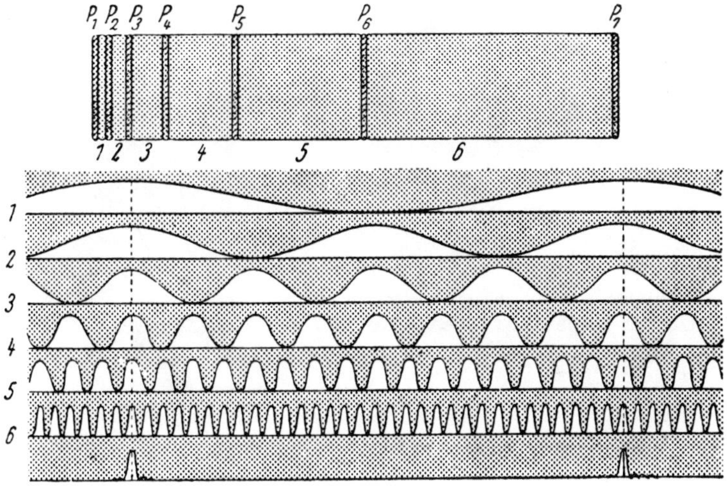

§ 6 Radio telescopes

Literature: J.D. Kraus 1966, *Radio Astronomy*, McGraw-Hill

W.N. Christiansen, and J.A. Högbom 1967, *Radiotelescopes*, Cambridge Univ. Press

Basic elements of radio astronomy instrumentation:

Antenna or array of antennae

series of amplifiers (maser or parametric amplifiers)

Integrator with recording device.

1) Dipole antenna ($\lambda/2$ antenna)

Simplest antenna; straight wire. Electrons are excited into

periodic oscillations by the electric forces of the incoming wave, → induced alternating current.

> Because of resonance:
> preferred wavelength = 2 times length of dipole

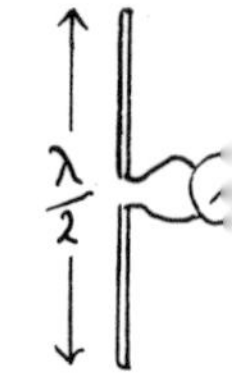

2) <u>Yagi antenna</u> (= usual television antenna)
A dipole augmented by several directors in front and a reflector behind. Hence more highly directive, though still not sufficiently so for common use.

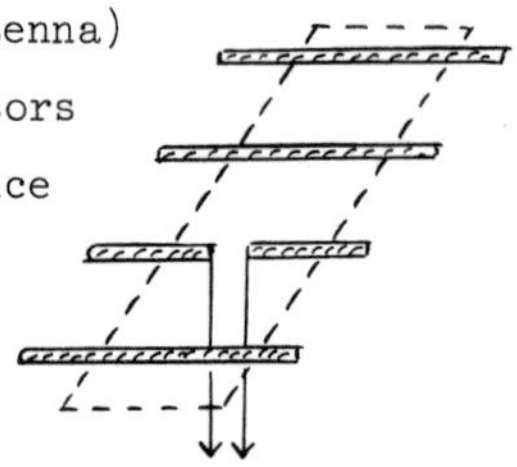

3) <u>Dipole array</u> (broadside arrays)
Several $\lambda/2$ dipoles arranged in a rectangular array providing greater directivity and sensitivity.

4) <u>Horn antenna</u>
Funnel-shaped wave guide. They make it possible to convert without special arrangements the traveling waves, which are circulating in the wave guide, into space waves.

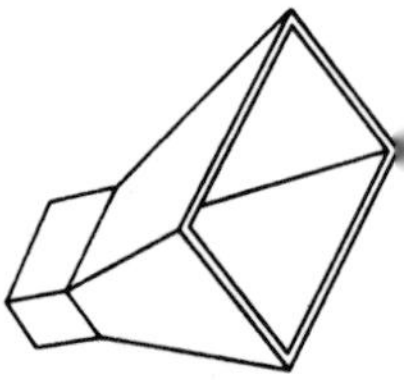

Preferred for absolute measurements
Chief application: feed for parabolic reflectors

5) <u>Parabolic antenna</u>
= parabolic reflecting surface (accuracy and width of meshes $\leq \lambda/10$) with feed antenna (dipole, horn antenna,...) at the focus.

Because of the analogy to a reflecting telescope, also called "radio telescope". This name is then carried over to all radio-wave detectors.

<u>Resolving power</u> for radio telescopes same as for optical telescopes (see 3.3.1) In this case, however, the diffraction pattern is usually given in polar coordinates. Width of the principal maximum characterized by the half-width, here called the "beam-width"

$$\boxed{A_{1/2} = 1.03\,\frac{\lambda}{D}}$$

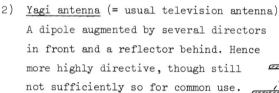

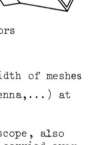

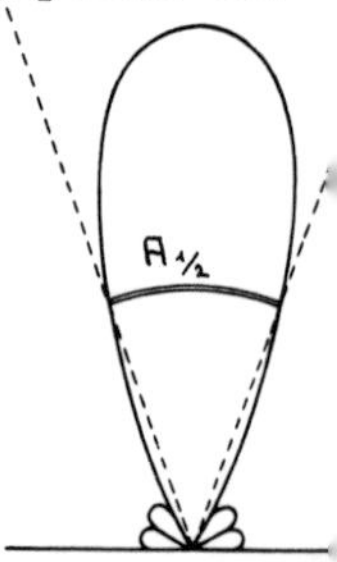

Because $\lambda_{radio} \gg \lambda_{optical}$ the resolving power of common parabolic antennae is very much lower.

To obtain at λ = 1 m the same resolving power as a 50 cm mirror at 5000 Å, the antenna has to have a diameter of 1000 km!

Resolving power of a 25 m dish: $2\overset{\circ}{.}5$ (= 5 times the moon's diameter)

Diameters of present radio telescopes: up to ~100 m

e.g. Max Planck Institute for Radio Astronomy (Bonn): 100 m. Fully steerable altazimuth

National Radio Astronomy Observatory (Green Bank): 300 ft. partially steerable meridian-transit type

Focal ratios: *f*/2 to *f*/4

6) Interferometers

Since only the diameter is important for the resolution, the surface in between the ends of an array need not be filled up; hence use electrically connected receivers with a large separation.
At present, have length up to 50 km or more.

No diffraction rings, but strips, i.e., resolution only in one coordinate, → "club-shaped".

Further increase by multi-element interferometers

Principle of the diffraction grating

(see 3.4.1)

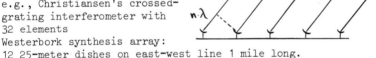

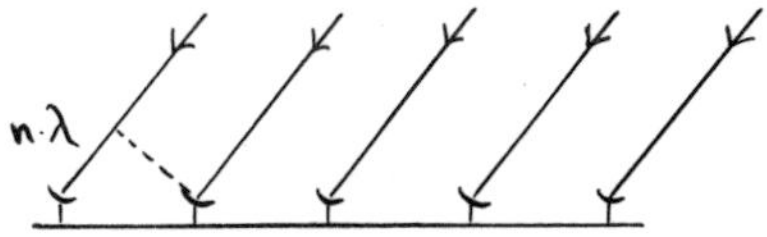

e.g., Christiansen's crossed-grating interferometer with 32 elements
Westerbork synthesis array:
12 25-meter dishes on east-west line 1 mile long.

Cross interferometer (= cross-shaped arrangement of the elements sometimes known as a Mills cross)

Resolution in two coordinates
e.g., Univ. of Sydney cross with base line nearly 1 mile long

At present, resolutions to less than 1" (similar to that of large optical telescopes).

Very-long-base-line techniques

Radiation is measured (and recorded on magnetic tape) by two telescopes separated by several thousand km distance; later, the measurements are correlated by an electric computer.

Resolution < 0".001 (much better than optical!)

Spectral resolution: by tuning of the receiver antennae.

4

BASIC PROPERTIES OF THE STARS

Literature: K.Aa Strand 1963, *Basic Astronomical Data*, vol. III of *Stars and Stellar Systems* (U. of Chicago Press).

Also most astronomy textbooks

Basic stellar properties are those which describe the star as a whole. The most important basic properties are:

apparent brightness*	mass	effective temperature
luminosity	radius	rotation
color	density	magnetic field
spectral type	surface gravity	chemical composition

*not truly basic, because dependent on the distance.

The basic properties are not all independent of one another, but are to some degree connected by simple or complicated relations. E.g. mass, radius, and density:
$$\rho = \frac{M}{{}^4/_3\ \pi\ R^3}$$

§ 1 Magnitude, color, luminosity

1.1 *Apparent brightness or apparent magnitude* = brightness as seen from earth

It is the oldest determined quantity and therefore (alas) laden with historical ballast.

Antiquity: division into "magnitudes". The brightest stars were of the first magnitude; the faintest naked eye stars were of the 6th magnitude.

Modern definition: (adapted as well as possible to original definition) The designations in antiquity were based on sense impressions for which the fundamental psycho-physical law of sensation by Fechner and Weber (1859) is valid:

⇒ Equal increases of sensation are produced by equal ratios of stimulus; hence, the perception is proportional to the logarithm of the stimulus.

Therefore: $\Longrightarrow$ apparent magnitude $m \propto \log s$

s = radiation flux arriving at the observer

= amount of light collected per unit of surface and of time

| Frequently -- but not correctly -- called "intensity" in the literature (see definition in 5.1.1)

The Pogson scale proposed in 1856 includes a constant of proportionality to give as good an approximation as possible to the historical scale:

$$m_1 - m_2 = -2.5 \log s_1/s_2 \qquad s_1/s_2 = 10^{-0.4(m_1-m_2)}$$

e.g., $\Delta m = 1 \longrightarrow s_1/s_2 = 10^{-0.4} = 1{:}2.512$

$\Delta m = 5 \longrightarrow s_1/s_2 = 10^{-2} = 1{:}100$

Zero-point now fixed by means of frequently-measured standard stars.
Formerly, the North Polar Sequence of standards was used. α UMi = Polaris: $2^{\mathrm{m}}\!.12$ (visual)

Unit designated by *mag* or *m* = magnitude

Note: Physical quantity (brightness) and unit of measurement (magnitude) are often confused in the literature.
We speak about measuring the "magnitude" of a star (properly: the "brightness" of a star) in "magnitudes", as we measure the "length" of a table in "meters".
The physical quantity as well as the unit of measurement are, unfortunately, nearly always designated by the same word, magnitude, and the same letter *m*.

Examples:

Vega 0.0 mag (or m = 0.0 or $0^{\mathrm{m}}\!.0$)

Sirius −1.6 mag

Sun −26.8 mag

$\Delta m \approx -25^{\mathrm{m}} \longrightarrow \dfrac{s(\text{Sirius})}{s(\text{Sun})} = 10^{-10}$

Limit for naked eye: 6th mag

Faintest objects measured so far: 23^{m} to 24^{m} (only a few percent of the night sky background)

Total range about 50^{m}, i.e., 20 factors of ten in radiation flux

Physical units

In physics the illumination is measured in lx = lux = meter-candle = lumen m^{-2} (= 1.5 erg cm^{-2} sec^{-1})

Sun at zenith:	-26.8 mag	=	137 000 lx
full moon:	-12.5	=	0.25 lx
star of 1st magnitude:	1.0	=	10^{-6} lx

A star of the 23rd magnitude corresponds to a candle at a distance of about 30 000 km.

Wavelength region

The emitted radiation of a star is not uniformly distributed over all wavelengths λ. The brightness, therefore, depends on the λ at which it is measured.

Hence, one distinguishes, for instance,

visual magnitude m_V

photographic magnitude m_{pg} (= brightness in the blue)

In general: m_λ (the wavelength region given as a subscript)

Apparent magnitudes in specifically defined wavelength regions are often designated by special letters (e.g., U,B,V, ...; see 4.1.2).

m (λ unspecified) usually means m_V.

Zero point: By common agreement, the A0 stars between $5\overset{m}{.}5$ and $6\overset{m}{.}5$ are defined to have the same magnitude at all wavelength Though inappropriate, this definition is maintained for historical continuity.

Bolometric magnitude: inclusion of the total spectrum; thus, a measure of the total radiation (just outside the terrestrial atmosphere)

Bolometric correction = *B. C.*:

Conversion of the "limited", especially the visual, magnitude to the bolometric one:

$$B.\,C. \doteq m_{bol} - m_V$$

Zero point defined such that for stars of solar type $B.\,C. = 0$

Because stars of solar type (G2V) have the maximum of their radiation in the visual range, the bolometric correction is always negative, for cooler as well as for hotter stars.

| (sometimes defined in reverse sense: always positive)

Approximate *B.C.*'s:				
	B0	- 3: mag	*G0*	- 0.1 mag
	B5	- 1.4	*K0*	- 0.2
	A0	- 0.4	*M0*	- 1
	F0	- 0.1	*M6*	- 3:

Relationship between magnitude and emitted energy

Let: R = radius of the star

r = distance

F_λ = mean intensity of radiation at wavelength λ emitted at the surface. πF_λ = radiation flux; (see 5.1.1)

Then $\pi f_\lambda = \dfrac{\pi R^2 F_\lambda}{r^2}$ is the radiation flux arriving above the terrestrial atmosphere.

Further, let:

E_λ = sensitivity function (transparency of the terrestrial atmosphere and the equipment (filters, etc.) and the sensitivity curve of the detector)

Then the amount of light received, $s = \int_0^\infty \pi f_\lambda\, E_\lambda\, d\lambda$

and hence:

$$m = \text{const} - 2.5 \log \int_0^\infty \frac{\pi R^2 F_\lambda}{r^2}\, E_\lambda\, d\lambda$$

Catalogues of apparent magnitudes of stars: see 4.1.3.

1.2 *Color*

Definition:

> Color index = difference between two magnitudes at different wavelengths
>
> $= m_{\text{short wavelength}} - m_{\text{long wavelength}}$
>
> Also known simply as "color".

e.g.: *C.I.* (color index) $= m_{pg} - m_v$

where $m_{pg} = m_{\text{photographic}} \approx m_{\text{blue}}$

|| positive: red brighter

|| negative: blue brighter

It follows from the above definition of the various magnitudes that the color index of *A0* stars is zero.

The effective wavelength, λ_{eff}, is defined by

$$\lambda_{eff} = \frac{\int_0^\infty \lambda\, I_\lambda\, s_\lambda\, f_\lambda\, q_\lambda\, p_\lambda^{F(z)}\, d\lambda}{\int_0^\infty I_\lambda\, s_\lambda\, f_\lambda\, q_\lambda\, p_\lambda^{F(z)}\, d\lambda}$$

where, at wavelength λ,

I_λ = energy distribution in stellar spectrum

s_λ = sensitivity of detector (photographic plate, etc)

f_λ = transmission of filter

q_λ = transmission of telescope

p_λ = zenith transmission coefficient of the atmosphere

$F(z)$ = air mass corresponding to the zenith distance

Effective wavelengths can be determined empirically from diffraction images produced by an objective grating.

Since λ_{eff} is dependent on I_λ, hence on temperature, (λ_{eff} greate for cool stars), the values in the table below are only approxim

Well-known systems (designations and effective wavelengths)

a)	International system	I_{pg}	4300 Å	(photographic)
	band pass pg ~1500 Å, pv ~ 800 Å	I_{pv}	5400	(photovisual)
b)	Standard system of Becker = "*RGU* system"	*U*	3690	(ultraviolet)
		G	4680	(green)
	band passes ~500-700 Å	*R*	6380	(red)
c)	Standard system of Johnson = "*UBV* system"	*U*	3500	(ultraviolet)
		B	4350	(blue)
	band passes ~800-1000 Å	*V*	5550	(visual)
d)	Six-color photometry (Stebbins, Whitford)	*U* 3550	*G* 5700	(*V* = violet
		V 4200	*R* 7200	*I* = infrared,
	band passes ~600-1500 Å	*B* 4900	*I* 10 300	rest as above)
e)	Four-color photometry of Strömgren = "*uvby* system"	*u*	3500	(ultraviolet)
		v	4100	(violet)
	band passes ~200 Å	*b*	4670	(blue)
		y	5470	(visual)

[Notation: The color $m_B - m_V$ in the *UBV* system is in short designated as *B-V*.

The *RGU* system is physically more meaningful than *UBV* because of bandpasses selected. But *RGU* can only be used photographically while the *UBV* system is defined for and adapted to photoelectric

Interpretation of wide-band magnitudes (*UBV*, *RGU*) is more ambiguous than that of intermediate-band magnitudes (*uvby*) because of greater difficulties in separating effects due to atmospheric extinction, color of star, spectral features such as the Balmer jump,... But wide-band measures require less telescope time.

Notice: The concept of "color" is used ambigiously: both in the strict definition as a difference of two magnitudes, and on the other hand for the individual wavelength regions (for instance in the phrase "three-color photometry").

Initially each series of observations has its own color system, as given by the sensitivity function of the receiver, transparancy of the optics and filter, etc. Through observation of "standard stars" (stars of known colors and magnitudes; see end of 4.1.3) one obtains equations for transformation of zero point and scale to one of the standard systems.
For photographic investigations (for instance of stellar clusters) one obtains--as far as possible--photoelectric standards.

Origin of the color:

1) Energy distribution in the stellar spectrum
→intrinsic color (subscript o) (see 4.2.2)
2) Interstellar reddening: blue light is more strongly absorbed by interstellar dust, so that the stars appear redder (see 9.1.5).

This supplementary color, not intrinsic to the star, is designated as "color excess" *E*.

Definition:

Color excess = measured color - intrinsic color

Notation: e.g.,

$$E_{B-V} = (B - V) - (B - V)_o$$

Because the intrinsic color is not known a priori, the separation of the two effects is problematical and only possible by iteration.

1.3 *Absolute magnitude or luminosity*

The apparent magnitude of a star depends on its intrinsic brightness (radiation energy) and on its distance (assuming no interstellar absorption). To obtain a measure of its true brightness, one refers to the unit distance of 10 pc (see 1.6) and defines:

Absolute magnitude M = apparent magnitude which a star would have at this distance of 10 pc

S = corresponding radiative flux

Then we have, analogously to §1.1,

$$M_1 - M_2 = -2.5 \log S_1/S_2$$
$$S_1/S_2 = 10^{-0.4(M_1-M_2)}$$

Because the magnitude increases with the square of the distance (as long as one disregards the interstellar absorption), the difference between apparent and absolute magnitude is a measure of the distance, the so-called uncorrected distance modulus:

$$m-M = 2.5 \log \frac{S}{s} = 2.5 \log \left(\frac{r}{R}\right)^2 = 5(\log r - \log R),$$

with R = unit distance = 10 pc, and

r[pc] = $1/\pi$ (π = parallax in arc sec)

If a star is dimmed A magnitudes by interstellar absorption, we can replace m with $m+A$ and write

Distance modulus: $m-M = 5 \log r - 5 - A = -5 \log \pi - 5 - A$

e.g., for A=0, and $m-M = -5^m \longrightarrow r =$ 1 pc
$= 0$ 10 pc (by definition)
$= 10$ 1 kpc
$= 25$ 1 Mpc

In general: change of the distance modulus by 5^m is equivalent to change of the distance by a factor 10.

The relation is often used for the determination of:

a) The absolute magnitude, if the distance and absorption are known;
b) the distance, if the absolute magnitude and absorption are known;
c) the absorption, if the absolute magnitude and distance are known.

⟹ Absolute magnitude of the sun: $\begin{cases} M_{pg} = +5.4 \\ M_v = +4.8 \end{cases}$

The absolute magnitudes of the stars extend from $M \cong -9$ to $M \cong +20$ (essentially instrumentally limited)(see 4.2.2)

The absolute bolometric magnitude of a star is a measure of its total energy emission. The corresponding radiation flux is called the "luminosity" L, measured in erg sec^{-1} or in solar units.

Relative to the sun ($M_{bol} = 4.72$), we have

$$M_{bol} - 4.72 = 2.5 \log L/L_\odot, \text{ where } L_\odot = 3.9 \times 10^{33} \text{ erg sec}^{-1}$$

Catalogues

The position catalogues mentioned in 1.9 also contain (estimated) data on apparent magnitudes.

Older catalogues of apparent magnitudes:

HR	Revised Harvard Photometry	m_v	9100	stars	1908
GA	Göttingen Aktinometrie	m_{pg}	3500	"	1910
PD	Potsdamer Durchmusterung	m_v	16000	"	1907/16
YA	Yerkes Actinometry	m_{pg}	2300	"	1931
HPP	Harvard Photographic Photometry	m_{pg}	6000	"	1935/37
HPP_v	Harvard Photovisual Photometry	m_{pv}	42000	"	1938

Numerous specialized works using standard systems

In the publication Landolt-Börnstein, New Series, Vol. VI/I *Astronomy*, are listed more than 200 catalogues giving apparent magnitudes and colors, as well as formulae for transforming individual systems from one to another.

UBVRI photometry of the 1325 brightest stars:
Arizona-Tonantzintla Catalogue: *Sky and Telescope* 1965,30,24:

Compilation of U, B, V mags for more than 20 000 stars:
V.M. Blanco, S. Demers, G.G. Douglass, and M.P. FitzGerald 1968, *Photoelectric Catalogue*,
Publ. U.S. Naval Obs. Washington, Vol. 21

§ 2 Spectral classification

Literature: P.C. Keenan 1963, in *Basic Astronomical Data*, *Stars and Stellar Systems* III, 78,

Ch. Fehrenbach 1958, *Hdb. Physik* 50, p.1
(summarizing articles with many references)

The spectral types (or spectral classes), as determined visually, are essentially defined by the appearance of the line spectrum. Absorption lines are the most important classification criteria, because they largely characterize the physical structure of the star. Quantitative spectral classification sometimes also includes measures of the continuum.

It would be ideal to classify the stars according to fundamental physical parameters, such as, for instance, the effective temperature and the surface gravity. These quantities, however, are not immediately accessible to observation. Therefore, at first, classification is purely phenomenological. It is one of the important tasks of astrophysics to determine the relations between the classification parameters and the basic parameters of stellar structure.

2.1 *Harvard system* (Pickering, Cannon, Maury...)
or Henry Draper (HD) system
= one-dimensional sequence, essentially a temperature series. Designation by capital letters, the order of which is of historical origin (original system in order of H strength instead of temperature)

⟶ *O B A F G K M (R N S)*

Mnemonic: Oh, be a fine girl, kiss me right now - smack!

99.95% of all stars brighter than 8^m } types *O* to *M* (= "normal stars")

Short description

O Hot stars with lines of multiply-ionized atoms, predominantly He II; H relatively faint. Occasionally have emission lines ("*Of*" stars, etc.)

B He II is absent; He I strong. Balmer series (H) is increasing in strength.

A H at maximum; faint lines of ionized metals (Ca II...)

F Ca II strong; ionized and neutral metals about equal in strength. H strength decreasing

G Solar spectrum. Ca II and CH (*G*-band) very strong; many neutral metals (Fe I...). H strength decreases further.

K Strong metal lines. Appearance of molecular bands

M Coolest normal stars, with neutral lines, especially Ca I; TiO bands

Scheme

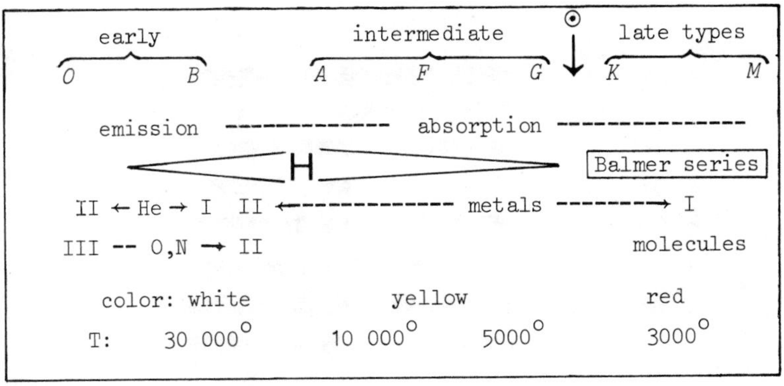

I = neutral; II = singly ionized; III = doubly ionized; ...

The designations "early, intermediate, late types" is of historical origin and has nothing to do with stellar evolution.

<u>Subdivision</u> into tenths: e.g., *A*0, *A*1, *A*2, ..., *A*9, *F*0, *F*1,...
(Not all subdivisions actually used)

<u>Criteria</u>: intensities and ratios of intensities of specified lines (mainly H, He, Ca, C, N, O, Mg, Si, CH, TiO)

<u>Extension</u>: special types: together about 0.05%

At the hot end:
- Planetary nebulae *P* (see 7.5)
- Wolf-Rayet stars *W* (see 7.4)
- Novae *Q* (see 7.3.1)

At the cool end:
- *S* stars
  strong bands of ZrO, YO, LaO
- Carbon stars: *R* stars (hotter), *N* stars (cooler) — today designed as *C* stars
  Strong carbon compounds (CN, CO, C_2).
  TiO is absent (see 4.9.2)

Neutral atomic lines in *S* and carbon stars are like those in *K* and *M* stars.

<u>The complete sequence</u>:

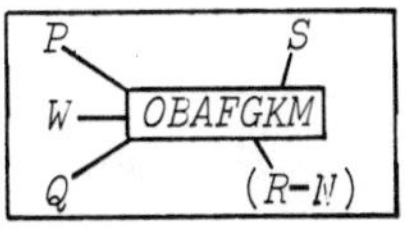

⟶ only giant stars (!)

⟶ only giant stars (!)

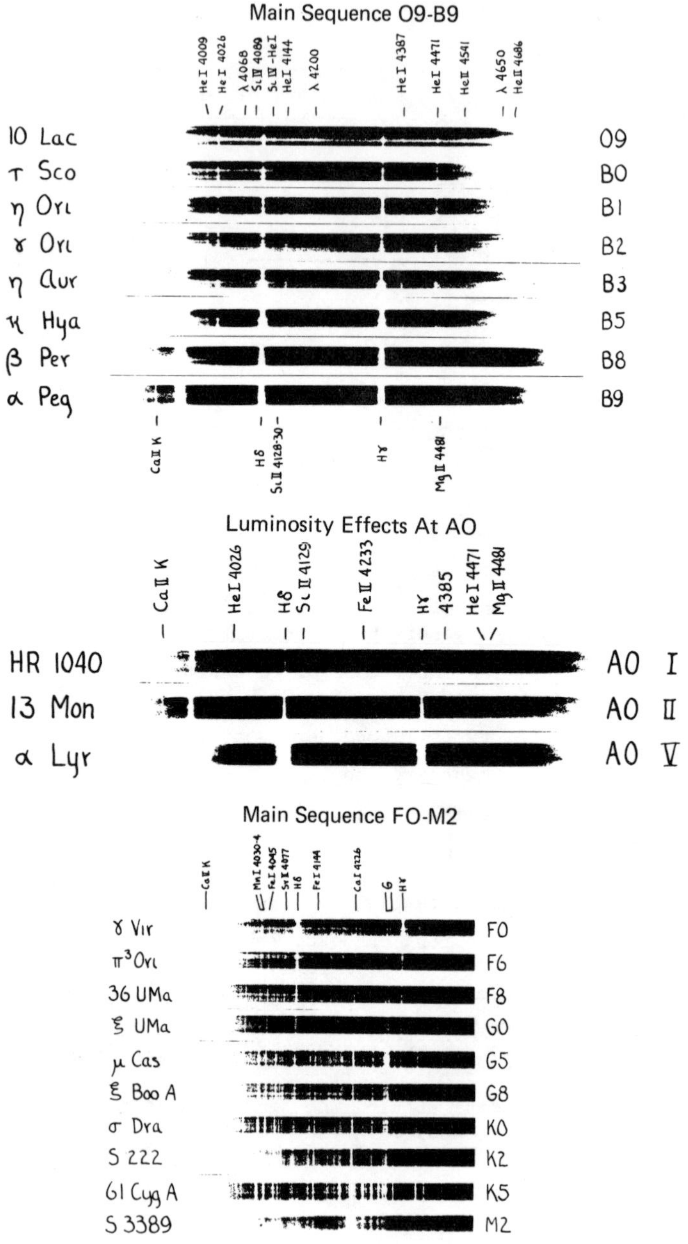

From Morgan, Keenan, Kellman 1943,
An Atlas of Stellar Spectra.

Prefixes to distinguish stars of the same type but of different luminosities:

The spectral type characterizes the surface temperature, but still says nothing about the luminosity of a star, which depends on both the temperature and the surface area. E.g., an *M* giant is about a million times brighter than an *M* dwarf. To the extent that these differences are detectable in the Harvard system they are characterized by prefixes. (Such prefixes are not used in the Henry Draper Catalogue, however.)

c:	supergiant	e.g., α Cyg (Deneb):	*cA*2
g:	giant	e.g., β Gem (Pollux):	*gK*0
d:	dwarf	e.g., the sun:	*dG*2
sd or *SD*:	subdwarf		
w or *D*:	white dwarf (see 7.6)		

Catalogues (objective-prism spectra)

HD	Henry Draper Catalogue (1918-1924)	(225 000 stars)
PSD	Potsdammer Spektraldurchmusterung (1929-1938)	(~ 65 000 stars)
BSD	Bergedorfer Spektraldurchmusterung (1935-1953)	(~170 000 stars)

2.2 *Yerkes or MK system* (MK = Morgan Keenan)

= further development to a completely two-dimensional classification, in order to indicate the difference in luminosity as well.

The l i n e spectrum is essentially determined by the degree of ionization, i.e., -- at a given chemical composition -- by temperature and electron pressure. Hence: two parameters necessary

First parameter: spectral type

Second parameter: luminosity class

(The calibration is, at present, kept open)

Spectral type

Harvard types, with some additions and omissions

P, *W*, *Q* not used

S, *N*, *R* not used in MK proper

Related system of Keenan for *S* stars and *C* stars (replaces *N* and *R*): temperature and molecular abundance parameters: e.g., *S* 3,9 and $C\,4_5$

Ap: peculiar *A* stars, most having strong magnetic field (Zeeman effect). Lines of individual elements considerably strengthened, e.g., Eu stars, Mn stars, etc. (see 4.8)

m[*Am*...*Fm*]: metallic-line stars. Anomalous intensity ratios of metals, especially Ca II abnormally faint. Reason unexplained (see 4.9.2).
About 10% of all *A*0 to *A*5 stars are *Am* stars.

Pecularities indicated by letters after spectral type:

n	(nebulous):	diffuse, broad lines	rapid rotation
nn	:	very diffuse lines	rapid rotation
s	(sharp) :	sharp lines	
e	(emission):	emission lines (extended shells, etc.)	
v	(variable):	variable spectrum	
k	(*K* line) :	strong interstellar calcium lines (*H* and *K*)	
p or pec	(peculiar):	pecularities which can be grasped only by detailed description	

Luminosity class

0	super supergiants	Each group, if necessary, subdivided into *a*, *ab*, *b*
I	supergiants	
II	bright giants	
III	giants	
IV	subgiants	
V	dwarfs = main-sequence stars	
VI	subdwarfs	

e.g.: sun *G*2 V; α Cyg *A*2 I*a*; β Gem *K*0 III

Determination of luminosity class is more difficult than determination of the spectral type, because differences are less evident for pressure-sensitive lines.

The criteria of the MK classification are based on a dispersion of ~125 Å/mm at Hγ. Convert from one instrumental system to another by observing "standard stars", the spectra of which are reproduced in the MK Atlas:

W.W. Morgan, P.C. Keenan, E. Kellman 1943, *An Atlas of Stellar Spectra*, Chicago

Revision: H.L. Johnson, W.W. Morgan 1953, *Ap. J.* 117, 313,

Relation between spectral type luminosity class luminosity (absolute magnitude)

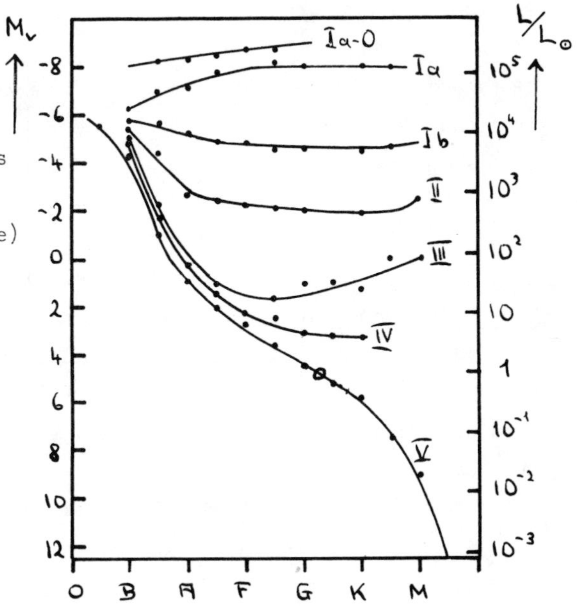

Absolute magnitude calibration of the main-sequence stars reliable; calibration of luminosity classes II and especially I still uncertain (problem of distance and interstellar absorption).

The absolute visual magnitudes of the MK types

Sp \ Lum	V	IV	III	II	I b	I a	I a-0	white dwarfs
*O*5	$-5^{\mathrm{M}}.6$							
*B*0	-4.2	$-4^{\mathrm{M}}.8$	$-5^{\mathrm{M}}.0$	$-5^{\mathrm{M}}.4$	$-5^{\mathrm{M}}.8$	$-6^{\mathrm{M}}.2$	$-8^{\mathrm{M}}.1$	$+10^{\mathrm{M}}.2$
5	-1.0	-1.8	-2.2	-4.4	-5.7	-7.0	-8.3	10.6
*A*0	+1.0	+0.3	(+0.1)		-5.2	-7.1	-8.4	11.2
5	2.1	1.4	1.1	-2.7	-4.8	-7.7	-8.5	12.3
*F*0	2.7	2.2	1.5	-2.5	-4.8	-8.5	-8.7	13.0
5	3.6	2.5	1.7	-2.3	-4.6	-8.2	-8.9	13.7
*G*0	4.6	3.0	(1.0)	-2.1	-4.6	-8.0	-9.0	14.4
5	5.2	3.1	(1.0)	-2.0	-4.6	-8.0		15.0
*K*0	5.8	3.2	1.2	-2.0	-4.5	-8.0		15.4
5	7.5		0.0	-2.0	-4.6	-8.0		
*M*0	8.9		-0.1	-2.5	-4.8	-7		
5	12.3							
8	(16.5)							

Apparent distribution of the (apparently) bright stars according to spectral type and luminosity:

lum	Type *O,B*	*A,F*	*G,K,M*	
I	3	4	4	%
II	2	1	6	%
III	6	5	25	%
IV	3	3	4	%
V	10	14	1	%
pec	5	5	-	%

True distribution in space completely different, because, in this table, the intrinsically bright stars are taken from a larger volume of space than the intrinsically faint stars. In the true distribution more than 99% of all stars belong to luminosity class V.

Advantages of the Harvard and MK classifications:

Spectral type is determined directly by visual inspection without measurements. Utilization of many criteria possible. Can process a large number of spectra readily.

Disadvantages: subjective, experience necessary, dependent on the instrument and hence on careful use of standards.

The intrinsic colors $(B-V)_0$ of the various MK types (see 4.1.2)

Sp \ Lum	V	III	I
O5	$-0\overset{m}{.}34$	$-0\overset{m}{.}34$	$-0\overset{m}{.}34$
B0	−0.30	−0.29	−0.22
B5	−0.18	−0.18	−0.10
A0	−0.02	−0.02	−0.03
A5	+0.15	+0.15	+0.06
F0	0.29	0.27	0.17
F5	0.42	0.42	0.36
G0	0.58	0.66	0.67
G5	0.68	(0.81)	1.08
K0	0.81	0.99	(1.35)
K5	1.15	1.50	1.60
M0	1.40	1.54	(1.80)
M5	1.58	(1.75)	(1.80)

2.3 *Paris classification* (Barbier, Chalonge, Divan)

Based on measurements of spectrum tracings: plots of log I (intensity) as a function of $1/\lambda$

AE = continuum to red of Balmer jump
CE = continuum to blue of Balmer jump

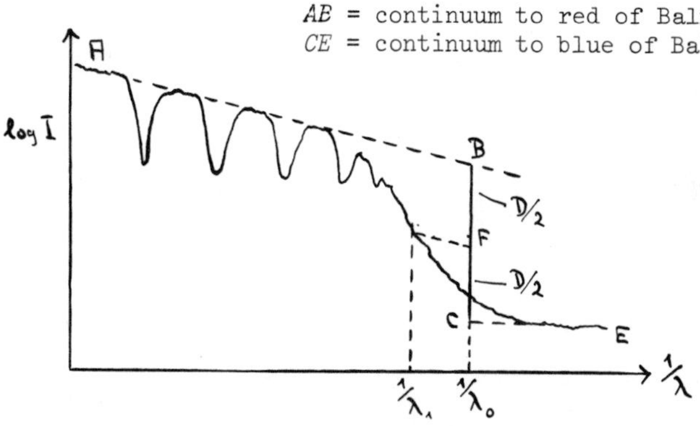

Criteria

1) Size of the Balmer jump D (at the wavelength λ_o = 3700 Å) = distance BC = Δ log I between the extended redward and blueward continua at 3700 Å.

2) Position of the Balmer jump λ_1 = intersection of the traced continuum with the line parallel to the redward continuum through the half-way point F of the Balmer jump.

The Balmer jump does not set in at the theoretical series limit, but earlier (at longer λ), because the high-order members blend into one another. The broader the lines are, i.e., the higher the electron pressure is, the earlier this blending occurs.

D predominantly determined by the temperature, therefore closely related to the spectral type.

λ_1 predominantly determined by the pressure, therefore closely related to the luminosity class.

Because the Balmer lines have a maximum at *A*0 this classification is ambiguous. In order to distinguish stars earlier than *A*0 from those later than *A*0, use a third parameter: gradient in the blue.

3) Blue continuum gradient ϕ_B (see 4.6)

= slope of continuum to redward of Balmer jump

(4000 Å < λ > 4900 Å)

$$\phi_B = 5\lambda - \frac{d(\ell n I)}{d(1/\lambda)}$$

$$= \frac{c_2}{T}\left(1 - e^{-c_2/\lambda T}\right)^{-1}$$ by differentiation of Planck's radiation law (3.2.1) for $I(\lambda)$

$$= \frac{c_2}{T}$$ by Wien's approximation

c_2 = 1.44 cm degree (radiation constant)

Hence ϕ_B merely a function of the temperature

In this way one obtains a three-dimensional classification and also picks out some types which are not in the MK scheme, e.g., metallic-line stars, etc. The "normal" stars fall on a curved surface in D, λ_1, ϕ_B space.

Advantages: Quantitative and objective; type defined by two or three numbers. Physical interpretation more obvious (related to pressure and temperature)

Disadvantages: For each star a rather high-dispersion (ca. 80 Å/mm) spectrum must be taken, traced, and measured; therefore applicable only to relatively bright stars. Not good for later type stars (late F, G...) because of the effect of metallic lines. ϕ_B affected by interstellar reddening.

2.4 *Classification by narrow-band photometry*

Measurement of the intensity at specified, useful positions in the spectrum (in the continuum as well as at positions which contain lines)

Two types of criteria:

a) Intensity criteria (usually a comparison of line λ with neighboring continuum)

$$= m(\lambda) - \tfrac{1}{2}[m(\lambda+\Delta\lambda) + m(\lambda-\Delta\lambda)]$$

b) Color criteria

$= m(\lambda_1) - m(\lambda_2)$

Measurement either photographically (tracings)

(Upsala and Stockholm classifications)

or photoelectrically directly at the telescope

(Strömgren, Gyldenkerne, Crawford, et. al.)

Band widths about 15 to 350 Å

In particular, numerous criteria,

e.g., H_β index: $\ell = m_{H\beta} - \frac{1}{2}(m_{4700} + m_{5000})$

Cyanogen index: $n = m_{4170} - m_{4240}$

Advantages: objective, highly accurate

Disadvantage: criteria unambiguous only in specified spectral intervals; therefore pre-selection according to MK types necessary

2.5 *Classification at low dispersion*

On objective-prism spectra, spectral types and, in several spectral intervals, luminosity classes can be determined using dispersions as low as 600 Å/mm.

Main criteria:
- strength and sharpness of the Balmer jump
- Intensity of the Balmer lines
- Intensity of other strong features (e.g., Ca II *K*-line, *G*-band, TiO,...)

e.g., *Luminous Stars in the Northern Milky Way*, I-VI.
1959 - 1965 Hamburg and Cleveland
~10 000 stars, types *O*, *B*, *A* I through *G* I

Certain types of stars can be picked out even at extremely low dispersion.

e.g., *OB* stars up to 30 000 Å/mm

§ 3 Radius

Directly measurable only for the sun: $R_\odot = 7.0 \times 10^5$ km

Stars: three geometric methods (§ 3.1 to 3.3)

- unfortunately, applicable only in a few cases;

one direct method (§ 3.4)

- widely applicable, but not very accurate

3.1 *Interferometer*

Fizeau 1868
present form: Michelson 1920

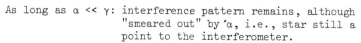

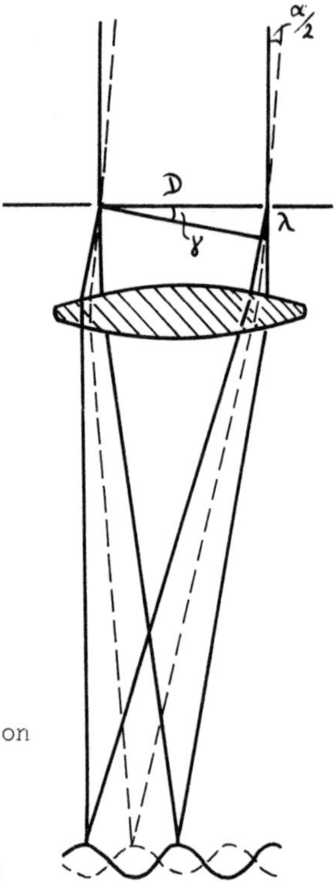

<u>Principle</u> (see sketch)

In front of the objective, a diaphragm with two slits of separation D = baseline. Wave from point source (——) produces a diffraction pattern (fringes);

maxima occur if the path difference is an integral multiple of the wavelength;

thus $\gamma = n \frac{\lambda}{D}$ $(n = 0,1,2,\ldots)$

Second plane wave (- - -) is at an angle $\alpha/2$ to the first one. It also produces a diffraction pattern. Interaction of the 2 diffraction patterns results in a interference pattern.

For $\alpha/2 = n \frac{\lambda}{D} \rightarrow$ amplification of fringes

For $\alpha/2 = (n + 1/2) \frac{\lambda}{D} \rightarrow$ mutual cancellation

Light from a star of angular diameter α:

Plane waves from the various parts of the stellar disk, hence all values between $-\alpha/2$ and $+\alpha/2$.
These diffraction patterns are superposed on one another.

As long as $\alpha \ll \gamma$: interference pattern remains, although "smeared out" by α, i.e., star still a point to the interferometer.

Enlarge $D \rightarrow$ decrease of γ; α remains constant

A spacing is eventually reached such that fringes coalesce into one another. The interference pattern disappears, and at that point $\alpha = \frac{\lambda}{D}$. (Exact theory yields $\alpha = 1.22 \frac{\lambda}{D}$; see 3.3.1)

Because γ and D are known, the angular diameter α is obtained, from which the true diameter follows, if distance known.

Application: Mt. Wilson 100" telescope; D = 6 m,
obtained via separate auxiliary mirrors in front of telescope tube.

Limit of measurement: $\sim 0\overset{''}{.}01$

Results obtained for about 10 large stars; e.g.:

		α	π	$R/R_\odot$
α Boo (Arcturus)	*K*2 III	0".022	0".090	26
α Tau (Aldebaran)	*K*5 III	0".020	0".048	48
α Sco (Antares)	*M*1 I	0".040	(0".006)	(700)

↳=trigonometric parallax

Intensity interferometer

R.H. Brown, R.Q. Twiss 1956 *Nature* 178, 1016

Whereas in the case of the Michelson stellar interferometer the rays must be compared in proper phase relationship, in this case the coherent intensity fluctuations are measured. Hence, separate telescopes, and therefore longer base lines possible.

Application: base line 30m. Only bright stars can be observed.

α CMa (Sirius)	*A*1 V:	α = 0".0068	π = 0".377	$R/R_\odot$ = 2.05
α Lyr (Vega)	*A*0 V:	0.0037	0.123	3.9

3.2 *Stellar occultation by the moon*

Principle: point source disappears instantaneously behind the moon's limb; a star with a measurable diameter fades gradually.

The diameter is derived from the duration of the decrease in brightness (which occurs in a fraction of a second).

Limit of measurement: $\alpha \approx 0''.002$

Complications:

a) Diffraction phenomena. Even a point source does not disappear instantaneously; diffraction pattern is moving past the observer. This diffraction pattern is smeared out in the case of a finite diameter.

b) Irregularities of the moon's limb. Path of star along limb about 100 m. Fluctuations > 100 m and < 1 m do not affect the result; irregularities between 10 and 25 m are critical. (solution: observations from several places or during several occultations)

Application in the optical region:

α Sco: α = 0".040, as with the interferometer

Extended applications in radio astronomy

3.3 *Eclipsing binaries* (see also 8.5)

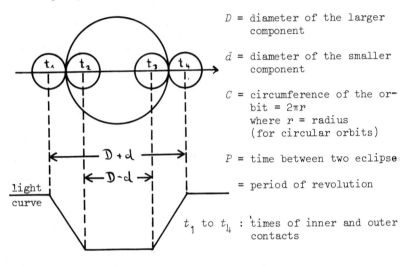

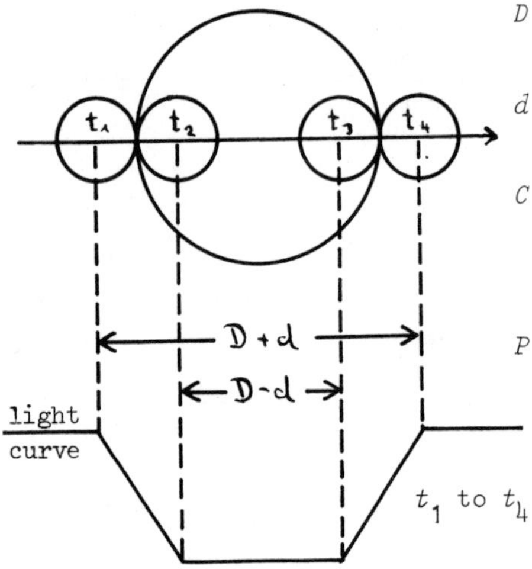

D = diameter of the larger component

d = diameter of the smaller component

C = circumference of the orbit = $2\pi r$ where r = radius (for circular orbits)

P = time between two eclipse

= period of revolution

t_1 to t_4 : times of inner and outer contacts

Then: $$\frac{t_4 - t_1}{P} = \frac{D+d}{C}$$

and $$\frac{t_3 - t_2}{P} = \frac{D-d}{C}$$

From this, by subtraction or addition, obtain

D/C and d/C, i.e., diameters in units of the circumference of the orbit.

If, in addition, the orbital velocity is known (from spectroscopic observations of the doppler effect) C can be found in linear measure and hence also

D and d in linear measure.

For circular orbits and assuming no stellar limb darkening, the procedure is simple and yields the most accurate values.

Complications

a) Elliptical orbits

b) Oblate stars (systems with small separation)

c) Limb darkening of the stellar disks

Application: up to now, about 20 stars, most reliable values

Greatest diameter derived up to now:

VV Cep(*M*2-supergiant): ~1200 $R_\odot$, more than Jupiter's orbit

3.4 *Radiated-energy method*

Principle:

apparent brightness, distance → luminosity (corresponds to total emitted energy)

spectrum → temperature → surface brightness (energy radiated per cm^2)

→ area of the radiating surface → radius

In practice:

Luminosity $L \propto$ energy per cm^2 per second × surface area $\propto F(T)R^2$,

where $F(T)$ = radiation flux

In solar units (see 4.1.3),

$$M - M_\odot = -2.5 \log \frac{L}{L_\odot} = -2.5 \log \frac{R^2 F(T)}{R_\odot^2 F(T_\odot)}$$

From this:

$$\log \frac{R}{R_\odot} = \frac{M_\odot - M}{5} - 0.5 \log \frac{F(T)}{F(T_\odot)}$$

Hence need $F(T)$ and M

Ideal case: $M = M_{bol}$ = bolometric magnitude

Star = black body, i.e., $F = \sigma T_e^4$ (3.2.1)

(T_e is temperature which gives total flux over all λ; see § 6.)

$T_\odot = 5700^\circ$

$(M_{bol})_\odot = +4.62$

In practice: observe M_v or M_{pg}, not M_{bol}

One needs the ratio, not of the total fluxes, but of the fluxes in the spectral region observed, or, equivalently, the ratio of intensities $\frac{B(T)}{B(T_\odot)}$.

For a rough estimate: Wien approximation to Planck's law (see 3.2.1):

$$\frac{B}{B_\odot} = \exp\left[\frac{hc}{k\lambda}\left(\frac{1}{T_{rad,\odot}} - \frac{1}{T_{rad}}\right)\right]$$

B = radiative intensity at λ

λ = wavelength of observation

T_{rad} = radiation temperature (see §6) for corresponding spectral region

Temperature

Comes either from quantitative analysis (model atmosphere) or from the color

However, color temperature not equal to radiation temperature (see §6). For hot stars one obtains values that are too low, for cool stars values too high.

$T_c \longrightarrow \sim T_{rad} \longrightarrow B/B_\odot$ which, with $M_V \longrightarrow \log R/R_\odot$

All methods for radius determination (although in detail often uncertain and independent of one another) yield the same results, as far as they overlap.

Numerical values at end of §4

§ 4 Mass, density, surface gravity

4.1 *Mass*

Direct determination possible only for binary stars from the effects of gravitational attraction

3rd law of Kepler: $\dfrac{(\mathbf{M}_1 + \mathbf{M}_2)\, P^2}{a^3} = \text{const} = 1$

(see 2.4.5)

where
- $\mathbf{M}$ in units of $\mathbf{M}_\odot = 1.985 \cdot 10^{33}$ g
- a in astronomical units $= 1.496 \times 10^8$ km
- P in years

Hence

$$\boxed{\mathbf{M}_1 + \mathbf{M}_2 = \frac{a^3}{P^2}}$$

From this: sum of masses if a and P known

A) Visual binary stars (see 8.2)

Direct observation yields a'' and P

One obtains:

a) Sum of the masses: if a is known in linear measure either by spectroscopic observations or because the distance is known

b) the mass ratio: if the absolute orbit (with respect to other stars) is known, i.e., the motion of the individual components around their common center of gravity; then we have

$$\mathbf{M}_1/\mathbf{M}_2 = a_2''/a_1'' \qquad a_1;\ a_2 = \text{semimajor axes of the absolute orbits}$$

c) Individual masses: If a) and b) are fulfilled

Results: up to now, only a few well-studied systems yielding reliable results

B) Astrometric binaries (stars with "invisible" companions)(8.3)

Fainter component not observable; only absolute orbit of the brighter component known.

Then, we have: $a_1/a = M_2(M_1 + M_2)$

and thus:
$$(M_1 + M_2)\left(\frac{M_2}{M_1 + M_2}\right)^3 = \frac{a_1^3}{P^2}$$

C) Spectroscopic binary stars (8.4)

Stars not resolved optically; binary nature detectable only from periodic shifting of the spectral lines (Doppler effect) revealing variations in radial velocity due to orbital motion

In general orbital inclination i unknown (angle between orbital plane and plane of sky); the observed radial velocity (RV) yields only the component of the orbital velocity v along the line of sight.

$$RV_{max} = v \sin i$$

Integration of the RV curve over a full period of revolution thus yields the projection of the orbit on the line of sight. The RV curve also allows determination of the projection of the semimajor axis on the line of sight:

a) $a_1 \sin i$ — if only one spectrum visible

b) $(a_1 + a_2) \sin i = a \sin i$ — if both spectra visible but line variation only measured relatively

c) $a_1 \sin i$, $a_2 \sin i$ — if both spectra visible and line variation measured absolutely

Then, from Kepler's law:

a) Single spectrum:
$$(M_1 + M_2)\left(\frac{M_2}{M_1 + M_2}\right)^3 \sin^3 i \equiv \underbrace{\frac{M_2^3 \sin^3 i}{(M_1 + M_2)^2}}_{\text{"mass function"}} = \frac{(a_1 \sin i)^3}{P^2}$$

where M_2 is the mass of the star not observed

b) Both spectra, relative orbit
$$(M_1 + M_2) \sin^3 i = \frac{(a \sin i)^3}{P^2}$$

c) Both spectra, absolute orbit — mass ratio
$$\frac{M_1}{M_2} = \frac{(a_2 \sin i)^3}{(a_1 \sin i)^3}$$

and from this: $M_1 \sin^3 i$ and $M_2 \sin^3 i$

Because $\sin i < 1$ one obtains lower limits for the mass.

In the statistical average (assuming uniform distribution of orbital inclinations) $\overline{\sin^3 i} = 0.59$,

but observational selection gives preference to large values of $\sin i$.

D) Spectroscopic eclipsing binaries (8.5)

Here $i \approx 90^\circ$ In this case, with favorable conditions direct determination of M_1 and M_2 possible

|| Reliable data, because distance need not be known

Limitation: only wide pairs

Close pairs often have a common envelope or gravitational distortion, so that Kepler's law can not be applied directly

Result: about 20 good mass determinations

however, all are main-sequence stars.

E) Relativistic red shift

Applicable to stars of high surface gravity (light "performs work" against gravitation), hence to white dwarfs.

Measured red shifts $\Delta\lambda/\lambda = \frac{GM}{c^2R} \approx 10^{-4}$

Problem: differentiating from effects of mass motions of gas in the atmosphere.

Summary

Apart from the main sequence reliable masses are known for

3 white dwarfs
2 subgiants
1 giant (Capella)
no supergiants

|| An accurate mass determination for even a single additional giant star would be of great help in developing the theory of stellar evolution!

4.2 *Density*

$$\rho = \text{mass/cm}^3 = \frac{M}{4/3\,\pi R^3}$$

// Without assumptions, can only be determined if mass and radius are known, i.e.,

⟹ for eclipsing binaries with known radial-velocity curves for both components

//For visual binaries:

Mass known (§4.1)
Radius from radiated energy (§3.4)

$L \propto T^4 R^2 \rightarrow R^3 \propto L^{3/2}\, T^{-6}$; hence $\rho \propto \boldsymbol{M} T^6 L^{-3/2}$

For the ratio of densities of two components, all constants are eliminated by division. Substitution of apparent magnitudes for luminosities gives:

$$\frac{\rho_1}{\rho_2} = \frac{\boldsymbol{M}_1}{\boldsymbol{M}_2} \left(\frac{T_1}{T_2}\right)^6 \cdot 10^{0.6(m_1 - m_2)}$$

independent of the orbital elements and of the distance!

However, temperature to the 6th power, hence poorly determined.

4.3 *Surface gravity*

$g = G \frac{\boldsymbol{M}}{R^2}$ $\qquad G$ = gravitational constant

Acceleration due to gravity, g, can be determined as above for the density,

> g can also be determined - with somewhat uncertainty - directly from an analysis of the spectrum and the theory of stellar atmospheres (see 5.2.4).

4.4 *Summary of data*

Mass: relatively small range: ~ 0.1 to $\sim 50\, \boldsymbol{M}_\odot$

Radius: large range: ~ 0.01 to more than $500\, R_\odot$

> Reason: various stages of stellar evolution; stars are able to expand and contract, but not to change their masses arbitrarily (see 6.5.4).

Luminosity $\propto R^2$ }
Density $\propto R^{-3}$ } very large range

The following table gives typical values obtained for stellar parameters as a function of spectral type, but should by no means be considered definitive! The values are given in solar units. The last line gives the data for the sun itself in *c g s* units.

Data Summary

Lum; Sp. Type	$L/L_\odot$	$M/M_\odot$	$R/R_\odot$	$\rho/\rho_\odot$	$g/g_\odot$	T_e
V *O5*	1.5×10^4	50	18	0.008	0.13	
V *B0*	4×10^3	17.5	7.5	0.025	0.30	37,800°
V *B5*	230	6.5	4.0	0.10	0.41	14,800
V *A0*	33	3.2	2.6	0.18	0.47	9,700
V *A5*	17	2.1	1.8	0.35	0.66	8,400
V *F0*	6.6	1.78	1.35	0.71	0.97	7,600
V *F5*	2.8	1.47	1.20	0.80	1.00	6,600
V *G0*	1.1	1.10	1.05	0.95	1.00	6,000
V *G5*	0.7	0.93	0.94	1.15	1.08	5,300
V *K0*	0.4	0.80	0.85	1.29	1.10	4,900
V *K5*	0.09	0.65	0.74	1.6	1.18	4,300
V *M0*	0.02	0.49	0.63	2.0	1.23	3,900
V *M5*	0.001	(0.2)	0.32	6.3	2.0	3,500
III *B0*	730		16			
III *A0*	70		6			
III *F0*	23		4			
III *G0*	30	2.5	6	0.01	0.06	5,400
III *K0*	30	3.5	16	8×10^{-4}	0.01	4,100
III *M0*	95	5.0	(40)	8×10^{-5}	0.003	2,900
I *B0*	2×10^4	50	20	6×10^{-3}	0.13	
I *A0*	6×10^4	16	40	2×10^{-4}	0.01	
I *F0*	1.8×10^5	12	60	5×10^{-5}	3×10^{-3}	6,400
I *G0*	1.2×10^5	10	100	1×10^{-5}	1×10^{-3}	5,400
I *K0*	1.2×10^5	13	200	6×10^{-6}	3×10^{-4}	4,000
I *M0*	5×10^4	17	500	1×10^{-7}	6×10^{-5}	2,800
white dwarfs	$10^{-2}..10^{-6}$	0.6	0.013	3×10^5	4×10^3	6,000 to 40,000
sun	4×10^{33} erg/sec	2×10^{33} g	7×10^{10} cm	1.41 g/cm³	2.7×10^4 cm/sec²	5,700°

§ 5 Relations among stellar properties

The diagrams discussed below indicate the relations among various stellar properties.

5.1 *Hertzsprung-Russell diagram* = HRD

Luminosity vs. spectral type

(Plots of closely related variables may also be referred to as HRD's: e.g., M_V vs. color or temperature.)

Stars of known spectral type and absolute magnitude are non-uniformly distributed in the HRD,

i.e., || some combinations of these parameters are preferred; others do not occur at all.

Schematic HRD of the stars to a certain limiting apparent magnitude (mainly Population I)

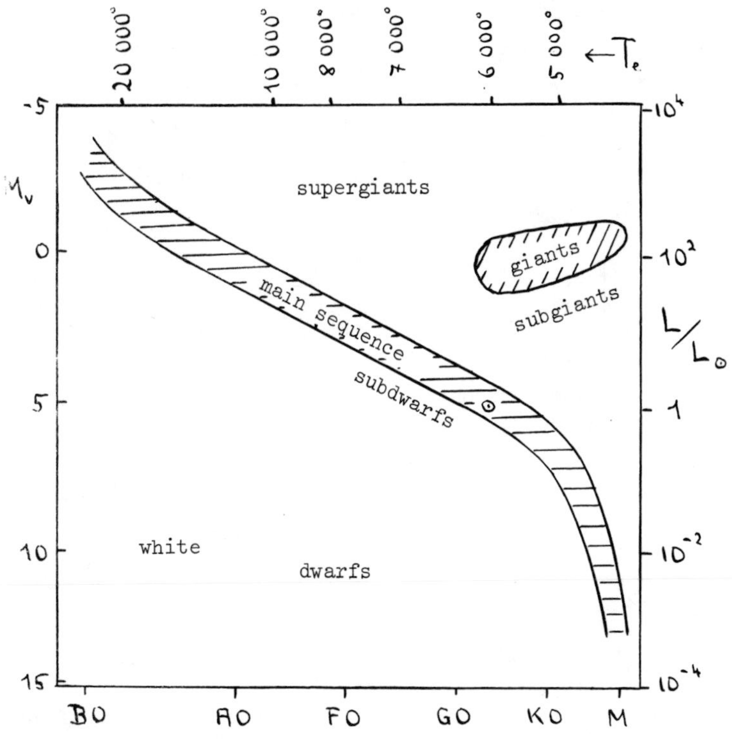

Main features

a) Majority of stars on a diagonal from ~1000 $L_\odot$ at *B*0 to 1/1000 $L_\odot$ at *M*

= main sequence, normal dwarf stars, lum. class V

b) Second, less sharp, branch, from about *G*0 to *M*, ~30-100 $L_\odot$. At the same spectral type - i.e., at about the same temperature and hence about the same surface brightness - these have higher luminosity, hence must have larger surface area.

= giant branch, normal giant stars, lum. class III

c) In the whole upper region scattered bright and very bright stars; uniformly, but sparsely, distributed

= bright giants and supergiants, lum. classes II and I

d) Stars scattered below the giant branch

= subgiants, lum. class IV

e) Stars scattered slightly below the main sequence

= subdwarfs, lum. class VI

f) Special group, lower left; hot but nevertheless low luminosity, hence must have very small surface area

= white dwarfs (see 7.6)

Note: The figure shows roughly the HRD of stars down to a certain limiting apparent brightness.

> This distribution is very different from the true distribution in space. Since it includes intrinsically bright stars (giant stars) from a large volume of space, but intrinsically faint stars only from the immediate solar neighborhood.

The true distribution, that is, the distribution of the stars in a specified volume, shows the following:

Up to 10 pc 254 stars are known, among them
- no supergiants
- 1 giant (Arcturus)
- 2 subgiants
- 7 white dwarfs
- 244 main sequence stars (96%)

-- and many stars at the lower end of the main sequence are undoubtedly still undetected.

The HRD of field stars contains a mixture of stars of various ages, of various evolutionary stages, and of various chemical compositions.

Hence, the HRD's of star clusters (stars presumably of the same age and of the same original chemical composition) (see ch. 8) are more important for problems of stellar evolution (chapter 6).

Relation to other basic properties

a) Temperature

Essentially correlated with spectral type, but not exactly. Spectral type based on the appearance of the line spectrum, i.e., determined principally by the degree of ionization. For supergiants, a given degree of ionization occurs at a lower temperature, because of the lower electron pressure (Saha formula: see 3.2.2). Lines of equal temperature, therefore, are somewhat inclined from upper left to lower right.

b) Radius

From T one gets the energy per cm^2, and from this the surface brightness. Surface brightness and total brightness define the size of the surface and, hence, the radius (see 4.3.4). Lines of constant radius from upper left to lower right.

c) Mass

The theory of stellar structure shows, that -- for a given chemical composition -- the mass at each point in the HRD can be specified. The relation, however, is complicated and is closely connected with the question of stellar evolution. (see chapter 6.5)

d) Surface gravity and density

For known mass and radius: trivial (see 4.4)

Hence:

In principle, the position in the HRD (i.e., the MK type) yields a large amount of physical information.

In practice, in most cases precise calibration of the relations is still not possible.

Populations:

W. Baade originally distinguished two "stellar populations" according to the distribution in the HRD of stars of different homogeneous groups (e.g., open star clusters and globular star clusters). Roughly we have:

Population I: Young stars, higher heavy element content (2 to 4% heavier than helium). Often all such elements are called "metals".

Population II: Old stars, 0.3 to 1% metals.

There is a continuous transition between the extreme populations. Further details on populations: see 9.3.5.

Nearly all stars can be arranged in this two-dimensional temperature-luminosity scheme, and, furthermore, all stars at a given location in the diagram seem to be essentially identical in all their intrinsic properties ($\boldsymbol{M}$, R, g,...). Thus it would appear that the structure of a star is essentially characterized by two parameters, e.g.,

- spectral type and luminosity
- color and luminosity

} observational parameters

- effective temperature and surface gravity or
- effective temperature and electron pressure (5.1.9)

} parameters of stellar atmospheres

- etc.

Complication: The original parameters of a star are its mass and chemical composition, which should completely and uniquely determine its structure (Russell-Vogt theorem). However, these do not define a point, but a line in the HRD -- the evolutionary track along which a star evolves as its properties change (6.5). Hence a third parameter necessary -- in this case, age.

Need for third parameter confirmed by observation that stars at a given point in HRD may have slightly different chemical compositions. Different compositions also produce different tracks, i.e., a different distribution of stars in the HRD.

Summary:

Fundamental parameters = mass, age, chemical composition

Composition is third parameter to be added to the pairs given above.

One of the main aims of astrophysics: to find relations among all these parameters.

5.2 *Color-magnitude and color-color diagrams*

For faint stars the spectral type can not be readily determined directly. Then, the color (4.1.2), which is correlated with the type via the temperature, serves as a substitute.

A) Color-magnitude diagram (CMD)

At first sight the CMD seems to be a last resort. However, it has proved to be a most important diagram, with far-reaching significance. Often referred to, loosely, as an HRD

Magnitude (absolute or apparent) vs. color

e.g., M_B vs $(B-V)$

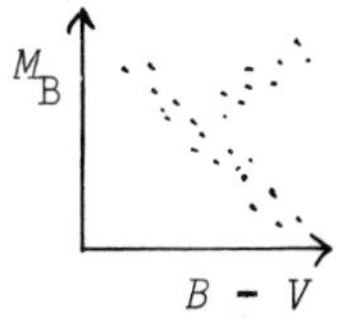

Main application is to stellar clusters (see 8.7 and following)

All stars at the same distance, hence apparent and absolute magnitude differ only by a constant. The shape of the CMD is found directly using apparent magnitude - e.g., B vs. $B-V$ - but the calibration of the ordinate remains open. This is derived by shifting the observed CMD of the cluster to coincide with the CMD of the stars in nearby clusters with known distances (e.g., the Hyades). The amount of the shift equals the distance modulus and hence yields distance (if absorption known from interstellar reddening; see B below and 9.1.5).

B) Color-color diagram

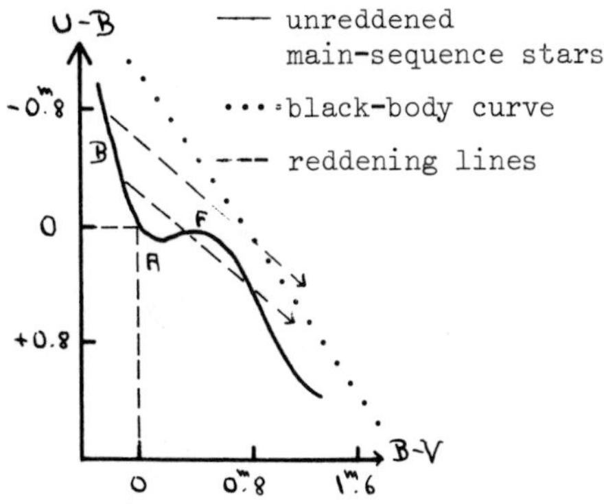

e.g., $(U-B)$ vs. $(B-V)$

$B-V$ function of temperature. Uniform increase of B with respect to V, from hot to cool stars, i.e., $(B-V)$ increases.

$U-B$
1) temperature dependent like $B-V$
2) Balmer depression increases U

Earlier than $A0$ 1) and 2) run parallel. Steep curve. From $A0$ on the Balmer depression decreases and U becomes brighter, contrary to the run of the temperature. Up to $F5$ the decrease of the Balmer depression prevails, thereafter the temperature dependence again dominates.

Hence the hump in the diagram.

Both colors are affected by interstellar reddening. If the reddening law (wave length dependence of absorption) of the interstellar dust is known we can compute "reddening lines" parallel to which a group of reddened stars will be displaced in the color-color diagram. The shift required to make an observed curve coincide with the standard curve yields the amount of interstellar reddening. This, with reddening law ⟶ absorption (see 9.1.5).

C) <u>Color-difference diagrams</u>

Difference of two colors vs. magnitude
or vs. color

e.g., $(B-V)$ - $(U-B)$ vs. B

$(B-V)$ - $(U-B)$ vs. $(B-V)$ ↘ (because of its shape also called "R diagram")

The color-difference diagrams are largely independent of the interstellar reddening.

Concerning their application (for instance, for the separation of giants and dwarfs) see, e.g., W. Becker 1951, *Zeitschrift für Astrophysik* 29, 66.

5.3 *Mass-luminosity relation*

For stars of the main sequence, mass and luminosity (or bolometric magnitude) are closely correlated:

In general:

$$\log \mathcal{M}/\mathcal{M}_\odot = -0.14\ M_{bol} + 0.55 \quad \text{or } L \propto \mathcal{M}^{2.85}$$

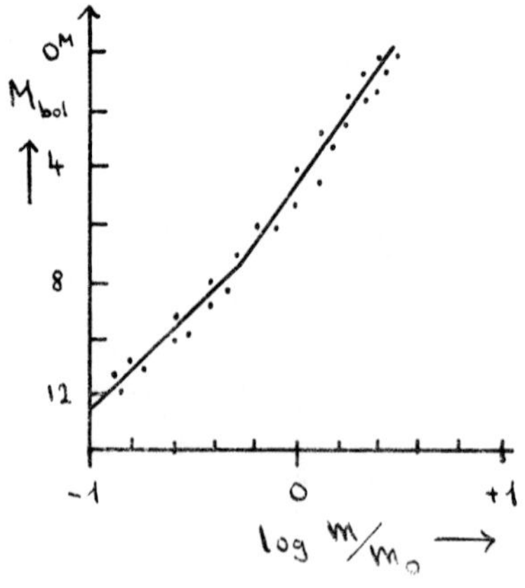

Reason: stars of the main sequence are constructed according to the same general scheme (see 6.5.3)

The mass determines the structure, and the structure determines the luminosity

For stars off the main sequence the relation (see next page) is not valid because of the different internal structure.

Better representation of population I by two relations:

$\log M/M_\odot = -0.10\, M_{bol} + 0.46$ or $L \propto M^{4.0}$
for $M_{bol} < 7.5$
(convective cores; see 6.5.3)

$\log M/M_\odot = -0.15\, M_{bol} + 0.75$ or $L \propto M^{2.7}$
for $M_{bol} > 7.5$
(non-convective cores)

§ 6 Temperatures

Temperature is neither a directly observable, nor, in general, a uniquely definable, quantity; it appears only as a parameter in equations yielding observable quantities (radiative intensity, electron velocity distribution, heat transfer ...). "The temperature" of an object can be viewed as simply that value which, in the appropriate equation, gives the correct result for the observable quantity.

> Hence each such equation defines a different T. Only in thermodynamic equilibrium (TE) are all T's equal, i.e., only a body in TE has a unique temperature (This can be considered the definition of TE)

A) Definitions based on Planck's radiation law

1) Effective temperature T_e

= temperature of that black body which radiates the same total energy.

2) Radiation temperature T_{rad}

= ... which radiates the same energy in the observed spectral region.

3) Black-body temperature or brightness temperature T_b

= ... which radiates the same energy at a specified wavelength.

> T_e is a true measure of the energy, a basic quantity; however, not directly measurable; transition from T_{rad} to T_e corresponds to the transition from M_{vis} to M_{bol}
>
> T_b = limit of T_{rad} for $\Delta\lambda \longrightarrow 0$

4) Color temperature T_c

= ... which, in the observed spectral region, shows the same run of intensity

5) <u>Gradient temperature</u> T_G

= [• • •] which, at a specified wavelength, shows the same intensity gradient

(= limit of T_c for $\Delta\lambda \to 0$)

<u>Scheme</u>:

	Energy	Shape of the Curve
Over all wavelengths	T_e	★
finite $\Delta\lambda$	T_{rad}	T_c
$\Delta\lambda \to 0$	T_b	T_G

★ Cannot fit Planck curve to a star over all λ, since star is not a black body.

6) <u>Wien temperature</u> T_W

= [• • •] which, according to the Wien approximation (see 3.2.1), has the same maximum-intensity wavelength.

Summary of some data

Type		T_e	T_c		T_{rad}		
			λ = 4250	λ = 5000	phot	vis	radio-meter
V	*B0*	37,000°	39,800°	33,500°			
	A0	9,710	16,700	15,300	10,900°	10,500°	10,100°
	F0	7,650	9,900	8,950	7,590	7,550	7,320
	G0	5,960			6,610	6,210	5,960
	K0	4,900			5,120	5,240	4,860
	M0	3,860			3,830	3,940	3,870
III	*G0*	5,400		6,000			
	K0	4,100		4,400			
	M0	2,900		3,400			
I	*G0*	5,400		6,200			
	K0	4,000		4,600			
	M0	2,800					

taken from Landolt-Börnstein, Astronomy volume.

Uncertainty for the hot stars is several thousand °K, for the cool stars several hundred °K. T_e even more uncertain for hot stars, for which bolometric corrections are hard to observe.

B) Definitions based on particles rather than radiation

7) Kinetic temperature T_{kin}

= temperature which is obtained from the observed velocity distribution of particles from Maxwell-Boltzmann law (kinetic theory of gases).

most probable velocity = thermal velocity $v_{th} = \sqrt{\frac{2RT}{\mu}} = \sqrt{\frac{2kT_{kin}}{m}}$

mean velocity $\bar{v} = \sqrt{\frac{8kT_{kin}}{m}} = \frac{2}{\sqrt{\pi}} v_{th}$

root-mean-square (rms) velocity $v_{rms} = \sqrt{\frac{3kT_{kin}}{m}} = \sqrt{\frac{3}{2}} v_{th}$

μ = molecular weight; m = mass of particle

R = gas constant = 8.32×10^7 erg deg^{-1} Mol^{-1}

k = Boltzmann constant = 1.38×10^{-16} erg deg^{-1}

The thermal velocity determines, for instance, the width of the spectral lines (statistical doppler effect); see 5.2.1

8) Electron temperature T_{el} (sometimes T_e)

= kinetic temperature of the electrons (μ = 1/1800)

9) Ionization temperature T_i or T_{ion}

= temperature which is obtained from the observed ratio of the number of atoms in the various stages of ionization, according to the Saha formula (3.2.2)

10) Excitation temperature T_{ex} or T_{exc}

= temperature obtained from the relative number of atoms in the various stages of excitation from the Boltzmann formula (3.2.2).

11) Molecular Band temperature (rotation or vibration temperature)

= T_{ex} based on the rotational and vibrational bands of the molecules

Calibration of the T scale with the temperature scale in physics by comparison of the stellar radiation with that of a black body (Heidelberg, Paris, Moscow)

C) Spectral intensity distribution

The spectral intensity distribution in the continuum is related to T_c and T_G. Here we give T_c as a function of gradient for a black body.

Definition:

$$\text{Absolute gradient } \phi = 5\lambda - \frac{d(\ln I)}{d(1/\lambda)}$$

For example:

ultraviolet gradient:	3150	< λ <	3700 Å
blue gradient:	3700		4900 Å
red gradient:	4900		8200 Å

Using Planck's radiation law (see 3.2.1) one obtains as in § 2.3

$$\phi = \frac{c_2}{T_c}\left(1 - e^{-c_2/\lambda T_c}\right)^{-1} \quad \text{where } c_2 = 1.44 \text{ cm degree}$$

In Wien's approximation (3.2.1)

$$\phi_w = \frac{c_2}{T_c} \quad \text{i.e. now merely a function of the color temperature}$$

The absolute gradient of the black body:

T_c [°K]	$\phi_w = c_2/T_c$ [10^{-4}cm]	ϕ [10^{-4}cm] 4000 Å	5000 Å	6000 Å
3,000	4.78	4.78	4.78	4.78
4,000	3.60	3.60	3.60	3.60
5,000	2.87	2.88	2.88	2.89
7,000	2.05	2.07	2.09	2.12
10,000	1.44	1.48	1.52	1.58
20,000	0.72	0.86	0.96	1.03
50,000	0.29	0.56	0.66	0.75
100,000	0.14	0.48	0.58	0.67
∞	0.00	0.40	0.50	0.60

The true intensity distribution in the spectra of stars deviates considerably from that of a black body, especially in the region of strong absorption (Balmer jump, Lyman jump, etc.) (see 5.1 and 5.2).

Calibration of stellar intensity distribution, and hence of T_e, made by comparing continuum radiation of star (e.g., Vega) directly with that of a standard black-body source.

§ 7 Rotation

A) Direct determination

Only for the sun and for a few eclipsing variables (see 8.5), if for at least a short time only the right- or left-hand limb of the star is visible.

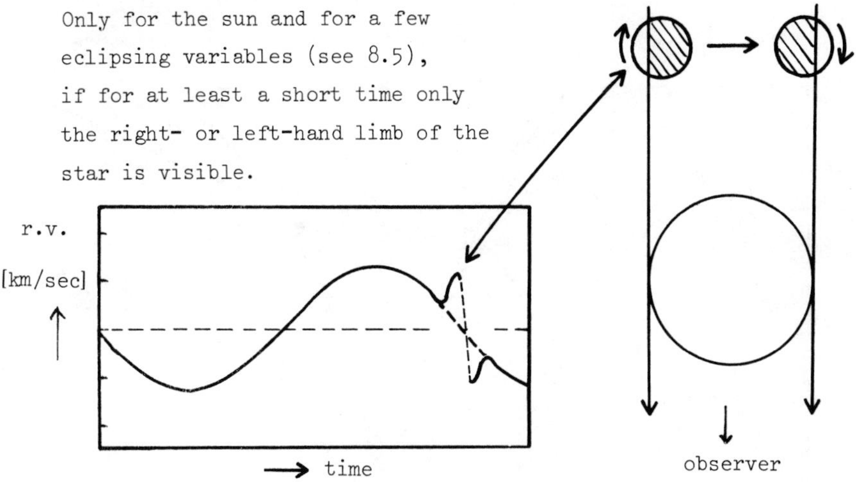

Normally the radial-velocity curve shows only the effect of orbital motion. Rotation -- because of averaging over the disk -- produces only broadened (see below), but not shifted, lines.

Note: close binaries usually rotate synchronously ($P_{rot} = P_{revolution}$).

B) Indirect determination

By the broadening of the lines caused by the doppler effect. (One limb of the star approaches the observer, the other recedes.)

Problem: Separation of the rotational broadening of the lines from other broadening mechanisms (temperature, turbulence, pressure broadening).

However, thermal and turbulent velocities decrease exponentially (5.2.1); on the contrary, for the rotational velocity a fixed maximum value (stellar limb) exists. Rotational broadening -- assuming no limb darkening -- results in a flat-bottomed, elliptically shaped line profile. Rapidly rotating stars, therefore, can be recognized by the relatively well defined edges of the absorption lines.

The determination of rotation in practice

One computes rotational profiles for specified types of lines and fits the observed profile to the theoretical family of curves. Limit of detection about 25 km/sec

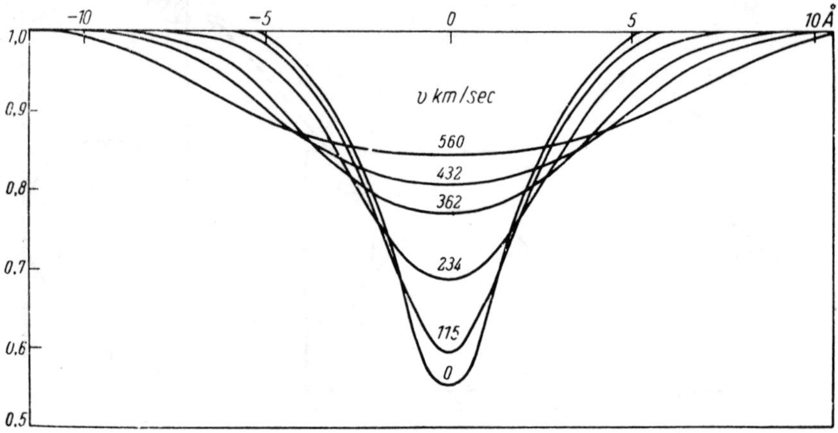

Because the inclination of the rotation axis is not known, one gets only

$v \sin i$ | v = rotational velocity at the equator; i = inclination of the axis of rotation to the line of sight

$i = 0$: pole toward observer, so called "pole-on stars"; no rotational broadening

Hence can obtain no individual values.

Statistically one can determine the distribution of the equatorial rotational velocities, if one assumes a uniform distribution of the axial inclinations:

$$\text{average value: } \bar{v} = \frac{4}{\pi}\,\overline{v \sin i}$$

Results: (from ~3000 stars)

1) Along the main sequence a clear dependence on spectral type; early types rotate faster.

Rough mean values:

B	stars	200-250	km/sec
A	"	100-200	"
F	"	15-100	"
G,K,M	"	< 15	"
Sun		2	"

2) Mean $v \sin i$ for *B* stars varies from cluster to cluster; thought to be caused by variation in frequency of spectroscopic binaries, which have anomalous velocities as a result of synchronous rotation.

3) For early types, dwarf stars rotate faster than giants; for later types (from ~*A*5 on) giants rotate faster.

> Consistent with the theory of stellar evolution: giants of intermediate spectral types originally were further up on the main sequence. Hence they have retained their fast rotation.

4) Supergiants presumably have no or only slow rotation

5) Early type stars with emission lines have faster rotation:

Oe, *Be*: 350 km/sec up to 500 km/sec

> Among the *Be* stars, there presumably exists no star with slow rotation. Causal relation:
>
> Because of rapid rotation →matter is thrown off
> →shell
> →emission lines

Correction to theory:

Rapidly rotating stars are oblate and have considerably higher surface gravity at the pole than at the equator. This causes different physical conditions in the atmospheres and hence different line profiles. Computations show that the simple model above results in rotational velocities that are too small.

Taking account of this oblateness effect shows that the *Be* stars indeed, rotate at the limit of stability.

Such rapid rotation affects both the star's luminosity (in either sense, depending on i) and apparent temperature (star reddened), as well as influencing its evolution.

Theoretical problem

Why is the angular momentum of stars -- especially for the late spectral types -- so small?

(see also cosmogony: 2.9.6)

Stars originate from interstellar gas clouds. These normally have appreciable angular momentum, no doubt, because of their turbulence. With contraction the rotational velocity should increase considerably -- because of the conservation of angular momentum.

Two possibilities:

a) Mechanical transfer of the angular momentum (binary stars, star clusters,...)

b) Dissipation of the angular momentum by magnetic fields (solar wind,...)

§ 8 Magnetic fields

Observation: By means of the Zeeman effect

> Because of the quantized orientation of the axis of angular momentum of atoms, in a magnetic field the terms and, consequently the lines, split up into several components. In the case of a weak magnetic field see merely a line broadening.

Distinguishing from rotational broadening etc.:

a) Zeeman effect dependent on quantum numbers. Some lines are not at all influenced by the magnetic field.

b) Zeeman components are differently polarized.

Stellar magnetic fields only observable if the lines are sharp and the fields are sufficiently strong.

Magnetic stars; A_p stars

Catalogue in Landolt-Börnstein (Babcock): 89 stars with an unambiguously strong magnetic field (most stronger than 500 gauss)

among these { 85 *A* stars and neighboring types (*Ap* stars, see 4.2.1)
4 late-type giants

In addition, a large number of stars have a probable, but not yet certain, magnetic field.

> Nearly all *A* stars with sharp lines are "magnetic stars". Presumably they are "pole-on stars"; i.e., probably all early-type stars have magnetic fields; however, the fields of the rapidly-rotating ones are not detectable because of the superposed rotation.

All magnetic stars show a variable magnetic field.

Period: of the order of several weeks
some regular, some irregular
often, but not always, with a reversal of the pola

Extreme cases: 53 Camelopardalis: +3750 to −5390 gauss
HD 215441 : ~34 000 gauss

<u>Models</u>: a) Magnetic oscillations of the star as a whole

⟹ b) Oblique rotator (magnetic axis does not coincide with the rotational axis)

c) Magnetic cycle like the sun's, but much stronger

<u>Spectrum</u>: Variations in the spectrum nearly always occur along with the magnetic variation.

Some groups of lines remain unchanged, others vary. Often Eu and Cr are sensitive, although in opposite sense (if Eu at maximum, Cr at minimum, and vice versa).

Besides the variations, have anomalous strengths of certain lines (Eu, Mg, Sr, Si, rare earths...). One talks about europium stars, etc.

These anomalies probably cannot be explained by physical conditions only but suggest anomalous abundances of elements (nuclear processes at the surface due to acceleration processes in the magnetic fields ??).

§ 9 Chemical composition

Direct knowledge very limited!

/Good: Meteorites, crust of the earth, solar atmosphere, atmospheres of about a dozen stars

/Qualitative: Atmospheres of more stars, a few planetary nebulae, interstellar matter

However: 1) Objects totally dissimilar (in distance, age, physical structure...) show nearly the same chemical composition

2) The abundances show theoretically explainable regularities

Hence, there exists something like a

⟶ cosmic element frequency distribution.

9.1 *General cosmic element abundance distribution*

Sources: Meteorites for heavy elements

These constituents have condensed at low temperatures, while volatile matter (H, He, C, N, O...) has evaporated.

Stellar atmospheres predominantly for light elements

Partly from sun, partly from hot stars, according to the excitation conditions required for observation (see also 5.2.6)

Result

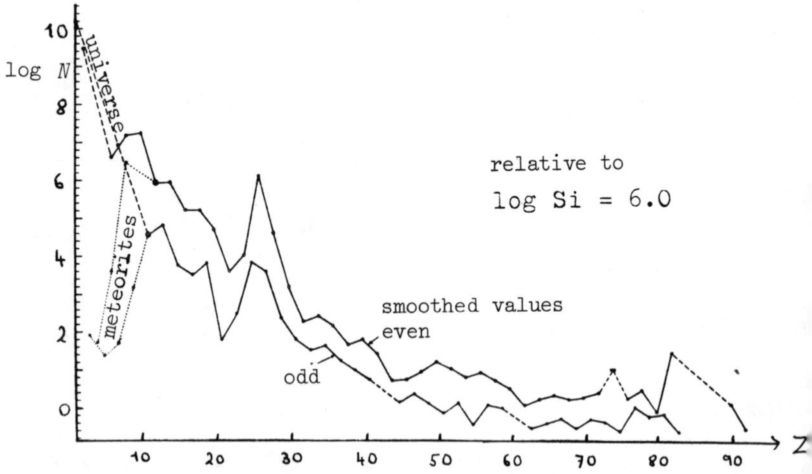

a) First rapid, then slower decrease with atomic number Z

b) Elements with even atomic number more frequent than neighboring odd elements (Harkin's rule)

c) Peaks at the "magic numbers" (2, 8, 14, 20, 28, 50, 82) (closed shells in the nucleus)

Further regularities are found if the mass number is taken into consideration in addition to the atomic number.

Accuracy: for abundant elements, about a factor of 2

for rare elements, " " " of 10

Data on individual stars: see 5.2.6

The 16 most abundant elements

Semi-empirical values according to Suess and Urey 1958, *Hdb. d. Physik* 51, 296, with corrections Urey 1967.

Quarterly J. Roy. Astr. Soc. 8, 23.

Values in the table are given in terms of percentage of numbers of atoms and percentage of mass

Z	El.	Number	Mass	Z	El.	Number	Mass
1	H	91.8	70.8	16	S	0.0021	0.050
2	He	8.0	24.7	26	Fe	.0005	.020
8	O	0.092	3.6	18	A	.0004	.012
6	C	.032	0.29	11	Na	.0002	.0030
10	Ne	.025	.38	13	Al	.0002	.0033
7	N	.009	.095	20	Ca	.0001	.0031
14	Si	.003	.063	28	Ni		.0020
12	Mg	.002	.043	15	P		.0007

By mass: $H : He : rest \equiv X : Y : Z \approx 71 : 25 : 4$

This corresponds approximately to average population I composition (see 9.3.5). For stars of population II the content of heavy metals is smaller by one order of magnitude (see 5.2.6).

9.2 *Anomalous abundances of elements*

Relatively infrequent, but obviously especially interesting.

In some cases it is not certain whether apparent anomalies are really due to anomalies or to special physical conditions.

1) <u>*C* and *S* stars</u> (see 4.2.1)

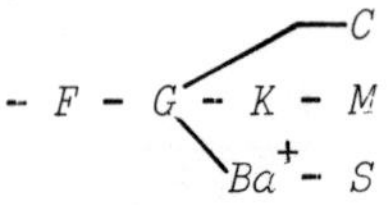

(The relatively infrequent Ba^+ stars are presumably rather hot *S* stars, hence, stars of the *S* series corresponding to type *K*.)

Reason for the division:

Differences in the C:O ratio

M	C:O	≈ 1:3	94%
S		≈ 1:1	1%
C		≈ 3:1	5%

(*S* and *C*:) Only giants!

Hence:

M: many oxides

C: many C compounds

S: all C and most of O consumed for CO, no excess of C for further C compounds, some O is left for further oxides. Stronger metal lines.

The strong ZrO, YO, LaO bands and the presence of nearly all rare earths in *S* stars cannot be explained only by this. Also anomalous abundances of Zr, Y, La .... The discovery of technetium (unstable) in some *S* stars shows that these elements have been generated in the star fairly recently.

2) <u>H-deficient stars</u>

Caused by nuclear processes in which the hydrogen is consumed

3) <u>Helium stars</u>

Some stars with hydrogen lines extremely faint or totally absent. He is the most abundant element.

Supposition: Matter from the interior, after having gone thro the H → He process, has somehow reached the surf

4) <u>Magnetic stars</u>, *Ap* → see 4.8

5) <u>Wolf-Rayet stars</u>, *W*

Nitrogen sequence *WN* } → see 7.4
Carbon sequence *WC* }

6) <u>Metallic-line stars</u>, *Am* ... *Fm* (see also 5.2.6)

Classified according to H lines: *A*5 to *F*0

Relative to the H type: majority of metallic lines too strong
Ca II (*H* and *K*), on the contrary, too

E.g., ε Ser: *A*3 according to Ca II lines
*A*5 according to Balmer lines
*F*0 according to metal lines

Not yet known, whether a chemical or physical anomaly.

9.3 *Origin of the elements, changing of the chemical composition*

Theory a: Origin of the frequency distribution of elements essentially at the "origin of the universe" (big bang). (see 10.6.3).
Later nuclear processes merely caused modifications.

Theory b: Originally only H. All others generated in the course of time in stellar interiors, in supernova explosions, etc. Initially only H stars, followed by present population II and then, present population I.

Theory c: Compromise: H and most He formed in big bang; others built up in stellar interiors, etc.

⟹ Cosmological findings now tend to support theory c.

Changes of chemical abundances by nuclear processes occur predominantly in stellar interiors, and possibly also in stellar atmospheres, in the interstellar space, and in catastrophic situations.

> The population, with the lower heavy element content (population II), is the older one. By nuclear processes higher elements formed. Interaction with interstellar space enriches it gradually with heavy elements. Stars generated later (young stars, population I) then, in general, have a higher content of heavy elements.

5

PHYSICS OF THE SOLAR AND STELLAR ATMOSPHERES

Prefatory remark: §1 and 2 of this chapter deal with fundamentals of the physics of stellar atmospheres. These are needed if one wants to deal with astrophysics in the narrower sense (physics of an individual star). In part, however, they exceed the scope of an introduction and could be skipped without detriment to one's understanding of later chapters

Literature: All text books on astrophysics. Especially:

L.H. Aller 1963, *Astrophysics*, vol. 1: *The Atmospheres of the Sun and Stars*, 2nd ed., Ronald, New York.

C.R. Cowley 1970, *The Theory of Stellar Spectra*, Gordon and Breach, New York.

J.L. Greenstein, ed. 1966, *Stars and Stellar Systems*, Vol. VI: *Stellar Atmospheres*, U. of Chicago Press.

D. Mihalas 1970, *Stellar Atmospheres*, Freeman, San Francisco.

T. Swihart 1971, *Basic Physics of Stellar Atmospheres*, Pachart, Tucson.

A. Unsöld 1955, *Physik der Sternatmosphären*, 2nd ed., Springer, New York.

H. Zirin 1966, *The Solar Atmosphere*, Blaisdell, Waltham (Mass)

In the physics of stellar atmospheres the sun serves as an ideal example. The methods tested there are then, as far as possible, transferred to other stellar atmospheres.

§ 1 Theory of the continuum

1.1 *Basic concepts of radiation theory*

A) Intensity

Surface $d\sigma$ in the radiation field

Normal **n**

Radiation in a direction given by the polar coordinates ϕ, θ

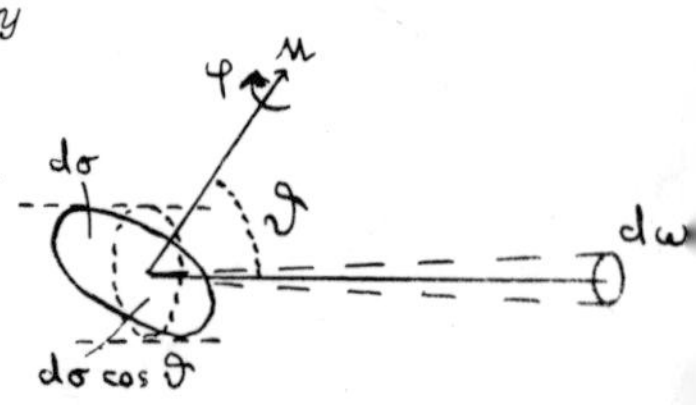

Then we have: Radiative energy passing in this direction per second through the surface dσ in element of solid angle dω in the frequency interval ν to ν + dν :

$$dE_\nu\,(\theta,\phi) = I_\nu\,(\theta,\phi)\,d\nu\,\cos\theta\,d\sigma\,d\omega$$

($\cos\theta\,d\sigma$ = projected surface area normal to the direction of the radiation)

This is the defining equation for the specific intensity I_ν, which appears here as a proportionality factor.

I.e., specific intensity = energy radiated per unit time, per unit frequency, per unit surface perpendicular to the direction of radiation, in a unit solid angle

Units: [erg sec^{-1} Hz^{-1} cm^{-2} $sterad^{-1}$]

If the intensity is referred to the unit of wavelength (cm), instead of to the unit of frequency, we have, according to 3.2.1, $I_\lambda = \frac{c}{\lambda^2} I_\nu$

(I_ν or I_λ sometimes called simply the intensity)

Total intensity (integrated over all frequencies):

$$I \equiv \int_0^\infty I_\nu\,d\nu = \int_0^\infty I_\lambda\,d\lambda \qquad (1)$$

Constancy of intensity with distance

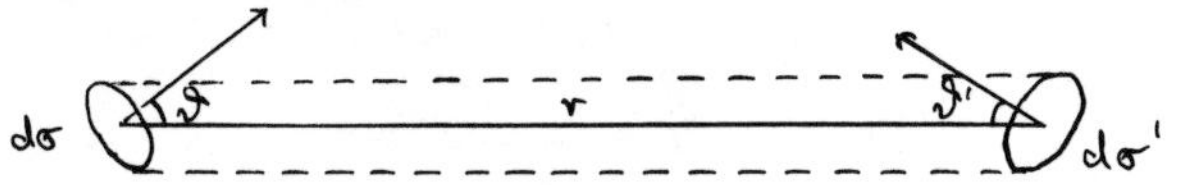

Consider energy radiated by surface dσ to surface dσ' at a distance r (essentially parallel beam).

Then dE across dσ = dE across dσ'

I_ν at dσ = $dE_\nu/d\nu\,\cos\theta\,d\sigma\,d\omega$

$$\left\{ \begin{aligned} d\omega &= \text{solid angle subtended by } d\sigma' \text{ as seen from } d\sigma \\ &= \frac{\cos\theta'\,d\sigma'}{r^2} \end{aligned} \right.$$

$= dE_\nu r^2/d\nu\,\cos\theta\,d\sigma\,\cos\theta'\,d\sigma'$

I_ν at dσ' = $dE_\nu/d\nu\,\cos\theta'\,d\sigma'\,d\omega'$

$$\left\{ \begin{aligned} d\omega' &= \text{solid angle subtended by } d\sigma \text{ as seen from } d\sigma' \\ &= \frac{\cos\theta\,d\sigma}{r^2} \end{aligned} \right.$$

$= dE_\nu r^2/d\nu\,\cos\theta'\,d\sigma'\,\cos\theta\,d\sigma \quad = I_\nu$ at dσ

Hence: The intensity of radiation is constant along a line -- i.e., independent of distance -- as long as there is no absorption.

The energy of the radiation falling on unit area changes, of course, with the square of the distance because of the decreasing solid angle.

B) Radiation flux (net flux) πF_ν

= net monochromatic radiation ($d\nu = 1$) flowing through unit area ($d\sigma = 1$) per unit time in all directions. Hence integrate $I \cos\theta$ over all solid angles, i.e., over the sphere:

$$\pi F_\nu = \int_O I_\nu(\theta,\phi)\cos\theta\, d\omega$$

Element of solid angle

$d\omega = \sin\theta\, d\theta\, d\phi$ ⟶

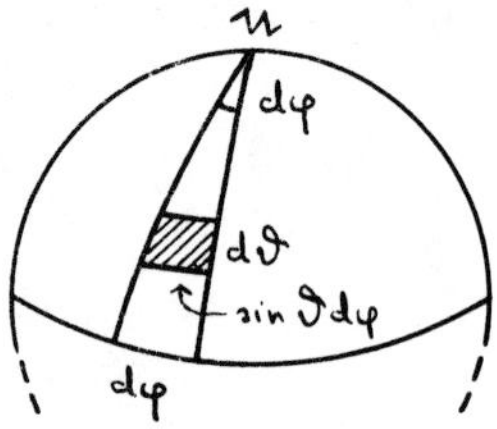

$$\boxed{\pi F_\nu = \int_{\theta=0}^{\pi}\int_{\phi=0}^{2\pi} I_\nu(\theta,\phi)\cos\theta\sin\theta\, d\theta\, d\phi} \tag{2}$$

The radiation flux is a function of the position, independent of the direction.

Note: Incidentally, also may be defined without the factor π, thus

$$\mathcal{F} = \iint \ldots$$

In an isotropic radiation field (I_ν independent of θ and ϕ)

$$\pi F_\nu = I_\nu \iint \cos\theta\sin\theta\, d\theta\, d\phi = 0$$

(equal radiation in all directions)

Integrated radiation flux:

$$\pi F = \int_0^\infty \pi F_\nu\, d\nu \tag{3}$$

Separate into 2 components, perpendicular to the surface of the star:

Outward radiation $0 < \theta < \frac{\pi}{2}$

$$\pi F_\nu^+ = \int_0^{\pi/2}\int_0^{2\pi} I_\nu \cos\theta\sin\theta\, d\theta\, d\phi$$

Inward radiation $\frac{\pi}{2} < \theta < \pi$

$$\pi F_\nu^- = \int_{\pi/2}^{\pi}\int_0^{2\pi} I_\nu \cos\theta\sin\theta\, d\theta\, d\phi$$

$$\pi F = \pi F^+ - \pi F^-$$

$$\text{Because} \int_0^{\pi/2} \int_0^{2\pi} \cos\theta \sin\theta \, d\theta \, d\phi = \pi$$

we have

$$F_\nu^+ = \frac{\iint I_\nu \cos\theta \sin\theta \, d\theta \, d\phi}{\iint \cos\theta \sin\theta \, d\theta \, d\phi} \equiv \overline{I_\nu^+} \qquad (4)$$

= mean value for the outgoing radiation.

On the other hand: mean value over the stellar disk

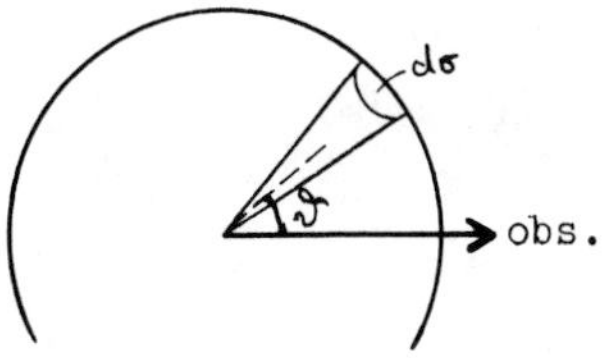

Surface element on the sphere

$d\sigma = R^2 d\omega = R^2 \sin\theta \, d\theta \, d\phi$

Surface in the direction of the observer

$d\sigma \cos\theta = R^2 \sin\theta \cos\theta \, d\theta \, d\phi$,

hence: mean intensity of the energy emitted from the disk of the star (size = πR^2) to the observer (integration over the disk):

$$\pi R^2 \overline{I_\nu} = \int_0^{\pi/2} \cdot \int_0^{2\pi} I_\nu(\theta,\phi) R^2 \cos\theta \sin\theta \, d\theta \, d\phi = \pi R^2 F_\nu^+$$

↳according to equation (2)

Because inward radiation at the surface = 0, we have

$$\boxed{\overline{I_\nu} = F_\nu} \qquad (5)$$

i.e., mean radiation intensity over the stellar disk

$= \frac{1}{\pi}$ radiation flux at the stellar surface.

Identity of equations (4) and (5) means:

F_ν = mean value of the radiation

a) from one point in all directions

b) from all points in one direction

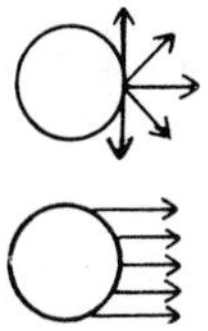

Intensity I_ν important for solar observations
Radiation flux F_ν important for stellar observations

At a large distance r from the star this comes from a solid angle $d\omega = \frac{\pi R^2}{r^2}$. Hence, the observed radiation flux becomes:

$$\pi f_\nu = I_\nu \, d\omega = \pi F_{\nu,\text{surface}} \cdot \frac{R^2}{r^2}$$

$\pi F_{\nu,\text{surface}} R^2$ is proportional to the "luminosity" of the star

πf_ν is a measure of the "apparent" brightness (see 4.1.3)

The total radiation flux is $\propto T^4$ according to the Stefan-Boltzmann law. The temperature as fixed by this is the effective temperature, thus

$$\boxed{\pi F = \sigma T_e^4} \qquad \text{with } \sigma = \frac{2\pi^5 k^4}{15c^2h^3} = 5.67\cdot 10^{-5}\ [\text{erg cm}^{-2}\ \text{sec}^{-1}\ \text{degree}^{-4}] \tag{6}$$

C) Optical depth

Let κ_ν = absorption coefficient

= relative decrease in intensity of a beam of intensity I_ν along a path dz

$$= -\frac{d\, I_\nu / I_\nu}{dz}$$

= property of the matter, dependent on chemical composition, frequency and physical conditions (density, pressure, temperature) $\longrightarrow$ see § 1.6

Dimension: [effective cross section per unit of volume]

$= [\text{cm}^2/\text{cm}^3] = [\text{cm}^{-1}]$

hence:
$$\frac{dI_\nu}{I_\nu} = -\kappa_\nu\, dz \quad \text{or} \quad \frac{dI_\nu}{dz_\nu} = -\kappa_\nu I_\nu \tag{7}$$

Definition of the optical depth

$$\boxed{d\tau_\nu \quad \kappa_\nu\, dz} \tag{8}$$

$d\tau_\nu$ element of optical depth
dz geometrical element } $\tau || z$

κ_ν absorption coefficient, see above

From $\frac{dI_\nu}{I_\nu} = \kappa_\nu\, dz = -d\tau_\nu$ integration $\longrightarrow I_\nu = I_o e^{-\tau_\nu}$

For $\tau_\nu = 1$ we have $I_\nu = \frac{1}{e} I_o$ i.e., intensity decreased by $1/e = 0.37$

The optical depth is a measure of the "transparency".

For κ_ν = const (i.e., independent of position, especially of depth, in the atmosphere) we have $\tau_\nu = \kappa_\nu z$

For $\kappa_\nu = \kappa_\nu(z)$ (general case) we have $\tau_\nu = \int_0^z \kappa_\nu \, dz$

In stellar atmospheres it is usual

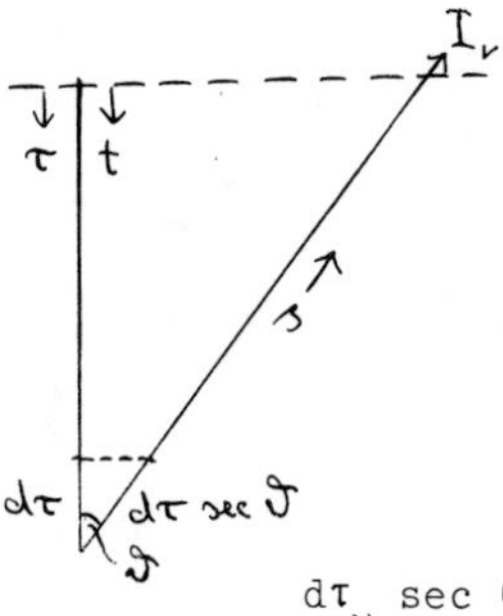

to measure the element of length in the direction of the radiation, but the optical depth from the surface of the the star perpendicularly inwards.

We then have for the radiation going out at an angle θ (sketch):

$$d\tau_\nu \sec\theta = -\kappa_\nu \, ds_\nu ; \; d\tau_\nu = -\kappa_\nu \, ds \cos\theta \quad (9)$$

1.2 *Equation of transfer*

Change of radiation intensity at the depth τ, at angle θ along the path ds

$$\frac{dI_\nu}{ds} = \text{loss (absorption)} + \text{gain (emission)}$$

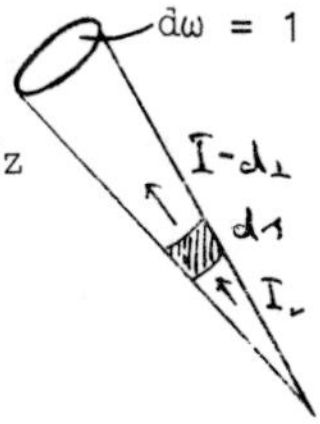

Loss = $-\kappa_\nu I_\nu(\theta)$ (see equation (7))

= energy absorbed per sec, per cm³, per Hz from the radiation coming from the solid angle dω = 1

Analogously one designates

Gain = ε_ν

= energy emitted per sec, per cm³, per Hz inside the solid angle 1

$\Longrightarrow$ ε_ν is independent of the direction.

Thus: $$\frac{d\,I_\nu(z,\theta)}{ds} = -\kappa_\nu I_\nu + \varepsilon_\nu$$

Introducing the optical depth according to equation (9) [division by $-\kappa_\nu$] yields:

$$\cos\theta \frac{dI_\nu}{d\tau_\nu} = + I_\nu - \frac{\varepsilon_\nu}{\kappa_\nu}$$

In thermal equilibrium: $dI_\nu = 0$, and then

$$\boxed{\frac{\varepsilon_\nu}{\kappa_\nu} = I_\nu} \qquad \text{Kirchhoff's law.}$$

We define, without assuming thermal equilibrium, an analogous function, the

$$\text{source function} \quad S_\nu \equiv \frac{\varepsilon_\nu}{\kappa_\nu} \tag{10}$$

and hence obtain the equation of transfer in its usual form:

$$\boxed{\cos\theta \frac{dI_\nu}{d\tau_\nu} = I_\nu(\tau,\theta) - S_\nu(\tau)} \tag{11}$$

Frequently, $\mu \equiv \cos\theta$ is used.

1.3 *Radiative transport*

Sun — Solve the equation of transfer for I_ν:

We put: $\tau/\cos\theta = \tau\sec\theta = \xi$

Then the equation of transfer is as follows:

$$\frac{dI}{d\xi} - I = S$$

Expand about $e^{-\xi}$ and apply the product rule:

$$\frac{d(Ie^{-\xi})}{d\xi} = -Se^{-\xi}$$

Integration: $$Ie^{-\xi} = \int^{\xi} Se^{-y}\,dy$$

or (substitute for ξ,
τ' = variable of integration, infinitely extended atmosphere)

$$I = -\int_{\infty}^{\tau} S(\tau')e^{-(\tau'-\tau)\sec\theta}\,d\tau'\sec$$

Important special case:

Outward radiation at the surface

i.e., $\tau = 0$, omit the prime on the integration variable exchange the limits:

$$\boxed{I_\nu(0,\theta) = \int_0^\infty S_\nu(\tau)\,e^{-\tau_\nu\sec\theta}\,d\tau_\nu\sec\theta} \tag{12}$$

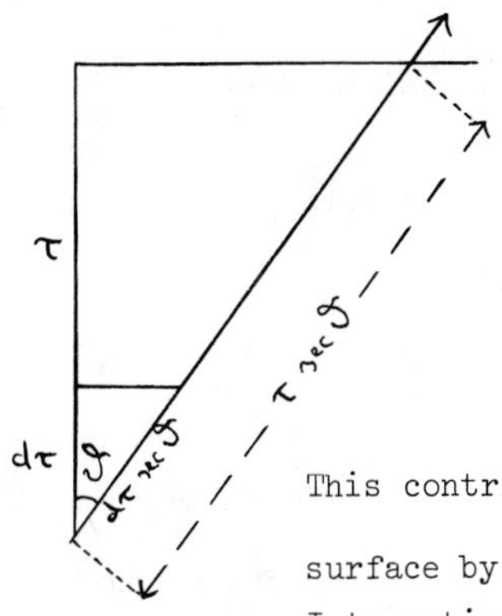

This equation can also be derived intuitively directly from the sketch: Contribution of an element of volume of thickness $d\tau_\nu$ at a depth τ_ν:

$$= S(\tau_\nu)\ \underbrace{d\tau_\nu \sec\theta}$$

→ element of optical path in direction θ

This contribution falls off in direction of the surface by the factor $e^{-\tau_\nu \sec\theta}$.
Integration over the whole path yields eqn. (12).

Special case: a) perpendicular view, hence $\theta = 0$
b) isothermal, i.e. S_ν independent of τ_ν

then: $I_\nu = S_\nu \int e^{-\tau_\nu}\, d\tau_\nu = S_\nu(1-e^{-\tau_\nu})$

$\tau >> 1$: optically thick: $I_\nu = S_\nu$

$\tau << 1$: optically thin: $I_\nu = S_\nu\, \tau_\nu$ | $e^{-\tau} = 1 - \tau$

i.e., as $\tau_\nu \to 0$, $I_\nu \to 0$
e.g., corona (where the density is extremely low, even the highest temperature does not produce appreciable radiation intensity.)

Significance of equation (12);

It gives the relation between the directly observable center-to-limb variation of the intensity $I_\nu(0,\theta)$ and the dependence of the source function $S_\nu(\tau_\nu)$ on the optical depth.

Former solution: Representation by analytic functions; e.g., expansion of S in a power series about τ yields, after a term-by-term integration, $I(0,\theta)$ as a power series in $\cos\theta$.

At present: Numerical procedures with the aid of computers

Eddington-Barbier Method: Expansion of S in a power series in τ about a point τ^*

$$S(\tau) = S(\tau^*) + (\tau-\tau^*)\left.\frac{dS}{d\tau}\right|_{\tau^*} + \frac{(\tau-\tau^*)^2}{2}\left.\frac{d^2S}{d\tau^2}\right|_{\tau^*} + \dots$$

Substituting, term-by-term integration:

$$I(0,\theta) = S(\tau^*) + [(\cos\theta - \tau^*)] \left.\frac{dS}{d\tau}\right|_{\tau^*} + \frac{1}{2}[\cos^2\theta + (\cos\theta - \tau^*)] \left.\frac{d^2S}{d\tau^2}\right|_{\tau^*}$$

For $\tau^* = \cos\theta$ the second term becomes = 0; the third term is at minimum, hence to a good approximation

$$\boxed{I_\nu(0,\theta) = S_{\tau=\cos\theta}} \qquad (13)$$

Simplest relation between the observed center-to-limb variation and the dependence of the source function on depth.

Stars Substitution of the intensity in the defining equation for the radiation flux (equation 2) gives, after some mathematical transformations, a relation for the radiation flux at the surface, analogous to equation (12):

$$\boxed{F_\nu(0) = 2\int_0^\infty S_\nu(\tau_\nu)\, E_2(\tau_\nu)\, d\tau_\nu} \qquad (14)$$

where E_2 is the 2nd exponential integral function:

$$E_2(y) = y\int_y^{+\infty} \frac{e^{-u}}{u^2}\, du$$

[sometimes designated by $K_2(y)$]

An expansion in series analogous to that above gives: $F_\nu(0) = S(\tau^*) + (\frac{2}{3} - \tau^*)\left(\frac{dS}{d\tau}\right)_{\tau^*} +$

and, hence

$$\boxed{F_\nu(0) = S_{[\tau = 2/3]}} \qquad (15)$$

i.e., the radiation flux corresponds to the source function at an optical depth $\tau = 2/3$

Combining with equation (13):

$$F_\nu(0) = I_\nu(0, \cos\theta = 2/3) \qquad (16)$$

1.4 *Equation of continuity* (Law of conservation of energy)

Assumption: Radiative equilibrium, i.e., energy is transported only by radiation.

Radiation integrated over all directions and wavelengths yields the total energy; this should be constant, hence change = 0, i.e., the equation of transfer (§ 1.2, equation (11); instead of optical depth, now geometrical depth) integrated over the sphere and all frequencies:

$$\frac{d}{dz}\int_0^\infty\int_0 \cos\theta\, I_\nu \frac{d\omega}{4\pi}\, d\nu = -\iint \kappa_\nu I_\nu \frac{d\omega}{4\pi}\, d\nu + \iint \kappa_\nu S_\nu \frac{d\omega}{4\pi}\, d\nu = 0$$

According to § 1.1 this statement is identical with the statement:

Integrated radiation flux = const, hence div $F = 0$.

With $J \equiv \int I_\nu \frac{d\omega}{4\pi}$ = intensity integrated over the sphere

and $\int S_\nu \frac{d\omega}{4\pi} = S_\nu$ because S_ν is independent of the direction and $\int \frac{d\omega}{4\pi} = 1$,

we get the equation of continuity,

$$\boxed{\int_0^\infty \kappa_\nu J_\nu\, d\nu = \int_0^\infty \kappa_\nu S_\nu\, d\nu} \qquad (17)$$

Note: J_ν = mean value of I_ν over the sphere

πF_ν = mean value of $I_\nu \cos\theta$ over the sphere

1.5 *Source function*

In fact, one should consider all the individual physical processes of absorption and emission. In complete generality this is not possible.

Limiting cases:

(a) Pure absorption or local thermodynamic equilibrium (LTE)

Independent of the kind of absorption, radiation is always re-emitted, corresponding to the local temperature, i.e., corresponding to Planck's radiation law (3.2.1).

Hence: $S_\nu = B_\nu = \frac{2h\nu^3}{c^2}\frac{1}{(e^{h\nu/kT}-1)}$ only $f(T)$

⟹ In practice the most important case

(b) Pure scattering or monochromatic equilibrium

Every quantum is re-emitted immediately at the same frequency at which it was absorbed.

Then: source function = sum of the total inward radiation

$S_\nu = \int I_\nu \frac{d\omega}{4\pi} \equiv J_\nu$ ⟶ according to the defining equation above i.e., in this case the equation of continuity is valid for each frequency and not only, as above, for the integral.

This S_ν substituted into transfer equation (11), yields an equation for I_ν, the so-called Milne integral equation; see equ.(19).

Here, one uses the scattering coefficient σ_ν instead of the absorption coefficient, and analogously, one has $d\tau_\nu = \sigma_\nu \, dz$.

(c) Absorption and scattering

One defines the total optical depth $d\tau_\nu = (\kappa_\nu + \sigma_\nu) \, dz$ and sets:

$$S_\nu(\tau_\nu) = \frac{\kappa_\nu}{\kappa_\nu + \sigma_\nu} B_\nu + \frac{\sigma_\nu}{\kappa_\nu + \sigma_\nu} J_\nu$$

For $\sigma_\nu = 0$ and $\kappa_\nu = 0$, this reduces to cases (a) and (b), respectively.

Note: The actual mechanism makes no difference in the absorption, but only in the re-emission.

1.6 *Absorption coefficient*

Essentially only bound-free and free-free transitions of electrons contribute to continuous absorption in stellar atmospheres (see 3.2.2).

Free-free absorption of electrons is only possible if they are in the field of influence of an atom or ion. Truly free electrons can absorb no appreciable energy because of the large mass difference between electron and photon.

The main contribution to the continuous absorption in the solar atmosphere is produced by the H^- ion ($\chi_i = 0.75$ eV). Additional contributions (especially in hotter stars): H, He I, He II. For cooler stars the series-limit continua of the metals produce a substantial contribution.

Scattering:

a) Thomson scattering (or electron scattering) by free electrons (predominantly in hot stars):

$$\sigma_{el} = \frac{8\pi}{3} \left(\frac{e^2}{mc^2}\right)^2 = 0.67 \times 10^{-24} \text{ cm}^2 \qquad (18)$$

independent of λ

b) Rayleigh scattering by atoms and molecules (predominantly in cool stars):

$$\sigma_R = \sigma_{el}\left(\frac{\lambda_o}{\lambda}\right)^4 \propto \lambda^{-4}$$

| This strong λ dependence of the Rayleigh scattering is the reason the sky is blue (blue light more strongly scattered)

Dimensions

//Absorption coefficient or scattering coefficient } per atom or per electron:

κ_{at}; σ_R; σ_{el} [cm^2] (= effective cross section)

//The same per cm^3:

$$\kappa_\nu = \kappa_{at} N \quad [cm^{-1}]$$ | N = absorbing or scattering particles per cm^3

//The same per gram

so-called mass-absorption coefficient

$$k_\nu = \frac{\kappa_\nu}{\rho} \quad [cm^2/g]$$ | ρ = density [g/cm^3]

Tables of the continuous absorption coefficient and scattering coefficient for "normal" chemical composition as a function of λ and T

e.g., E.Vitense 1951, *Z.f. Ap.* **28**, 81

See also Landolt-Börnstein, Vol. *Astronomy*, Section 5.3.1.3.4

1.7 *Gray atmosphere; dependence of temperature on depth*

Gray atmosphere means:

Absorption coefficient κ_ν independent of the frequency. The "gray atmosphere" is popular, because it is easily handled; but it is not a good representation.

In addition, as before, we assume radiative equilibrium.

In the equation of continuity (equation 17), the κ's can be taken out of the integrals and hence vanish. Integration over ν can be performed, and we obtain:

$$S = J = \int I \frac{d\omega}{4\pi}$$

Hence, the equation of transfer (equation (11)) becomes:

$$\cos\theta \frac{dI}{d\tau} = I - \int I \frac{d\omega}{4\pi} \qquad (19)$$

Starting with:

$$I(\tau,\theta) = I_o(\tau) + I_1(\tau)\cos\theta$$

Substitute in the radiation flux (§ 1.1.B)

$$\pi F = \int I \cos\theta\, d\omega = I_o \underbrace{\int \cos\theta\, d\omega}_{=0} + I_1 \underbrace{\int \cos^2\theta\, d\omega}_{=4\pi/3} = \frac{4\pi}{3} I_1$$

hence $I_1 = \frac{3}{4}F$, thus constant, independent of τ.

Substitute in the equation of transfer:

$$\cos\theta\frac{dI_o}{d\tau} + \underbrace{\cos^2\theta\frac{dI_1}{d\tau}}_{=0,\ \text{because}\ I_1 = \text{const}} = I_o + I_1\cos\theta - I_o\underbrace{\int\frac{d\omega}{4\pi}}_{=1} - I_1\underbrace{\int\cos\theta\frac{d\omega}{4\pi}}_{=0}$$

hence $\frac{dI_o}{d\tau} = I_1 \longrightarrow I_o = I_1\tau + b = \frac{3}{4}F\tau + b$

Substitute in the initial equation:

$$I(\tau,\theta) = \frac{3}{4}F\tau + b + \frac{3}{4}F\cos\theta$$

Constant b determined by boundary condition: no inward radiation at the surface (see § 1.1):

$$-\pi F^-(0) = \int_{\pi/2}^{\pi}\int_o^{2\pi} I(0)\cos\theta\, d\omega = b\underbrace{\iint\cos\theta\, d\omega}_{=-\pi} + \frac{3}{4}F\underbrace{\iint\cos^2\theta}_{=2/3}$$

hence $-\pi b + \frac{\pi}{2}F = 0 \longrightarrow b = \frac{F}{2}$

from this $\quad I_o = \frac{3}{4}F\tau + \frac{F}{2} = \frac{3}{4}F\left(\tau + \frac{2}{3}\right) = \frac{F}{2}\left(1 + \frac{3}{2}\tau\right)$ (20)

and therefore:

$$I(\tau,\theta) = \frac{F}{2}\left(1 + \frac{3}{2}\tau + \frac{3}{2}\cos\theta\right) = \frac{3}{4}F(\tau + \cos\theta$$

= Eddington approximation (21)

For $\tau=0$ and $\cos\theta = \frac{2}{3}$ it follows immediately from this that $F(0) = I(0, \cos\theta = \frac{2}{3}) \longrightarrow$ hence equation (16)

$I(\tau,\theta)$ contains an isotropic part: $1 + \frac{3}{2}\tau$

and an anisotropic part: $\frac{3}{2}\cos\theta$

The anisotropic portion becomes more and more important as $\tau \ll 1$, i.e., when approaching the surface.

For $\tau >> 1$ the radiation becomes more and more isotropic.

At the surface: $$I(0,\theta) = \frac{F}{2}\left(1 + \frac{3}{2}\cos\theta\right) \quad (22)$$

Hence center-to-limb variation:

$$\frac{I(0,\theta)}{I(0,0)} = \frac{2}{5}\left(1 + \frac{3}{2}\cos\theta\right)$$

Sun:

$r/R = \sin\theta$	$\frac{I(0,\theta)}{I(0,0)}$	observed
0.0	1.00	1.00
.2	0.99	0.99
.4	.95	.95
.6	.88	.92
.7	.83	.87
.8	.76	.81
.9	.66	.70
.96	.57	.59
.98	.52	.49
1.00	.40	-

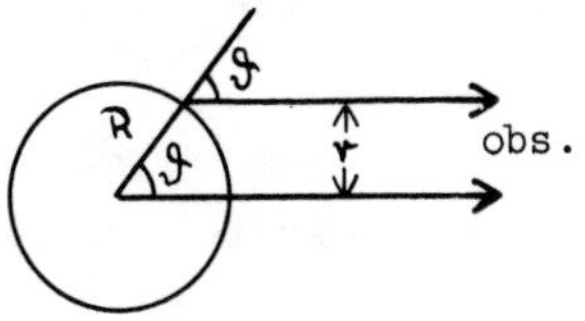

$r/R = \sin\theta$
= distance from the center of the disk in units of the solar radius

Agreement with observations astonishingly good.

$r/R = 0$
→ center of sun's disk

$r/R = 1$ ⟶ limb of sun

Temperature as a function of τ in Eddington approximation

An unambiguous determination of the temperature is not possible in an anisotropic radiation field. We must try to define the temperature as significantly as possible.

In the framework of Eddington's approximation, we have:

$$J \equiv \int I \frac{d\omega}{4\pi} = I_o \underbrace{\int \frac{d\omega}{4\pi}}_{1} + I_1 \underbrace{\int \cos\theta \frac{d\omega}{4\pi}}_{0} = I_o = \frac{F}{2}\left(1 + \frac{3}{2}\tau\right) \quad (23)$$

→ according to equation (20)

From this: $J(0) = F/2$ and $\frac{dJ}{d\tau} = \frac{3}{4}F$

Then, equation (22) can be written as:

$$I(0,\theta) = \underbrace{J(0)}_{\text{isotropic}} + \underbrace{\frac{dJ}{d\tau}\cos\theta}_{\text{anisotropic}} \text{ part.}$$

In the isotropic field, because I is then independent of θ, we have, according to equation (5) } $J = I \int \frac{d\omega}{4\pi} = I$

In thermal equilibrium (Stefan-Boltzmann law) } $\pi I = \sigma T^4$

hence in the isotropic case ⟶ $\pi J = \sigma T^4$

This relation should also be preserved in the anisotropic case. Hence we define T in such a way that

$$\pi\ J\ (\tau) = \sigma\ T^4\ (\tau)$$

in other words: T should - when used in the Stefan-Boltzmann law - yield the right "mean radiation intensity".

Substitute $J(\tau)$ according to equation (23):

$$\sigma\ T^4(\tau) = \frac{\pi}{2}\ F\ (1 + \frac{3}{2}\ \tau)$$

Hence surface temperature: $\sigma\ T^4(0) = \frac{\pi}{2}\ F$

On the other hand, the effective temperature is defined, according to equation (6), § 1.1, by: $\sigma\ T_e^{\ 4} = \pi F$

Hence, finally, the following relations result:

$$\left.\boxed{\begin{aligned} T^4\ (\tau) &= T_o^{\ 4}\ (1 + \frac{3}{2}\ \tau) \\ &= \frac{1}{2}\ T_e^{\ 4}\ (1 + \frac{3}{2}\ \tau) \end{aligned}}\ \right\} \qquad T_o^{\ 4} = \frac{1}{2}\ T_e^{\ 4} \qquad (24)$$

This equation says that $T = T_e$ at $\tau = 2/3$, in agreement with equation (15).

1.8 *Opacity (absorption coefficient)*

The absorption, in reality, is frequency dependent. Nevertheless in order to be able to utilize the integral quantities I, J and F, one needs a suitable mean value, the so-called opacity or the mean absorption coefficient $\bar{\kappa}$.

Definition such that the total radiant flux is preserved (law of conservation of energy), hence $\int_o^\infty F_\nu\ \mathrm{d}\nu = F$

After some manipulation the above leads to

$$\frac{1}{\bar{\kappa}} = \frac{\int_o^\infty \frac{1}{\kappa_\nu} \frac{\mathrm{d}K_\nu}{\mathrm{d}z}\ \mathrm{d}\nu}{\int_o^\infty \frac{\mathrm{d}K_\nu}{\mathrm{d}z}\ \mathrm{d}\nu} \qquad \text{with } K_\nu = \int_o I \cos^2\theta\ \frac{\mathrm{d}\omega}{4\pi}$$

Problem: K_ν unknown

For large optical depths the radiation field becomes isotropic and we can set

$$\overline{\cos^2\theta} = \frac{1}{3}\,; \quad \text{hence } K_\nu \approx \frac{1}{3} J_\nu$$

For a gray atmosphere (§ 1.7): $J_\nu = S_\nu$

For local thermodynamic equilibrium (§ 1.5): $S_\nu = B_\nu$

$$\Bigg\} \quad K_\nu \longrightarrow \frac{1}{3} B_\nu$$

Hence, because T is an unambiguous function of the depth, we set:

$$\frac{dK}{dz} = \frac{1}{3}\frac{dB}{dz} = \frac{1}{3}\frac{dB}{dT}\frac{dT}{dz}$$

Then:

$$\boxed{\frac{1}{\kappa} = \frac{\displaystyle\int_0^\infty \frac{1}{\kappa_\nu}\frac{dB_\nu}{dT}\,d\nu}{\displaystyle\int_0^\infty \frac{dB_\nu}{dT}\,d\nu} = \frac{\pi}{4\,\sigma T^3}\int_0^\infty \frac{1}{\kappa_\nu}\frac{dB_\nu}{dT}\,d\nu = \text{Rosseland mean}} \qquad (25)$$

└see 3.2.1 with $\displaystyle\int \frac{dB_\nu}{dT}\,d\nu = \frac{dB}{dT}$

i.e. a harmonic mean value weighted by the gradient of Planck's law.

For the corrresponding optical depths, analogous to § 1.1, we have

optical depth of the total radiation: $d\overline{\tau} = \overline{\kappa}\ dz$

optical depth of the radiation at frequency: $d\tau_\nu = \kappa_\nu\ dz$

$$\tau_\nu = \int_0^{\overline{\tau}} \frac{\kappa_\nu}{\overline{\kappa}}\,d\overline{\tau} \qquad (26)$$

1.9 *Pressure as function of* τ

A) Gas pressure

Equation of hydrostatic equilibrium

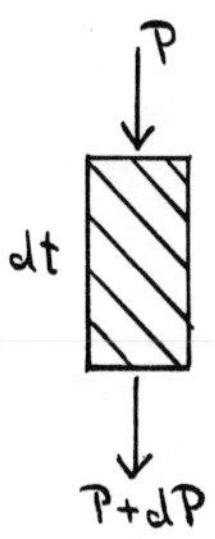

In hydrostatic equilibrium gas pressure supports the weight of the overlying layers

Pressure difference corresponds to weight of a volume element of surface area 1 cm^2 and height dz

$dP = g\rho\ dz$

Introducing the optical depth $\overline{\tau} = \overline{\kappa}\ dz = \overline{k}\ \rho\ dz$

$$\boxed{\frac{dP}{d\overline{\tau}} = \frac{g\rho}{\overline{\kappa}} = \frac{g}{\overline{k}}} \qquad (27)$$

$\bar{\kappa}$ = mean absorption coefficient or opacity [cm^{-1}]
$\bar{k}$ = mean absorption coefficient or opacity per gram matter
} See § 1.6

Dependence of temperature on depth, $T(\tau)$, assumed to be known.

$\bar{\kappa}$ itself is a function of T and P

Boundary condition: for $\bar{\tau} = 0$ (surface): $P = 0$

Solving the equation of hydrostatic equilibrium iteratively then yields step by step the run of pressure with depth.

B) Radiation pressure (also see 6.2.2)

For hot stars the radiation pressure has to be taken into account in addition to the gas pressure. Each photon ($E = h\nu$) possesses a momentum $h\nu/c$ in the direction of motion; upon absorption this momentum is transferred to the absorbing atom.

Radiation per second through an arbitrarily chosen unit area at an angle θ with the normal in the solid angle dω will be $I \cos\theta \, d\omega$. The corresponding amount of momentum transported is $(1/c) \cdot I \cos\theta \, d\omega$. Component of momentum normal to the surface: $\dfrac{I \cos\theta \, d\omega}{c} \cos\theta$

Hence radiation pressure

$$\boxed{P_r = \frac{1}{c} \int_0 I \cos^2\theta \, d\omega} \tag{28a}$$

For isotropic radiation:

$$P_r = \frac{I}{c} \int_0 \cos^2\theta \, d\omega = \frac{4\pi}{3} \frac{I}{c} = \frac{u}{3} \tag{28b}$$

with $u = \dfrac{4\pi \, I}{c}$ = radiation density

Analogously to equation (27) we get a radiation acceleration

$$g_{rad} = \bar{k} \frac{dP_r}{d\bar{\tau}} = \bar{k} \frac{4\pi}{3c} \frac{dI}{d\bar{\tau}} \quad \text{(eqn. (28b))}$$

Using Eddington approximation (equation (21)) we have

$\dfrac{dI}{d\tau} = \dfrac{3}{4} F$ and thus

$$\boxed{g_{rad} = \bar{k} \frac{\pi F}{c} = \bar{k} \frac{\sigma T_e^4}{c}} \tag{28c}$$

(eqn. (6))

This is in the opposite direction to the acceleration of gravity g, hence, "effective acceleration" $g_{eff} = g - g_{rad}$

C) Electron pressure P_e = partial pressure exerted by the electrons; related to the degree of ionization. For a given chemical composition P_e follows unambiguously from P and T.

Let: ε_i = abundance of the ith element [number/cm^3]

x = fraction of the atoms which are singly ionized

x' = fraction of the atoms which are doubly ionized

} Saha formula (3.2.2)

In practice 2nd ionization sets in only when the first is complete, hence if $x \simeq 1$.

Number of free electrons per atomic nucleus is then

$$E = \frac{\Sigma\, \varepsilon_i\, (x_i + x'_i)}{\Sigma\, \varepsilon_i} = f(T, P_e) = f(T, P)$$

Higher degrees of ionization are unimportant, for by the time the third ionization of the heavier elements sets in, H is totally ionized and produces, because of its abundance, practically all the electrons.

Gas pressure: atoms + electrons
Electron pressure: electrons

$$\frac{P}{P_e} = \frac{1 + E}{E}$$

Tables: $P_e = P_e(T, P)$ e.g. A. Rosa 1948, *Z.f.Ap.* 25,1.

D) Effective molecular weight (see also 6.2.1)

For un-ionized matter:

$$\mu_o = \frac{\Sigma\, \varepsilon_i\, \mu_i}{\Sigma\, \varepsilon_i} = 1.5$$ for normal chemical composition

In general:

$$\mu_{eff} = \frac{\mu_o}{1 + E}$$

For matter predominantly consisting of ionized hydrogen $\mu_o \rightarrow 1$; $E \rightarrow 1$, hence $\mu_{eff} \rightarrow 1/2$.

1.10 *Convection and radiative equilibrium*

Up to now we have assumed transport of energy only by radiation.

When is this valid?

Criterion according to Schwarzschild (intuitive, exact derivation below in c))

Given an atmosphere in radiative equilibrium, temperature decreasing outward, let a mass of gas rise, by a chance perturbation; it expands adiabatically, i.e., without heat exchange and so the temperature of the gas decreases; if it gets cooler and hence denser and heavier than the surroundings, it sinks back again. The stratification remains stable, the matter essentially at rest.

If, however, it remains warmer than the surroundings in spite of the adiabatic cooling, then it is less dense and moves still further upwards,

i.e., convective motions set in as soon as there is a slight perturbation.

Hence: Convection streams or cells originate if the adiabatic temperature gradient is smaller than the temperature gradient for radiative equilibrium

$$\left|\frac{dT}{dz}\right|_{ad} < \left|\frac{dT}{dz}\right|_{rad}$$

Using the equation of hydrostatic equilibrium (see above § 1.9, and the ideal gas law (paragraph b) below) we obtain:

$$\frac{1}{P} \cdot \frac{dP}{dz} = \frac{g\mu}{\mathcal{R}T}$$ z = geometric depth (measured from surface inward)

from this (multiplication by dT)

$$\frac{dT}{dz} = \frac{g\mu}{\mathcal{R}} \cdot \frac{dT/T}{dP/P} = \frac{g\mu}{\mathcal{R}} \cdot \frac{d\ \ln T}{d\ \ln P}$$ $\mathcal{R}$ = gas constant

The criterion for convection (convective equilibrium)

then becomes:

$$\left(\frac{d\ \ln T}{d\ \ln P}\right)_{ad} < \left(\frac{d\ \ln T}{d\ \ln P}\right)_{rad} \qquad (29)$$

or with the usual symbol ∇ = nabla $\equiv \frac{d\ \ln T}{d\ \ln P}$

$$\nabla_{ad} < \nabla_{rad}$$

∇ indicates how much T changes as P varies (with depth)

∇ describes the local variation. Not to be confused with the variation of P with changes in the conditions of an element of gas

a) Calculation of ∇_{rad} (= temperature gradient for radiative equilibrium)

In the framework of Eddington's approximation (§ 1.7) the following relations are valid:

$$I_o = J = \frac{\sigma}{\pi} T^4 \ ; \quad I_1 = \frac{dI_o}{d\bar{\tau}} = \frac{3}{4} F$$

From this: $$\pi F = \frac{4}{3}\,\sigma\,\frac{d(T^4)}{d\,\bar{\tau}} = \underbrace{\frac{16}{3}\,\sigma\,\frac{1}{\bar{k}\,\rho}}_{=\text{ " conductivity"}}\,T^3\,\frac{dT}{dz}$$

or
$$\boxed{\frac{dT}{dz} = \frac{3\,\bar{k}\,\rho}{16\,\sigma\,T^3}\,\pi\,F} \qquad (30)$$

This equation gives the temperature gradient which occurs for a given radiation flux πF

It is valid not only in the atmosphere, but even more so in the deep interior, because Eddington's approximation is not valid right at the surface (strong anisotropy).

Note: In the stellar interior (chapter 6) one uses the radial distance from the center of the star (from inside to outside) instead of the geometrical depth (from outside to inside). Because $dz = -\,dr$, in that case the signs in the corresponding equations change!

Occasionally one may also write: $$\frac{dT}{dz} = \frac{3\ \bar{k}\ \rho}{4\ ac\ T^3}\,\pi\ F \qquad (31)$$

where $a = \frac{4\sigma}{c} = \frac{8\ \pi^5\ k^4}{15\ c^3\ h^3} = 7.6 \times 10^{-15}$ erg cm^{-3} degree^{-4}

(k = Boltzmann's constant)

Variation of pressure $\Big\}$ $\frac{dP}{dz} = g\rho$ (equation of hydrostatic equilibrium; see § 1.9)

substituting this: $$\frac{dT}{dP} = \frac{3\ \bar{k}}{16\sigma\ gT^3}\,\pi\ F$$

and, therefore:
$$\nabla_{rad} \equiv \left(\frac{d\ \ln\ T}{d\ \ln\ P}\right)_{rad} = \frac{dT/T}{dP/P} = \frac{3\ \bar{k}\ P}{16\sigma\ gT^4}\,\pi\ F \qquad (32)$$

With $g = \frac{G\,M_r}{r^2}$ (see 2.4.1)

M_r = mass inside the radius r

$L_r = 4\ \pi\ r^2 \cdot \pi\ F$ = luminosity at distance r from the center

= total radiation energy, which passes per sec through a sphere of radius r

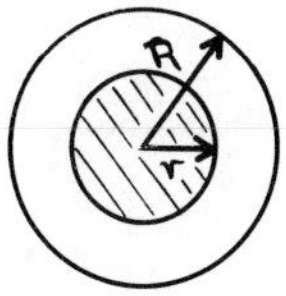

Finally one gets
$$\boxed{\nabla_{rad} = \frac{3}{64\ \pi\sigma G}\cdot\frac{\bar{k}\ L_r\ P}{M_r\ T^4}} \qquad (33)$$

b) Adiabatic stratification

i.e., pressure balance (expansion or contraction), but no heat balance

Adiabatic process for ideal gases (see text books on thermodynamics); constancy of entropy

$$dQ = c_v dT + P\,d(1/\rho) = c_v dT - \frac{P}{\rho^2}\,d\rho = 0$$

hence: $c_v \dfrac{dT}{T} = \dfrac{P}{\rho T} \cdot \dfrac{d\rho}{\rho}$

ideal gas: $P = \dfrac{\mathcal{R}}{\mu}\,\rho\,P \longrightarrow \dfrac{P}{\rho T} = \dfrac{\mathcal{R}}{\mu}$

differentiated: $\dfrac{dP}{P} = \dfrac{d\rho}{\rho} + \dfrac{dT}{T} \longrightarrow \dfrac{d\rho}{\rho} = \dfrac{dP}{P} - \dfrac{dT}{T}$

further: $\dfrac{\mathcal{R}}{\mu} = c_p - c_v$

[$c_{p,v}$ = specific heat at constant pressure and volume, respectively

$\gamma = c_p/c_v = 1 + 2/n$, where n = number of degrees of freedom of atom or molecule]

Substituting this:

$$c_v \frac{dT}{T} = (c_p - c_v)\left(\frac{dP}{P} - \frac{dT}{T}\right) \longrightarrow c_p \frac{dT}{T} = (c_p - c_v)\frac{dP}{P}$$

or, finally:

$$\boxed{\nabla_{ad} \equiv \left(\frac{d\,\ell n\,T}{d\,\ell n\,T}\right)_{ad} = \frac{dT/T}{dP/P} = 1 - \frac{c_v}{c_p} = 1 - \frac{1}{\gamma}} \qquad (34)$$

For monatomic gases $\gamma = \frac{5}{3}$, hence $\nabla_{ad} = 0.40$

Because ∇_{rad} is $\propto P$, at the stellar surface $\nabla_{rad} \rightarrow 0$ i.e., there always $\nabla_{ad} > \nabla_{rad}$, hence no convection.

$\Longrightarrow$ **The outermost layers of a star are always in radiative equilibrium.**

c) Derivation of Schwarzschild's criterion

I z; P; T; ρ

↓

II $z + dz$; $P + dP$; $T + dT$

Element sinks from layer I into lower layer II.

or $P(1 + \frac{\Delta P}{P})$; $T(1 + \frac{\Delta T}{T})$ [Δz, ΔP, ΔT; all > 0]

$$\Delta P = \frac{dP}{dz} \cdot \Delta z; \; \Delta T = \frac{dT}{dz} \Delta z$$

Definition:

Pressure scale height / Homogeneous thickness of a layer

$$H_p \equiv \frac{\mathcal{R}T}{g\mu} = \frac{dz}{d\,\ell n\,P} = \frac{dz}{dP/P} > 0 \quad (35)$$

(↑ see above)

Herewith, we have $\frac{\Delta P}{P} = \frac{dP/P}{dz} \Delta z = \frac{\Delta z}{H_p}$

and $\frac{\Delta T}{T} = \frac{dT/T}{dz} \Delta z = \frac{dT/T}{dP/P} \cdot \frac{dP/P}{dz} \Delta z = \nabla \frac{\Delta z}{H_p}$

Taking account of $\frac{d\rho}{\rho} = \frac{dP}{P} - \frac{dT}{T}$ (see above)

the following values in layer II result

	Pressure	Temperature	Density
Surroundings	$P(1+\frac{\Delta z}{H_p})$	$T(1+\nabla_{rad}\frac{\Delta z}{H_p})$	$\rho(1+\frac{\Delta P}{P} - \nabla_{rad}\frac{\Delta z}{H_p}) = \rho_s$
Element	$P(1+\frac{\Delta z}{H_p})$	$T(1+\nabla_{ad}\frac{\Delta z}{H_p})$	$\rho(1+\frac{\Delta P}{P} - \nabla_{ad}\frac{\Delta z}{H_p}) = \rho_E$

Hence: $\rho_E - \rho_s = \rho(\nabla_{rad} - \nabla_{ad}) \frac{\Delta z}{H_p}$

$\nabla_{ad} < \nabla_{rad}$: sign of $(\rho_E - \rho_s)$ = sign of Δz

i.e., for descending ($\Delta z > 0$) we have $\rho_E > \rho_s$

⟶ further descending ⟶ convection

same for ascending ($\Delta z < 0$) ⟶ $\rho_E < \rho_s$

further ascending ⟶ convection

$\nabla_{ad} > \nabla_{rad}$: sign of $(\rho_E - \rho_s)$ = − sign Δz

i.e., for descending ($\Delta z > 0$) we have $\rho_E < \rho_s$

⟶ rising ⟶ no convection.

The same for ascending ⟶ descending

d) Convection zones:

From the above considerations it follows that convection is induced by a large temperature gradient for radiative equilibrium and by a small adiabatic temperature gradient.

Both conditions occur if an abundant element is ionized, namely H, eventually He I and He II.

Increase in the gradient for radiative equilibrium because of increase of the opacity in the region of ionization.

Reduction of the adiabatic gradient: Besides the translation energy, during ionization work must be done; the separated electrons must receive energy 3/2 kT. The gas approaches a polyatomic gas; its effective γ and, hence, also ∇_{ad}, decreases. Even a change in the degree of hydrogen ionization by 1% from 0 or 1 causes a considerable decrease of ∇_{ad} relative to the value 0.40 in the case of a neutral or completely ionized gas.

In those regions, consequently, there are developed

→ hydrogen convection zones
or: 1st and 2nd helium convection zones

If convection starts, hence $\nabla_{ad} < \nabla_{rad}$, then a real temperature gradient ∇_{conv} sets in, and we have

$$\nabla_{ad} < \nabla_{conv} < \nabla_{rad}.$$

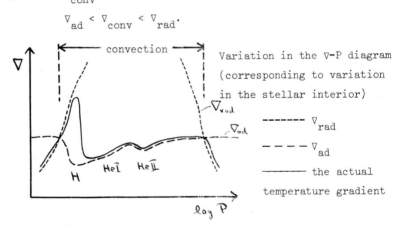

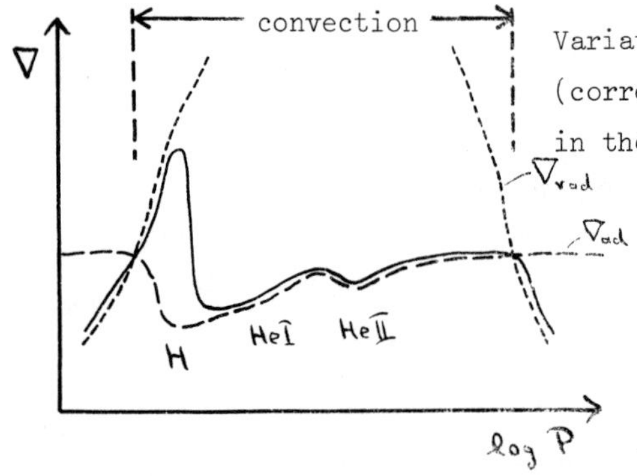

Variation in the ∇-P diagram (corresponding to variation in the stellar interior)

------- ∇_{rad}

– – – – ∇_{ad}

——— the actual temperature gradient

In the deep interior of the convection zone we have as a good approximation

$$\boxed{\nabla_{conv} = \nabla_{ad}} \tag{36}$$

In the convection zones near the surface the actual temperature gradient deviates only slightly from the one for radiative equilibrium.

1.11 *Model atmospheres*

Sun

A) Empirical model

Observed: $I_\nu (0,\theta)$ = center-to-limb variation (see § 4)

from this, according to § 1.3 ⟶ source function $S_\nu (\tau)$

In the sun predominantly absorption rather than scattering,

hence $S_\nu = B_\nu$

yields: $T(\tau)$

result: $T_0 \approx 4000^\circ$

$T_{\tau=2} \approx 7000^\circ$

Then, can get pressure as a function of τ according to § 1.9

B) Theoretical model: Two conditions must be fulfilled:

a) The total radiation must yield the right luminosity, ⟶ T_{eff} ("fixing of the zero point")

b) The law of conservation of energy must be satisfied at every depth (equation of continuity).

Vary the starting approximation until these conditions are fulfilled. In all generality solved by K. H. Böhm.

Agreement with the empirical model:

For $\tau > 0.05$	good (computing and observing accuracy: $\Delta T < 50^\circ$
for $\tau < 0.05$	worse and worse with smaller τ, i.e., theory of radiative equilibrium no longer holds. One is already in the chromosphere.

Stars

Only the total radiation observable, a direct, empirical determination of the dependence of temperature on depth, therefore, is not possible.

General procedure:

a) From a coarse analysis of the line spectrum (see 5.2.4)

⟶ { T_{eff}, chemical composition, gravity }

b) Approximate dependence of temperature on optical depth according to § 1.7, equation (24)

⟶ "Zero-th approximation" $T^{(o)}(\tau)$

c) Pressure as a function of τ according to § 1.9.

⟶ "zero-th approximation" $P^{(o)}(\tau)$

Because $\overline{\kappa}$ itself is a function of T and P, this step must be iterated until $\overline{\kappa}$, P and T converge.

d) Principal iteration (Transition from gray to non-gray atmosphere)

Compute radiation flux $\pi F(\tau)$ through the atmosphere (§ 1.1) and check whether constant. If not, vary $T(\tau)$ by means of certain procedures, especially developed for this,

e.g., "Flux-iteration procedure": From the difference between the flux $F(\tau)$, as computed at various depths, and the mean value corresponding to T_{eff}, hence $\Delta F = F(\tau) - \overline{F}$, a correction follows for the source function, $\Delta S(\tau)$, and, from this, $\Delta T(\tau)$.

This yields the 1st approximation of the run of temperature $T^{(1)}(\tau)$.

e) If $T^{(1)}(\tau)$ differs considerably from $T^{(0)}(\tau)$, iterate the whole from c) on again and repeat until the τ-dependence stabilizes, i.e., until πF is sufficiently constant.

Further refinement of the analysis not possible without the help of the line spectrum. See § 2.

§ 2 Theory of absorption (Fraunhofer) lines

Because the continuous absorption coefficient does not change in the vicinity of a spectral line, in this section we let

κ (without subscript) = continuous absorption coefficient

κ_ν or κ_ω (with subscript) = line absorption coefficient

2.1 *The line profile; broadening mechanisms*

In the ideal case:

Jump of the electron between two precisely sharp levels $\Delta E = h\nu$. Absorption coefficient in this case a δ function.

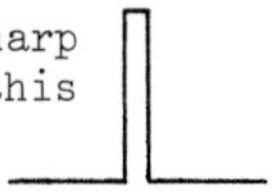

This corresponds to an infinitely extended wave train of frequency ν.

In reality:

Only finite wave train of duration t; this yields a broadening of ΔE. Expressed differently; diffuse terms in the energy-level diagram

$\Longrightarrow$ Natural line width (radiation damping of the classical oscillator)

In general, the time interval is interrupted by interactions with particles.

$\Longrightarrow$ Pressure broadening (damping)

The individual atoms absorb at different frequencies because of their motion (doppler effect).

$\Longrightarrow$ Thermal and turbulence broadening

A) Natural broadening (= radiation damping)

For classical oscillator one gets:

$\Delta\lambda_N$ (half width) = 1.2×10^{-4} Å (independent of λ)

For astronomy, in general, irrelevant, because the other broadening mechanisms are considerably stronger.

B) Pressure broadening (shock damping)

For a transient wave train with damping constant γ, the absorption coefficient is given by the so-called dispersion profile or Lorentz profile

$$\kappa_\omega = \frac{\pi e^2}{mc} N \cdot f \frac{\gamma}{(\omega-\omega_0)^2 + (\gamma/2)^2} \qquad (1)$$

$\omega = 2\pi\nu$ angular frequency

$\omega_0 =$ angular frequency of the undisturbed line center (= eigenfrequency of the classical oscillator)

$f =$ oscillator strength

$\gamma =$ damping constant

$\gamma/2$ = number of effective interactions per sec
= half width of the absorption coefficient, for: at

$\omega-\omega_0 = \gamma/2$ one has $\kappa_\omega = \frac{1}{2}\kappa_{(\omega=\omega_0)} = \frac{1}{2}\kappa_{\omega,max}$

$2/\gamma$ = average time interval between two interactions

Integration over all frequencies (over the whole line)

$$\int \kappa_\nu \, d\nu = \frac{1}{2\pi} \int \kappa_\omega d\omega \qquad (2)$$

$$= \frac{\pi e^2}{mc} N \cdot f \cdot \frac{1}{\pi}\frac{1}{2} \underbrace{\int \frac{\gamma \, d(\omega-\omega_0)}{(\omega-\omega_0)^2 + (\gamma/2)^2}} = \frac{\pi e^2}{mc} \cdot N \cdot f$$

with $x = \frac{2(\omega-\omega_0)}{\gamma}$ one gets $\rightarrow = \int \frac{dx}{x^2+1} = \pi$

The classical theory of electrons yields only $\frac{\pi e^2}{mc} N$, i.e., $f = 1$. f is a measure of the strength of the classical oscillator and is necessary for agreement with quantum theory. f indicates how many classical oscillators correspond to one absorbing atom.

Equation (2) can be considered as the defining equation for the oscillator strength.

Quantum mechanics yields for the phase shift in general:

$$\omega-\omega_0 = \frac{2\pi C}{r^n}$$

C = constant of the interaction effect

r = distance of the particles

$n = 2$ linear Stark effect: perturbations of hydrogen and some helium terms by electric fields of ions and electrons moving along.

$n = 4$ quadratic Stark effect: perturbations of heavier elements by ions and electrons.

$n = 6$ Van der Waals forces: perturbations by neutral particles, mostly hydrogen.

Herewith, the damping constant γ is

$\propto P$ for Van der Waals forces

$\propto P_e$ for linear and quadratic Stark effect

> Concerning the derivation of equation (1) and further details about the mutual perturbation of the particles one must refer to the specialized literature mentioned at the beginning of the section or to the corresponding physics text books.

C) Doppler broadening

Thermal motion and microturbulence. Maxwellian velocity distribution yields for the fraction of atoms with radial velocities between

ξ and $\xi + d\xi$

$$\frac{dN}{N} = \frac{1}{\sqrt{\pi}} e^{-(\xi/\xi_o)} \frac{d\xi}{\xi_o} = \text{"Doppler profile"}$$

Doppler effect: ξ_o = most probable velocity

$$\frac{\xi}{c} = \frac{\Delta\omega}{\omega} = \frac{\Delta\lambda}{\lambda}$$

Definition of doppler width $\Delta\omega_D$ or $\Delta\lambda_D$:

$$\frac{\Delta\omega_D}{\omega} = \frac{\Delta\lambda_D}{\lambda} = \frac{\xi_o}{c} = \left\{\begin{array}{l}\text{the doppler shift of}\\ \text{the most probable velocity}\end{array}\right.$$

According to thermodynamics, we have

$$\left.\begin{array}{lll} & \xi_o = \sqrt{\dfrac{2\mathcal{R}T}{\mu}} \quad \text{and hence} & \Delta\lambda_D = \dfrac{\lambda}{c}\sqrt{\dfrac{2\mathcal{R}T}{\mu}} \\ \text{or} & \xi_o = \sqrt{\dfrac{2\mathcal{R}T}{\mu} + \xi_T^2} \quad \text{and hence} & \Delta\lambda_D = \dfrac{\lambda}{c}\sqrt{\dfrac{2\mathcal{R}T}{\mu} + \xi_T^2} \end{array}\right\} \quad (3)$$

$\mathcal{R}$ = gas constant = $8.31 \cdot 10^7$ erg degree^{-1} mol^{-1}
μ = molecular weight
ξ_T = radial component of the turbulent velocity

Intuitive meaning

For optically thin lines we have $I \propto N$ and, hence, the relative intensity distribution in the line:

$$\frac{dI}{I} = \frac{1}{\sqrt{\pi}} e^{-\left(\frac{\Delta\lambda}{\Delta\lambda_D}\right)^2} \frac{d(\Delta\lambda)}{\Delta\lambda_D}$$

i.e., $\Delta\lambda_D$ = 1/e width,

for, at $\Delta\lambda = \Delta\lambda_D$, I has decreased to $I/e = 0.37\ I$

Half width:

I is reduced to half its value if $e^{-\left(\frac{\Delta\lambda}{\Delta\lambda_D}\right)^2} = \frac{1}{2}$

i.e., $\Delta\lambda_{h\omega} = \Delta\lambda_D \sqrt{\ln 2}$

Example: Hβ at $T = 5700^\circ \longrightarrow \xi_o = 9.7$ km/sec

$\Delta\lambda_D = 0.16$ Å

Multiply the first equation above (Doppler profile) by N and integrate:

$$\int_{-\infty}^{+\infty} dN = N = \frac{1}{\sqrt{\pi}} \int N e^{-\left(\frac{\Delta\omega}{\Delta\omega_D}\right)^2} \frac{d(\Delta\omega)}{\Delta\omega_D} \qquad (4)$$

Phase shift $\Delta\omega$ means that the basic frequency ω changes to $\omega + \Delta\omega$.

D) Doppler effect + damping; Voigt profile

Substitute equation (4) into equation (1) for the absorption coefficient:

$$\kappa_\omega = \frac{\pi e^2}{mc} \gamma \int \frac{Nf}{\sqrt{\pi}} \cdot \frac{d(\Delta\omega)}{\Delta\omega_D} e^{-\left(\frac{\Delta\omega}{\Delta\omega_D}\right)^2} \frac{1}{(\omega-\omega_o-\Delta\omega)^2 + (\gamma/2)^2}$$

= convolution of a doppler and a dispersion profile

Every "strip" in the dispersion profile is smeared out by the doppler effect.

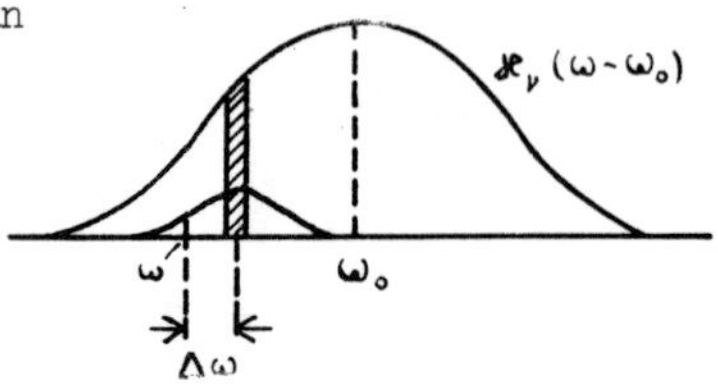

Multiply nominator and denominator by $1/(\Delta\omega_D)^2$.

Introduce the following dimensionless quantities (in units of the doppler width):

$$\left.\begin{array}{lll} \text{integration variable} & y = \frac{\Delta\omega}{\Delta\omega_D} = \frac{\Delta\lambda}{\Delta\lambda_D} \\ \text{distance from line center } (\upsilon = \text{small Greek upsilon}) & \upsilon = \frac{\omega-\omega_o}{\Delta\omega_D} = \frac{\lambda-\lambda_o}{\Delta\lambda_D} \\ \text{half the damping constant} & a = \frac{\gamma}{2\Delta\omega_D} \end{array}\right\} \qquad (5)$$

Introduce abbreviating notation $\kappa_c = \frac{2\pi^{3/2}e^2}{mc} \cdot \frac{Nf}{\Delta\omega_D}$ (6)

The above equation then becomes

$$\frac{\kappa(\upsilon)}{\kappa_c} = \frac{a}{\pi} \int \frac{e^{-y^2}}{(\upsilon-y)^2 + a^2}\, dy \;\equiv\; H(a,\upsilon) \qquad (7)$$

The function defined by this is

$H(a,\upsilon)$ = Voigt function (W. Voigt, theoretical physicist, 1850-1919)

It has, as can be proved by Fourier transformation, the property that the convolution of two Voigt functions is again a Voigt function with different parameters.

Integration of eqn.(7) [see also eqn.(9)] shows $H(0,0) = 1$; from this follows for the quantity κ_c defined by equation (6):

→ ‖ κ_c = absorption coefficient at the line center for negligeable damping ($a \to 0$)

Occasionally one also meets the definition

$$V(a,\upsilon) = \frac{1}{\sqrt{\pi}\,\Delta\omega_D}\; H(a,\upsilon). \qquad (8)$$

Whereas H is normalized to the central value $H(0,0) = 1$, V is normalized to the area $\int_{-\infty}^{+\infty} V d\upsilon = 1$

Variation:

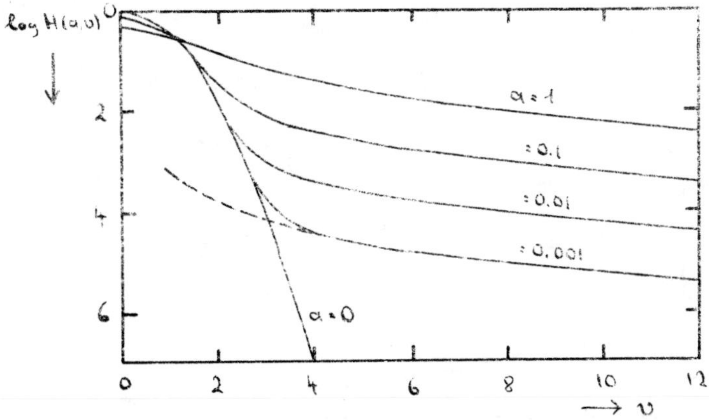

At the center the doppler portion predominates (because in astrophysics always $a \ll 1$). However, because this decreases exponentially, and the dispersion part only as $1/\Delta\lambda^2$, damping plays a decisive role in the wings of strong lines.

For $a \ll 1$ there exists a rather complicated mathematical transformation (Fourier transform, expansion in series):

$$H(a,\upsilon) = e^{-\upsilon^2} - \frac{2a}{\sqrt{\pi}} \left[1 - \upsilon\, F(\upsilon)\right] \tag{9}$$

where $F(\upsilon) = e^{-\upsilon^2} \int_0^{\upsilon} e^{z^2}\, dz$

The functions $H(a,\upsilon)$ and $F(\upsilon)$ are tabulated in several text books (Unsöld, *Physik der Sternatmosphären*, Landolt-Börnstein, etc.)

Limiting cases for the profile of strong lines:

with equation (7) and (6) and with

$$\Delta\omega_D = \frac{2\pi c}{\lambda^2} \Delta\lambda_D$$

Doppler nucleus:

$$\left.\begin{matrix} \upsilon \ll 1 \\ a \ll 1 \end{matrix}\right\} \qquad H(a,\upsilon) = e^{-\upsilon^2} \tag{10}$$

$$\text{i.e.,} \quad \kappa_\lambda = \sqrt{\pi}\, \frac{e^2}{mc^2} \cdot \frac{\lambda^2 N f}{\Delta\lambda_D}\, e^{-\left(\frac{\Delta\lambda}{\Delta\lambda_D}\right)^2}$$

Wings of a line:

$$\upsilon \gg 1 \qquad H(a,\upsilon) = \frac{a}{\sqrt{\pi}} \frac{1}{\upsilon^2} \tag{11}$$

$$\text{i.e.,} \quad \kappa_\lambda = \frac{1}{4\pi} \cdot \frac{e^2}{mc^2} \cdot \frac{\lambda^4}{c} \frac{N f \gamma}{\Delta\lambda^2}$$

This last equation follows also directly from equation (1) with

$$\Delta\,\omega = \frac{2\pi c}{\lambda^2} \Delta\lambda\ .$$

$\frac{e^2}{mc^2}$ = so-called classical radius of an electron $= 2.82 \cdot 10^{-13}$ cm

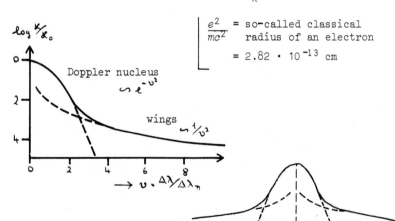

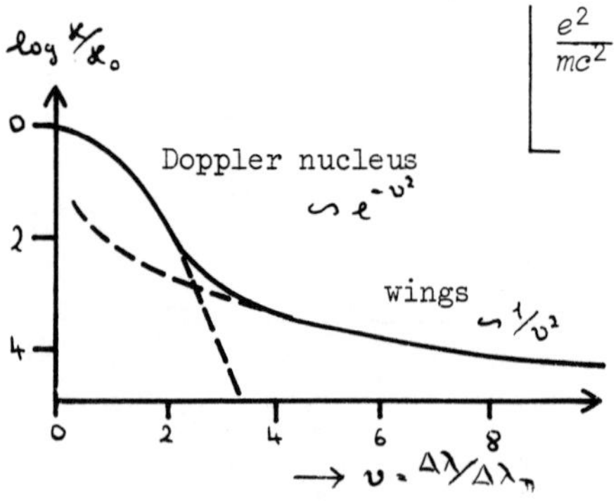

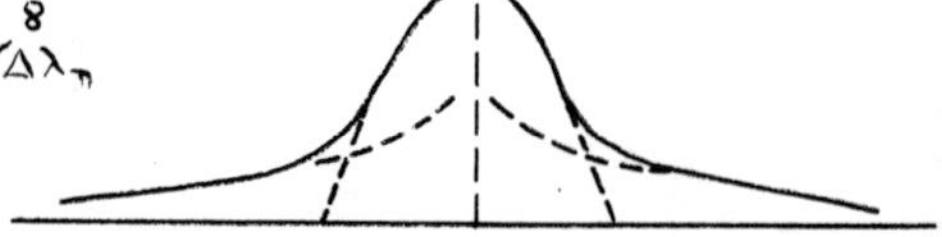

E) Depth of a line

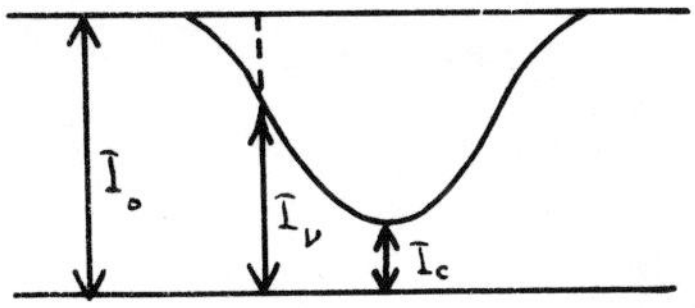

I_o = intensity of the adjacent continuum

I_ν = intensity inside the line at frequency ν

I_c = intensity at the center of the line
= residual intensity

F_o, F_ν, F_c : the same for the radiation flux (see 5.1.1)

Definition of the depth of a line
(= depression in units of the adjacent continuum)

	Sun	Star
Depth of a line:	$r_\nu = \frac{I_o(0,\theta) - I_\nu(0,\theta)}{I_o(0,\theta)}$;	$R_\nu = \frac{F_o(0) - F_\nu(0)}{F_o(0)}$
Central depth:	$r_c = \frac{I_o(0,\theta) - I_c(0,\theta)}{I_o(0,\theta)}$;	$R_c = \frac{F_o(0) - F_c(0)}{F_o(0)}$

(12)

2.2 *Radiative transfer, computation of the line profile*

In the case of lines, bound-bound transitions are involved. The treatment in § 1 on the continuum has to be extended. Again, the absorption ($= \kappa_\nu I_\nu$) itself is not important, but the problem of where the absorbed energy goes, hence, the problem of the re-emission.

Preliminary considerations same as in § 1.5

a) Scattering (= monochromatic equilibrium)

Each light quantum is re-emitted at the same wavelength. Happens in the case of resonance lines, where the electron has no other possibility than to perform the same "jump-back". Re-emission distributed uniformly over all directions (independent of θ),

hence

$$= \sigma \int I_\nu \frac{d\omega}{4\pi} \equiv \sigma_\nu \boldsymbol{J}_\nu \quad \Big| \; \sigma_\nu = \text{scattering coefficient}$$

b) Pure absorption (local thermodynamic equilibrium = LTE)

In a complex scheme of terms it is improbable that exactly the inverse emission process follows an absorption process.

The re-emission, rather, occurs according to Kirchhoff's law, i.e., depending on the local temperature, hence

$$= \kappa_\nu B_\nu$$

Other mechanisms...

Noncoherent scattering (re-emission in the same line, but distributed over the line)

Extinction (no re-emission)

... play only a minor role.

As in § 1.5, all these mechanisms can be combined to obtain a total source function.

Below we restrict ourselves to the most important case:

Pure absorption

In the equation of transfer, § 1.2, now the continuous line absorptions must be taken into account, hence:

$$\cos\theta \frac{dI_\nu}{dz} = (\kappa + \kappa_\nu)\, I_\nu - (\kappa + \kappa_\nu)\, B_\nu$$

Introduce the total optical depth (see § 1.1)

$$d\tau' = d\tau_\nu + d\tau = \kappa_\nu\, dz + \kappa dz = (\kappa_\nu + \kappa)\, dz$$

τ = optical depth of the continuum

τ_ν = optical depth of the line absorption only

Note: there is no standard notation for the above quantities; it varies widely.

Then obtain the equation of transfer in the well-known form:

$$\cos\theta \frac{dI_\nu}{d\tau'} = I_\nu\,(\tau',\theta) - B_\nu(\tau') \tag{13}$$

In its mathematical structure this equation is identical to equation (11) in § 1.2, hence the same mathematical formalism, especially

Total radiation at the surface:
[equations (12) and (14), § 1.3]

Sun

$$I_\nu(0,\theta) = \int_0^\infty B(\tau')\, e^{-\tau'/\sec\theta}\, d\tau' \sec\theta \tag{14}$$

Star

$$F_\nu(0) = 2\int_0^\infty B(\tau')\, K_2\,(\tau')\, d\tau' \tag{15}$$

Note: Formulae only formally identical with the equations in § 1.3.

Difference: $B(\tau')$ is a different function from $B(\tau)$, because $\tau' = 1$ corresponds to a geometrical depth different from $\tau = 1$.

$\tau = 1$ (continuum) lies geometrically deeper, therefore $T_{(\tau = 1)} > T_{(\tau' = 1)}$

Hence for known temperature dependence on depth and known absorption coefficient, $I_\nu(0,\theta)$ or $F_\nu(0)$ can be computed for various points in the line, and, hence, for the line profile by equation (12).

In particular, the Eddington approximation yields according to equation (13) or (15) in § 1.3:

Sun $$r_\nu = \frac{B_\nu(\tau = \cos\theta) - B_\nu(\tau' = \cos\theta)}{B_\nu(\tau = \cos\theta)}$$

Star $$R_\nu = \frac{B_\nu(\tau = 2/3) - B_\nu(\tau' = 2/3)}{B_\nu(\tau = 2/3)}$$

Remark on practical procedure:

At present, in concrete cases one always solves the equation directly numerically.

To obtain general results, one often uses analytical expressions or schematic models which allow a closed solution.

E.g., Linear expression of the Kirchhoff-Planck function

$$B(\tau) = a + b\tau \quad \text{or} \quad = B_0(1 + \beta_0\tau)$$

Milne-Eddington model: Ratio of line absorption to continuous absorption independent of the depth so, that κ_ν/κ can be taken out of the integral. Also, continuum source function is a linear function of τ. For many absorption lines the ME model is a very good approximation.

Schuster-Schwarzschild model:

Lines originate in a very thin layer at the surface (= reversing layer), in which noticeable continuous absorption no longer occurs.

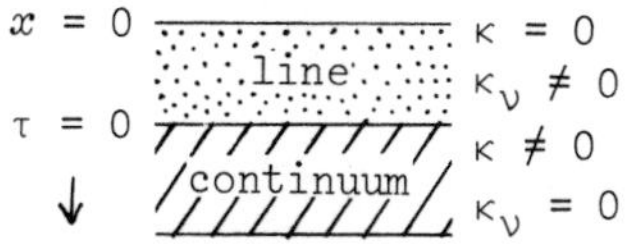

2.3 *Curve of growth*

Equivalent width

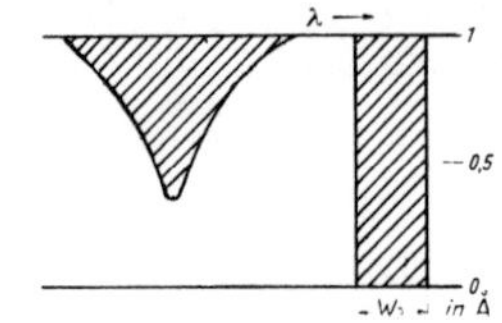

W_λ = width of a rectangular absorption strip with 100% absorption, the area of which is equal to the area of the line

Dimension: [Å]

= measure of the total absorbed energy

At lower dispersion may be more accurately determined than the line profile, because independent of the instrumental profile.

According to equation (12)

$$W_\lambda = \int_{-\infty}^{+\infty} r \, d\lambda = \int \frac{I_o - I_\lambda}{I_o} d\lambda \text{ or } \int \frac{F_o - F_\lambda}{F_o} d\lambda \qquad (16)$$

or, with the variable of integration (according to equation (5)) $\quad \upsilon = \frac{\Delta\lambda}{\Delta\lambda_D} = \frac{\Delta\omega}{\Delta\omega_D}$

$$\frac{W_\lambda}{2\,\Delta\lambda_D} = \frac{W_\omega}{2\,\Delta\omega_D} = \int_0^\infty r \, d\upsilon \qquad (17)$$

‖ If I_o and I_ν (or F_o and F_ν for stars) are known, W_λ can be computed from this.

So long as the dependence of T on depth is not known, one must be content with preliminary "coarse analysis", with an interpolation formula for r (see below) and the relation, resulting from this, between the equivalent width and the number of absorbing atoms (= curve of growth)

Assumption: Absorption coefficient k_λ independent of the depth i.e., the atmosphere characterized by a uniform mean temperature.

Limiting cases:

(a) Weak lines (or wings of strong lines)

Treat as an absorbing column

According to § 1.2 $\quad I_\lambda = I_o e^{-\tau_\lambda}$

herewith: $r_{wing} = 1 - e^{-\tau_\lambda} \approx \tau_\lambda$

[for $\tau \ll 1$ we have $e^{-\tau} = 1 - \tau$

(b) Center of strong lines

$\tau_\lambda \rightarrow \infty$, all absorbed. No radiation comes from deeper layers.

Have residual central intensity I_c = Kirchhoff-Planck function of the boundary temperature

To this corresponds the central depth $r_c' = 1 - \frac{I_c}{I_o}$; usually ≈ 1

Note: r_c' is not the central depth of the investigated line, but the limiting value of the central depth of very strong lines.

Interpolation formula (according to Minnaert)

$$\boxed{\frac{1}{r} = \frac{1}{\tau_\lambda} + \frac{1}{r_c'}} \longrightarrow r = \frac{r_c'}{1 + r_c'/\tau_\lambda} \tag{18}$$

Now, we have

$\tau = k \cdot \ell$

where ℓ is = length of the absorbing column

for $\tau_\lambda \ll 1$ $\quad r \rightarrow \tau_\lambda$

for $\tau_\lambda \gg 1$ $\quad r \rightarrow r_c'$

Then, we have:

$$\left.\begin{aligned} \frac{\tau_\upsilon}{r_c'} = \underbrace{\frac{k(\upsilon)\ell}{r_c'}}_{\text{equation (7)}} = \frac{k_c \ell H(a,\upsilon)}{r_c'} \overset{\text{equation (6)}}{=} \underbrace{\frac{2\pi^{3/2}e^2}{mc}}_{K} \cdot \frac{N\ell f}{r_c' \, \Delta\omega_D} \cdot H(a,\upsilon) \\ = K \underbrace{\frac{N\ell f}{r_c' \, \Delta\omega_D}}_{} \cdot H(a,\upsilon) \\ = C \cdot H(a,\upsilon) \end{aligned}\right\} \tag{19}$$

Substituting this into equation(18) and then into (16) and (17)

$$\boxed{\frac{W_\lambda}{2\, r_c' \, \Delta\lambda_D} = \int_0^\infty \frac{d\upsilon}{1 + \frac{1}{C \cdot H(a,\upsilon)}}} \tag{20}$$

This relation, which states how the equivalent width varies with the number of absorbing atoms (with the damping parameter "a") can be calculated once and for all

$\Longrightarrow$ curve of growth

Ordinate: $\log \dfrac{W_\lambda}{2r_c \ \Delta\lambda_D}$

Abscissa: $\log C = \log \dfrac{N\ell f}{r_c{}' \ \Delta\omega_D} + \underbrace{\log \dfrac{2\pi^{3/2} e^2}{mc}}_{= \log K = -1.03}$

or $\log \dfrac{N\ell f}{r_c{}' \ \Delta\omega_D}$; in this case $\log K$ is included in a zero-point shift in the abscissa.

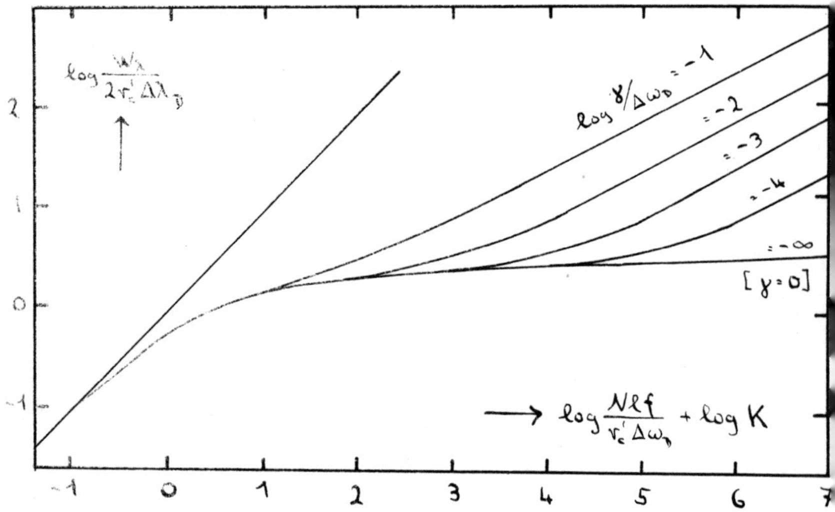

Finally, the curve of growth thus contains:

$W_\lambda = f(N\ell, a)$ | where $N\ell$ = number of absorbing atoms per column of 1 cm^2; a = damping parameter

Properties of the curve of growth

The limiting cases $C \ll 1$ and $C \gg 1$ can be calculated analytically, the transition region by numerical integration:

(a) Linear portion

Line optically thin;

For the whole line: $\tau \ll 1$, i.e., $CH \ll 1$

For weak lines damping plays no role, hence, according to equation (10) $H(a,\upsilon) = e^{-\upsilon^2}$

This, substituted into equation (20),

$$\frac{1}{r_c'}\,\frac{W_\lambda}{2\Delta\lambda_D} = C\int_0^\infty e^{-\upsilon}\,d\upsilon = \frac{\sqrt{\pi}}{2}\,\underset{\substack{\big\downarrow\\ \text{equation (19)}}}{C} = \frac{\sqrt{\pi}}{2}\,K\,\frac{N\ell f}{r_c'\,\Delta\omega_D} = \frac{\pi^2 e^2}{mc}\cdot\frac{N\ell f}{r_c'\,\Delta\omega_D} \qquad (21)$$

= total absorption for an optically thin layer

$W_\lambda \propto N$, i.e., all atoms participate in the absorption.

$$\log\frac{\sqrt{\pi}}{2} = -\,0.05$$

According to whether the constant log K is included in the scale of the abscissa or not, at abscissa = 0 the value of the ordinate is

$$-\,1.03 - 0.05 = -\,1.08$$

or $-\,0.05$

(b) Damping portion

Very strong lines $C \gg 1$

Then, according to equation (11): $H(a,\upsilon) = \frac{a}{\sqrt{\pi}}\,\frac{1}{\upsilon^2}$

Substitute into equation (20):

$$\frac{W_\lambda}{r_c'\,2\Delta\lambda_D} = \int\frac{d\upsilon}{1+\frac{\sqrt{\pi}\,\upsilon^2}{a\,C}} = \text{----} = \sqrt{\frac{a\,C}{\sqrt{\pi}}}\;\underbrace{\int\frac{dy}{1+y^2}}_{\arctan Y\,\big|_0^\infty\,=\,\frac{\pi}{2}} = \frac{\pi}{2}\sqrt{\frac{a\,C}{\pi}} = \text{---}$$

[Substitution: $\frac{\sqrt{\pi}\,\upsilon^2}{a\,C} = y^2$; $\upsilon = \sqrt{\frac{a\,C}{\sqrt{\pi}}}\cdot y$; $d\upsilon = \sqrt{\dots}\;dy$

$$\text{---} = \frac{\pi}{2}\left(\frac{2\pi e^2}{mc}\right)^{1/2}\sqrt{\frac{N\ell f a}{r_c'\,\Delta\omega_D}} = \text{const.}\;\frac{\sqrt{N\ell f\gamma}}{\Delta\omega_D\,\sqrt{2r_c'}} \qquad (22)$$

$$a = \gamma/2\Delta\omega_D \;\text{[equation (5)]}$$

i.e., $\propto\sqrt{N\ell\gamma}$, therefore also called "square-root portion"

Because of the logarithmic representation, straight line with an inclination of 1/2. Parallel straight lines for different values of γ

Only the product $N\ell\gamma$; i.e., number of atoms and damping can not be separated by means of equivalent widths of strong lines alone, but indeed only from strong <u>and</u> weak lines.

(c) Flat portion

Transition region. Line saturated in the center, core becomes optically thick, but line not so strong that the wings stand out noticeably.

Historical remark:

E. v. d. Held dealt with the whole problem of the curve of growth, primarily according to the model of the absorbing column. Then, we have (with above notation)

$$r = 1 - e^{-\tau_\lambda} \quad \text{and} \quad \frac{W_\lambda}{2\Delta\lambda_D} = \int_0^\infty [1 - e^{-k_\upsilon \ell H(a,\upsilon)}]\,d\upsilon$$

For $k_c << 1$ and $H = e^{-\upsilon^2}$ we then get - except for the factor r_c' in both coordinates - equation (21)

For $k_c >> 1$ and $H = \frac{a}{\sqrt{\pi}} \frac{1}{\upsilon^2}$ we obtain with the substitution

$z = \frac{a k_c \ell}{\sqrt{\pi}\,\upsilon^2}$ the same result as equation (22), only again

with $r_c' = 1$ and the factor $\sqrt{\pi} = 1.77$ instead of the factor

$\frac{\pi}{2} = 1.57$ occurring in equation (22).

Hence the curves of growth differ only slightly.

Remark:

If the dependence of temperature and pressure on depth are known, we are able to calculate with the help of the Saha and Boltzmann formulae the fraction ζ of the atoms which participate in the absorption (= number of the atoms in the initial level of the line) for each depth. In this case too one can use the curve of growth.

Instead of the factor $N\ell$ we then have for the abscissa

$\varepsilon_i \int_0^\infty \zeta\, g\, d\tau$ where ε_i = abundance of the element considered

and g = weighting function, which takes account of the contributions of the individual layers in a suitable manner.

$g(\tau)$ is only a function of the temperature dependence on depth ($T(\tau)$) in the continuum and not of the specific line.

However, in practice, one uses, at present, the curve of growth only for a coarse analysis (with unknown $T(\tau)$), whereas in case of a known $T(\tau)$ one prefers to calculate the equivalent widths directly according to equation (16) because of the schematical procedures in the case of the curve of growth.

2.4 *Coarse analysis*

Principle: Measured: r_c' and W_λ

Compute $\Delta\lambda_D$ and $\Delta\omega_D$ for an assumed temperature (not so critical, because only $\propto\sqrt{T}$)

Enter the curve of growth with $\dfrac{W_\lambda}{2\, r_c'\, \Delta\lambda_D}$

Yields C

From this - for known oscillator strength - $N\ell$

$N\ell$ = number of absorbing atoms per column of 1 cm^2, i.e., the number of atoms in the initial level of the line; hence better $N_{r,s}\,\ell$

In practice: Because of the dispersion in the measured values, in general it is meaningless to enter the curve of growth for each line separately. One combines several lines of a multiplet, a supermultiplet or a transition array and constructs from this an "empirical curve of growth", which is shifted horizontally as a whole upon the theoretical curve of growth. Lines are combined by means of the Boltzmann formula

$$N_s = N_o \frac{g_s}{g_o} e^{-\chi/kT} = N_o\, g\, e^{-\chi/kT} \qquad \text{(see 3.2.2)}$$

$g = g_s/g_o$ = relative statistical weight

N_o = number of atoms in the ground state. If only excited levels are involved an arbitrary level of average excitation can be taken as reference instead of the ground level, in order to keep uncertainties in the temperature as small as possible (small $\Delta\chi$).

Take the logarithm and substitute into the abscissa of the curve of growth:

$$\log \frac{1}{r_c'} \frac{N\ell f}{\Delta\omega_D} = \log \frac{1}{r_c'} + \log N_o\ell + \log \frac{gf}{D} - \frac{5040}{T}\chi_s \qquad (23)$$

$\log N_o\ell$ is the proper unknown; however, it is the same additive constant for all lines at the same ionization level.

Procedure for the coarse analysis

(a) Compute an empirical curve of growth according to the above procedure for several lines; these should have states of excitation as nearly equal as possible but covering a wide range in intensity.

(b) The same for a group of lines of the same element having the same degree of ionization, but covering as wide a range of excitation as possible.
According to equation (23) the horizontal difference between two empirical curves of growth is equal to

$$\frac{5040}{T}\,\Delta\chi$$

Because $\Delta\chi$ is known, we get from this

the excitation temperature $\boxed{T_{ex}}$

/ If T_{ex} is greatly different from the temperature assumed in the beginning: Re-compute $\Delta\lambda_D$ or $\Delta\omega_D$
and repeat procedures (a) and (b).

/ In the case of too few lines one can relate lines of various excitations to one another by means of equation (23) using a provisionally assumed temperature, the individual χ's being known.

(c) Shifting the empirical curve of growth for a specified degree of ionization, obtained as described, horizontally upon the theoretical curve of growth, yields $N_0 \ell$ and, hence, by the Boltzmann formula the

total number of atoms having this degree of ionization $\boxed{\mathcal{N}_r \ell}$

(d) Because in the linear portion the shifting of the curve of growth is unambiguous the strong lines yield the

damping $\boxed{\gamma}$

(e) For lines of the same element but at different levels of ionization using the Saha formula (with a temperature according to (b)) the same procedure yields the

electron pressure $\boxed{P_e}$

(f) If two or more elements are observable at several levels of ionization, the corresponding Saha equations yield, in addition to P_e, the ionization temperature $\boxed{T_{ion}}$

> This determination of the temperature is more accurate than the one mentioned in (b) from various states of excitation. If necessary, repeat the whole procedure from here with a revised temperature.

(g) Summation of each element over the Saha formulae yields the total number of atoms of each element per column of 1 cm^2, hence, the relative abundance $\sum_r N_r \ell = \boxed{\varepsilon_i \ell}$

> If no f values are known, at least one can perform a relative abundance comparison (for instance with respect to the solar atmosphere).

(h) If microturbulence (see below) is present, according to equation (3) $\Delta\lambda_D$ becomes larger than that computed using only T. This will affect the ordinate and the abscissa in the same way. Both become too large (because computed by using too small a $\Delta\lambda_D$, caused only by thermal motions). In the linear part not detectable, because the curve of growth is shifted by a 45° line to the upper right; however, the flat portion is too high. From the necessary vertical shift one gets

$$\log \frac{\Delta\lambda_D \text{ (thermal)}}{\Delta\lambda_D \text{ (thermal + turbulent)}}$$

and hence microturbulence $\boxed{\xi_T}$

(i) In hot stars practically all hydrogen is ionized, then $P_e = \frac{1}{2} P$, hence: gas pressure $\boxed{P}$

(j) If results for the most abundant elements are derived from the analysis, we get, by means of the relation, pressure at the base of the atmosphere P_o =

= mass of the column × acceleration of gravity

and using $P_o \simeq 2P$ and mass = $\sum_i \varepsilon_i \mu_i \ell$,

the acceleration of gravity $\boxed{g}$

2.5 *Turbulence*

Microturbulence

Mean free path of the photons > diameter of the turbulent element

Effects mimic an increased thermal velocity. Each atom absorbs corresponding to its individual velocity.

Optically thin lines: Only broadening, no change of equivalent width

Optically thick lines: with high turbulence, atoms, which otherwise do not take part in the absorption, play a role.

Hence, influence on $W_\lambda \rightarrow$ influence on curve of growth.

Increasing in $\Delta\lambda_D$ (see (h) above)

Macroturbulence

Mean free path of the light quanta < diameter of the turbulent element

Line as a whole is shifted. The individual shifted components are combined into one broadened line, whose total equivalent width is not changed.

Extreme case: Unresolved double star, rapidly-rotating star...

Hence: By utilizing the curve of growth and the line profile it is possible in principle to distinguish between the two limiting cases.

2.6 *Principle of the fine analysis (model atmospheres)*

With the aid of the average values of T, P, g and the chemical composition as derived by the coarse analysis one computes according to the principles of § 1.11

$\longrightarrow$ a model atmosphere

For the model atmosphere the equivalent width for the individual lines are computed and compared with the observati

From the difference (observation-computation) get correctio

ΔT; ΔP; Δg; $\Delta\ \varepsilon_i$ result.

Iterate this procedure until computation and observation ag

Ultimately, every star has to be treated individually; a "general formula" cannot be given.

N o t e The temperature and pressure dependence on depth and the chemical composition are connected with one another. They can only be determined by their mutual effects. The "entrance" into this vicious circle is given by the coarse analysis.

Often even the coarse analysis yields rather useful values, which are sufficient for many problems.

Aim: Fine analysis for some typical stars of different spectral types to obtain "standard points" in the Hertzsprung-Russell diagram.

Good model-atmosphere analyses are available for stars of early types, to ~ G0. Still problematic: Stars of late types (molecules, convection zones ...)

Examples

Z	*El*	τ Sco B0 V	55 Cyg B3 Ia	α Lyr A0 V	Sun G2 V	HD 140283 1)	53 Tau 2)
1	H	10.50	10.50	10.50	10.50	10.50	10.50
2	He	9.73	9.68	9.64	9.71	-	-
6	C	6.20	6.91	-	7.22	-	7.65
7	N	6.76	7.13	-	6.48	-	-
8	O	7.13	7.48	7.67	7.46	-	-
10	Ne	7.36	-	-	-	-	-
11	Na	-	-	6.35	(3.94)	-	-
12	Mg	6.80	-	6.50	5.90	4.03	(5.27)
13	Al	4.90	-	4.51	4.98	2.25	-
14	Si	6.13	5.96	6.04	6.00	3.77	5.20
20	Ca	-	-	5.00	4.54	2.57	3.01
21	Sc	-	-	2.58	1.30	-1.04	-
22	Ti	-	-	3.59	3.08	1.30	3.72
23	V	-	-	3.12	2.62	0.86	-
24	Cr	-	-	4.36	3.40	1.80	2.51
25	Mn	-	-	2.95	3.30	1.31	5.06
26	Fe	-	-	5.85	5.34	3.36	5.09
27	Co	-	-	-	3.20	1.75	-
28	Ni	-	-	6.16	4.45	3.03	-
38	Sr	-	-	1.92	1.20	-0.83	2.70
39	Y	-	-	0.89	(1.70)	-0.84	3.04
40	Zr	-	-	1.64	1.15	-1.15	2.85
56	Ba	-	-	-	1.00	-1.59	-
		Population I				Pop.II	Mn-star

Table:

Chemical composition for 4 stars of population I, and for one metal-poor and one metal-rich star.

Given: log N relative to log H = 10.5 (this corresponds approximately to the normalization to log Si = 6.00 as otherwise frequently used).

1) Subdwarf of population II : H type F5; metal type A5

2) Metallic-line star ("Manganese star") : H type F0; metal type F5 (see 4.9.2)

General information on chemical composition, see 4.9

§ 3 Solar spectrum

Survey

Components of the solar atmosphere

a) Photosphere = visible disk; layer from which visible spectrum originates. Thickness about 200 km

See §4

b) Chromosphere = "color sphere"; relatively transparent gas directly visible only at eclipses above advancing limb of moon. Thickness about 10 000 km

See §5

c) Corona = outermost envelope; rarified atmosphere, only fully visible during solar eclipses. Merges with solar wind (2.9.5) at a few solar radii above limb

See §6

The Solar Spectrum

Radio region (about 1 mm < λ < 10 m ground-based limit): Only continuum.

Long-wave limit: reflection by the terrestrial ionosphere

Short-wave limit: absorption in the terrestrial atmosphere

Only wavelengths below ≈ 3 mm stem from the photosphere (= thermal radiation, $T \approx 6000^\circ$). Going to longer wavelengths, to start with the chromosphere and later the corona too are opaque, see § 5 and § 6. Numerous phenomena in connection with the solar activity (see disturbed radio radiation, § 7.5)

Infrared region (7000 Å < λ < 1 mm)

Extensively absorbed by molecular bands of the terrestrial atmosphere (O_3, CO_2, N_2O, ...). Broad "windows" in between th

Continuous spectrum with absorption lines from the photosphere, see § 4.

Visible region

Continuous spectrum with numerous (up to 10 000) absorption lines. Number of lines increases more and more toward the short wavelengths.

Origin of the radiation: photosphere, see § 4.

Near-ultraviolet (down to ~1700 Å)

(below 3000 Å absorbed in the terrestrial atmosphere) = normal continuation of the visible absorption-line spectrum, but so many lines that it is questionable whether a "true continuum" is ever reached in between them.

Origin: photosphere, see § 4.

Shortest observed wavelength of absorption line at approximately 1520 Å

Longest observed wavelength of emission line: C I at 1993 Å

i.e., between 1500 and 2000 Å have superposition of photospheric absorption lines and chromospheric emission lines. Origin in the neighborhood of the temperature minimum.

Far-ultraviolet (down to 100 Å)

Radiation no longer from the photosphere = below about 1520 Å.

Quasi-continuous absorption in the sun:

due to neutral silicon; possibly CO bands; absorption continua of Al, Ca, CO, NO, ...

Emission lines and, in part, faint emission continuum from the chromosphere (see § 5); toward shorter wavelengths more and more from the corona (see § 6).

X-ray radiation (λ < 100 Å)

Emission lines of highly-ionized atoms from the corona (see § 6). Quasi-thermal continuum (recombination and free-free radiation). Only during flares (see § 7.4) non-thermal bremsstrahlung, synchrotron radiation.

Energy distribution in the range 20 ... 100 Å:
2/3 lines, 1/3 continuum. Below 20 Å the continuum predominates more and more. Shortest identified emission line: 13.8 Å (Fe XVII and Ne IX).
observed line at λ 1.9 Å (Fe XXVI ?).

Solar constant

= total radiation energy arriving at the earth (outside the terrestrial atmosphere)

$= 1.99 \pm 0.02$ cal cm^{-2} min^{-1} $= 1.39 \times 10^6$ erg cm^{-2} sec^{-1}
1.39 kWatt/m^2

From this $T_e = 5800°$

§ 4 Photosphere

= Layer having a thickness of ~200 km (very roughly), from which the visible light originates, hence, the "visible solar disk".

4.1 *Dependence of T on depth, spectrum*

Center-to-limb variation or limb darkening

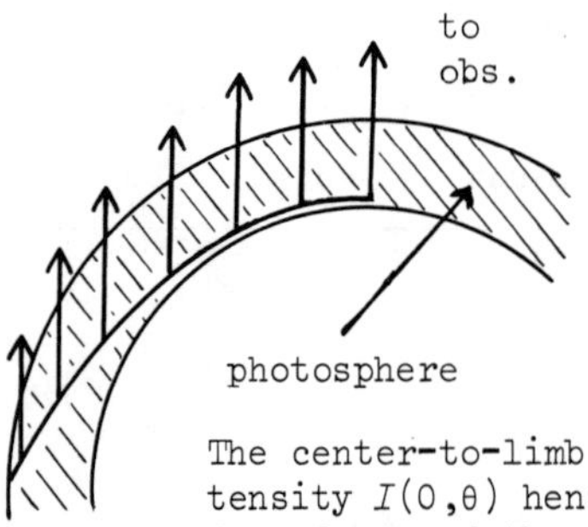

Intuitively:

At the center of the solar disk (viewing perpendicularly) one is receiving radiation from deeper, hotter layers; at the solar limb (viewing at an angle), however, from higher, cool layers. Hence, limb radiati fainter, solar limb darker.

The center-to-limb variation of the observed intensity $I(0,\theta)$ hence directly reflects the depth dependence of the temperature in the photosphere.

Determination of an empirical $T(\tau)$ (see § 1.11)
Quantitative treatment: § 1.3

$T(\tau)$ of the photosphere for $\lambda = 5000$ Å

Gas pressure P_g and electron pressure P_e in [dyn/cm^2]

According to
E. Böhm-Vitense 1954,
Z. f. Ap. 34, 209
(see also § 1.11)

τ_{5000}	T °K	log P_g	log P_e
0	4006	$-\infty$	$-\infty$
0.001	4164	3.29	-0.62
0.01	4700	3.95	+0.10
0.1	5066	4.53	0.71
0.2	5310	4.68	0.90
0.4	5680	4.86	1.17
0.6	5965	4.94	1.43
0.8	6200	4.99	1.65
1.0	6405	5.02	1.78

Continuous spectrum

Free-free transitions and bound-free transitions (see 3.2.2) predominantly of the H^- ion (see § 1.6)

Intensity distribution of the continuum corresponds to about $T \approx 5700^{\circ}$

> Not "black-body radiation"; exact measurements with an absolute calibration show differences between different spectral regions.

Excess of radiation (> 6000°) at about 16,000 Å

> Reason: Minimum of continuous H^{-} absorption; i.e., here the photosphere is especially transparent; one looks into deeper layers.

Measurements out to about 24 μ; still about 2 orders of magnitude below the radio radiation.

Spectral energy distribution

F_{λ} = radiation flux just outside the terrestrial atmosphere

[erg cm^{-2} sec^{-1} $Å^{-1}$]

λ[Å]	F_{λ}
2500	6.4
3000	61
4000	154
5000	198
6000	181
7000	144
8000	113
9000	89.5
10000	72.5
20000	10.8
30000	2.7
40000	1.0
50000	0.4

Theory of continuous radiation: see § 1

Line spectrum

Known from 1500 to 237,000 Å

(with gaps; for extended regions in the infrared there are still no rocket observations)

Numerous atlases, e.g.,

λ	
1800 - 2965 Å:	H.C. McAllister 1960, Boulder, Colorado
2988 - 3629	G. Brückner 1960, = "Göttingen Atlas"
3332 - 8771	M. Minnaert et al., 1940, = "Utrecht Atlas"
7498 - 12,016	L. Debouille et al., 1963, Liège
8465 - 25,242	O.C. Mohler et al., 1950, McMath-Hulbert Obs.
28,000 - 237,000	(2.8 - 23.7 μ) M. Migeotte 1956, Liège.

and tabular publications, e.g.,

"Revised Rowland Table of Solar Spectrum Wavelengths" (C.E. John, C.E. Moore, et al., 1928, Washington)

Contains: Wavelength, element identification, intensity both in the photosphere and in the sunspot spectrum, excitation potential, pressure and temperature classification

Range: 2975 ... 10,193 Å

The solar spectrum 2973-8770 Å; Second Revision of Rowland's Preliminary Table of Solar Spectrum Wavelengths. C. Moore, M. Minnaert, J. Houtgast 1966; National Bureau of Standards, Washington.
(Contains, among other data, the equivalent widths of the lines)

The infrared atlases show:

$\sim$11 500 telluric absorption lines
$\sim$ 2000 solar lines

of which $\sim$1000 of CO (in the sun!)
$\sim$ 500 of atomic origin
$\sim$ 500 not yet identified

Lines in the near ultraviolet predominantly of Fe I and II, and other metallic lines. Resonance doublet of Mg II at 2795 and 2803 Å with a width of 50 Å = strongest absorption line in the solar spectrum (analogous to the Ca II lines H and K).

→Theory of the Fraunhofer lines: see § 2.

Analysis

Carrying out a fine analysis according to the methods as described in § 1 and 2 shows:

> It is not possible to explain satisfactorily all absorption lines with a homogeneous model.

Extensions to model:

(a) Deviations from local thermodynamical equilibrium (NLTE, see § 1.5), especially in the higher layers (transition into the chromosphere with outwardly increasing temperature).

> Up to now, only treated formally: at any time use different temperature T_e, T_{ion}, T_{kin}, ..., in the corresponding formulae.

This would correct model by considering atomic processes in detail instead of using macroscopic equations. As of now, no useful practical method.

(b) Inhomogeneities, see § 4.2

(c) Taking account of magnetic fields and hydrodynamic effets. Still rudimentary. Have no great influence in the undisturbed photosphere, but important in active regions.

4.2 *Structure of the photosphere*

Granulation: Surface of the undisturbed photosphere shows a honeycombed or cellular structure. The elements are the granules = hot eddies ascending from the hydrogen convection zone (see § 1.10) in the photosphere

Diameters: ~ 700 - 1000 km (= about 1")

Life time: about eight minutes

Horizontal fluctuations in temperature between granules and intergranule region: several hundred degrees

Velocity of ascent: several km/sec.

Consequence of the granulation: Inhomogeneities in the photosphere. Different contributions to the lines from the hot and cool regions, respectively:

(a) Temperature effect: Variation of ionization and excitation, hence variation of the number of absorbing atoms. Ionized and highly excited lines are stronger in the hot regions, and vice versa. Moreover, different contribution from the neighboring continuum.

(b) Doppler effect: Lines of the rising, hot elements shifted to the blue, those of the descending cooler regions to the red.

The observed line represents a mixture of all these constituents.

Analysis: 1) by the so-called "multi-stream models". The contributions of the individual elements are computed and superposed.

2) direct observation of spectra of individual granules (because of disturbance of earth's atmosphere, possibilities marginal)

In high-resolution spectra taken in good seeing the slit overlaps several granules (hence see red and blue shifts) ⟶ so-called "wiggly lines"

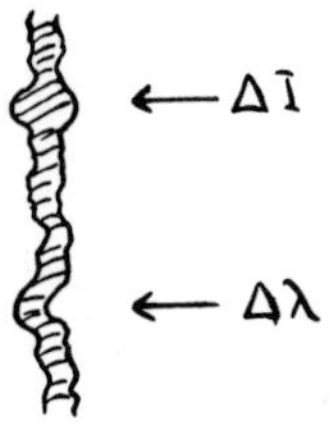

Direct pictures of the granulation at higher resolution: from balloon telescopes.

Photospheric Oscillations:

Period ~ 300^s

Dimension of coherent oscillations uncertain; different observers give values from 5" (~ 4000 km) to 2' (~ 100 000 km).

Supergranulation:

Extended structure, diameter about 40" (= 30 000 km)

Can be made visible by carefully superposing copies of solar images in the wings of the lines, so that doppler shifts are detectable as intensity fluctuations)

Identical with the "network" in H_α and Ca-K- spectroheliograms. Not visible in white light, hence no (or only small) temperature fluctuations.

> Doppler spectroheliograms indicate radial flow within supergranules, gas flowing horizontally from center to edge.

The boundaries of the supergranulation are co-spatial with lines of increased magnetic field strength (up to ~100 gauss).

Photosphere of stars

//Only visible range (observation of the UV from rockets and satellites just starting)

//Only total radiation (because stars are unresolved)

hence: no center-to-limb variation } can be observed
no fine structure }

Analysis, see § 2.6

4.3 *Rotation*

Equatorial speed about 2 km/sec (slightly faster as judged from sunspots, slightly slower as judged by doppler shifts). Rotates fastest at equator, more slowly at higher latitudes, hence ⟹ Differential rotation

From sunspots, sidereal rate is

$$14\overset{\circ}{.}38 - 2\overset{\circ}{.}7 \sin^2 \text{(latitude) per day.}$$

This gives a sidereal rotation time of 25.4 days for the main sunspot zone (~16°). Synodic rotation (because of the earth's motion) 27.3 days.

There is observational evidence to suggest that sidereal rate also depends on altitude above photosphere.

§ 5 Chromosphere

Thickness: up to 10 000 km, hence >> photosphere

Density: very low, factor 10^3 to 10^4 less than in the photosphere; optical depth in the continuum ~0.03

Flux: emitted radiation only several thousandths of the photospheric value

Investigation difficult

/Observation: Many details observable only during the few seconds immediately before and after a total eclipse

/Theory: Transition from $T = 4300^{\circ}$ at the limb of the sun (photosphere) to $T \geqslant 10^6$ degrees in the corona.

Spectrum: So-called "flash spectrum", because it "flashes" bright briefly just before and after eclipse totality

= emission spectrum (more than 3500 lines known)

(Absorption ceases at the solar limb because of the tangential view, only the re-emission remains)

Outside eclipse only the strongest lines are visible; the fainter ones disappear in the scattered light of the photosphere.

In the flash spectrum: Ionized lines strengthened, neutral lines fainter than in the photosphere

$\Longrightarrow$ higher temperature

No systematic change with height; neutral and highly-ionized lines obviously exist in proximity at the same time

$\Longrightarrow$ inhomogeneities

(regions of high and low temperature next to another)

Structure

Observed at the solar limb in the center of H_α or Ca II K

Residual intensity of these strong lines originates almost entirely in the chromosphere; that means, in the H_α filter for instance solar disk and chromosphere at the limb are about equally bright.

Appearance is like a "burning prairie", so-called spicules

On average 700 or 800 km thick and 3000 km high.
Height of the longest spicule $\approx 20{,}000$ km
At the poles somewhat longer and slightly inclined because of the magnetic field.

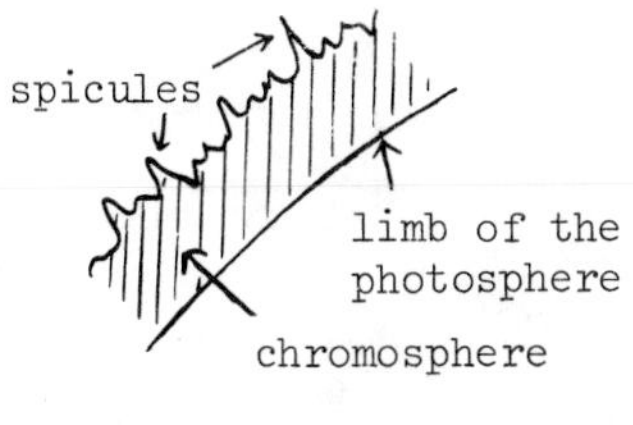

Lifetime: several minutes

Observation on the solar disk

The optical depth at the center of strong lines remains > 1 even far above the photosphere,

i.e. the chromosphere is optically thick here

(a) Narrow interference filters in the center of certain lines. According to the choice of lines one "sees" different layers.

(b) Spectroheliograms (monochromatic images of the sun in the light of certain lines)

H_α or Ca II faculae = bright regions on the H_α or Ca II filtergrams

Bright means: Higher residual intensities, i.e., shallower lines.

Reasons: Smaller number of absorbing atoms
different temperature conditions
different stratification
systematic motions (doppler effect)

Filtergrams and spectroheliograms contain much information; interpretation complicated (no thermodynamical equilibrium!...)

Observation in the far UV (λ < 1600 Å) from rockets and satellites

Only emission lines; continuous radiation from the photosphere absorbed.

Several hundred emission lines identified

Strongest line L_α = 1215.7 Å (about 90% of the emission in this region)

Line amazingly narrow, half width ~ 1 Å.
Originates at base of the narrow chromosphere-coronal transition region where the density is still high enough and the temperature already high enough.

Further lines: Lyman series, Lyman limit (918 Å)

He II; C I, II, III, IV; N V; O I, O VI, ...

Resonance line of neutral He: 584 Å
" " " ionized He: 304 Å

Center-to-limb variation, for instance, shows that O I is emitted in deeper layers, O VI, however, in higher layers.

Physical structure

Perturbations from the hydrogen convection zone run like sound waves through the photosphere.

Energy flux of a sound wave:

$$\rho\, \overline{v_p^2}\, v_s$$

| ρ = density
| v_p = velocity of particles
| v_s = velocity of sound

Chromosphere so thin that radiation small,

i.e., energy remains approximately constant

hence, because ρ decreases, $v_p \longrightarrow 1/\sqrt{\rho\, v_s}$ increases,

finally, $v_p \rightarrow v_s$, hence sound wave → shock wave (spicules?)

Irreversible entropy changes in gas overtaken by shock wave result in heating of gas

heating of the chromosphere and the corona.

Computations complicated: a) non-linear equations

b) ionized matter, hence influence of magnetic fields

Radio radiation (thermal)

In the case of radio radiation the absorption is larger ($\tau \sim \lambda^2$)

// cm radiation: originates from the lower chromosphere, $T = 6000°$

Variation: Over the disk rather regular, then strong limb brightening (one looks tangentially along chromosphere, hence emitting layer much thicker than if viewed along radial direction); outwards from limb, rapid decrease

// dm radiation: already a noticeable contribution from the corona; contribution from the chromosphere small.

Ring effect no longer holds, because the chromosphere already is optically thick. Outward decrease slower.

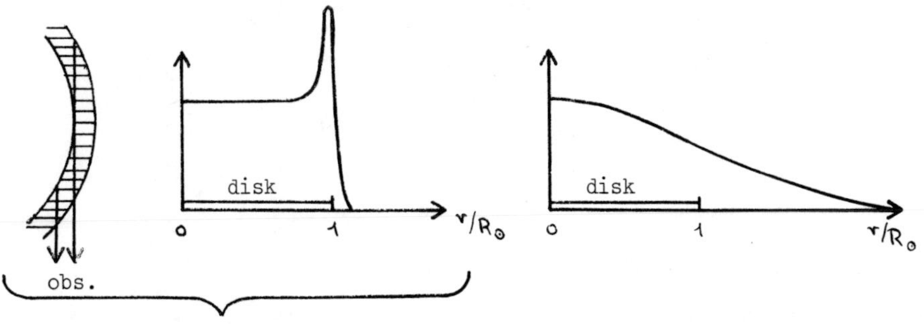

cm-radiation m-radiation

§ 6 Corona

Envelope of very low-density gas

Total brightness: $\sim 10^{-6}$ that of the photosphere

Slow density decrease outward, no limit specifiable, a continuous transition into the solar wind and zodiacal light (see 2.9.5)

6.1 *Observation*

a) Eclipse

Outer corona and many details observable only at a total solar eclipse, because scattering of the sun's light in the terrestrial atmosphere brighter than the light of the corona.

Hence, large expeditions for a few minutes of data collection

> In total since the middle of the last century about 2^h observing time. Our knowledge about the corona is partly due to these two hours. Recently survey from satellites (scattered light from the earth's atmosphere ceases)

b) Coronograph (Lyot, 1930)

Using this, the inner corona can be seen from high-altitude sites (with excellent optics) even without an eclipse.

(A scratch on the optics yields more scattered light than the brightness of the corona).

Principle:

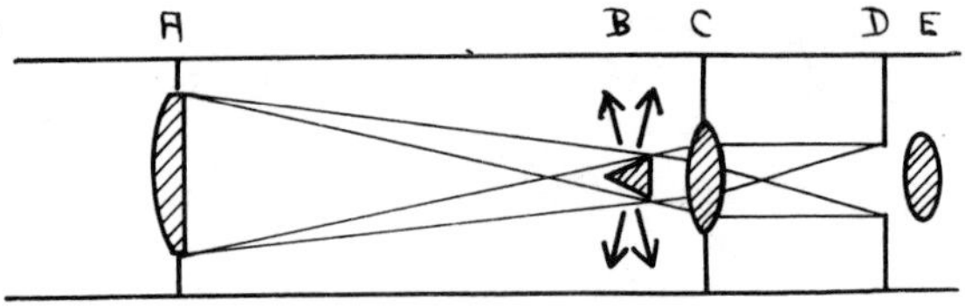

A simple plano - convex lens

B conical diaphragm at the position of the solar image (diameter somewhat larger than the solar image) suppresses the direct solar image

C field lens, produces image of *A* at *D*

D ring-shaped diaphragm removes the light bent at the edge of the objective at *A*

E ocular, secondary image, etc.

At present, cooperation of 7 high-altitude stations makes possible a nearly uninterrupted survey of the corona.

c) <u>Rockets and satellites</u> X-ray region < 100 Å

Faint continuum, predominantly emission lines. In this spectral region only the corona is hot enough to emit radiation, hence the photosphere is not seen. The spectral slope of the quiet sun is very steep at λ 7Å, so that negligible radiation is seen λ < 6Å.

d) <u>Radio region</u>

Corona optically thick to meter waves. Hence, here one observes the corona directly. (see § 6.3)

Diameter radio sun > diameter optical sun

6.2 *Structure and spectrum*

Continuous radiation; about 99% of the total light

<u>Shape</u>: extremely variable

Sunspot minimum: extension in equatorial zone, polar rays

Sunspot maximum: quite symmetric in all directions

Arches, rays, no detailed structure

occasionally bright knots (so-called coronal condensations)

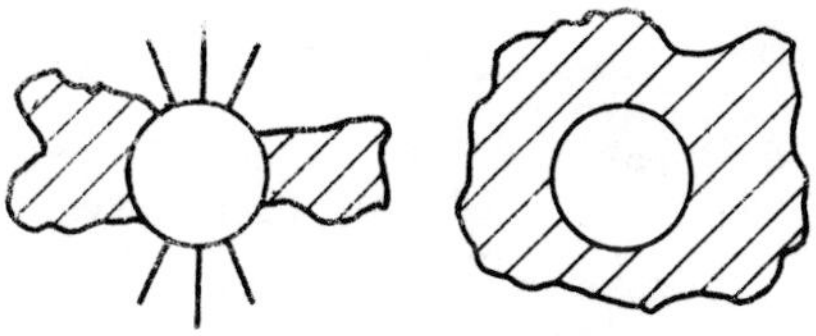

minimum corona maximum corona

Middle corona has temperature of about 2×10^6 °K.

<u>Spectrum</u>:	Inner:	emission lines	|*L* corona|
	Middle:	pure continuum, without absorption lines	|*K* corona|
	Outer:	normal solar spectrum	|*F* corona|

F corona: Scattering by dust far removed from the sun (interplanetary dust), hence normal <u>F</u>raunhofer spectrum of the photosphere (see 2.9.5)

K corona: Scattering by free electrons (polarization). Velocity of the electrons about 8000 km/sec →lines wholly smeared out by doppler effect, hence continuum (<u>K</u>ontinuum) $T_{el} = 10^6$ degrees

L corona: Emission <u>l</u>ines = light produced by the corona itself about 1% of total

<u>Emission lines</u> about 30 in the visible region
numerous in the X ray region

// Visible region: Identification problematic for a time, - tentatively a new element "coronium" was introduced.

9 to 15 times ionized Fe, Ca, Ni, ...

brightest lines:	green coronal line	Fe XIV	5303 Å
	red " "	Fe X	6374
	yellow " "	Ca XV	5694
	infrared " "	Fe XIII	10747, 10798

Isophotes of these lines can be measured with a coronograph.

// X-ray region: Highly ionized atoms

Interesting lines:	L_α of C VI		33.7 Å
	" of N VII		24.8
	" of O VIII		18.8

Shortest observed line: 1.9 Å (Fe XXVI ?)

Limit of line emission certainly at L_α of Fe XXVI, 1.9 Å
(heavier elements are too rare)

// Ionization temperatures: 2 to 3 × 10^6 degrees.

6.3 *Radio radiation*

For λ > 5 m besides absorption also refraction
(diffraction of rays) becomes important.

Rays describe curved paths, are totally reflected in a specified layer having a sufficiently high electron density. With increasing λ, the reflection sets in at a lower density, i.e., further outward.

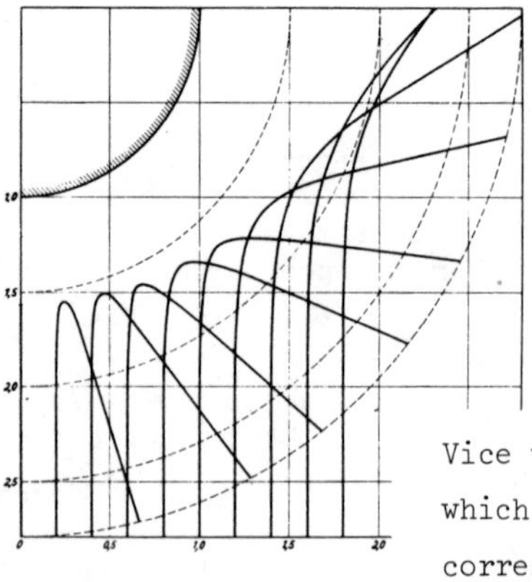

Run of radiation for

λ = 10 m

(radiation originates essentially from the "boundary layer" corresponding to this wave length).

I.e., a certain boundary depth corresponds to each wave length.

Vice versa: A limiting wave length, which just comes through, corresponds to each depth, hence || the long-wave radio radiation allows observation of the individual layers.

According to 3.2.2 the relation between boundary frequency and electron density

$$\nu_o = \sqrt{\frac{e^2 N_e}{\pi m}} = 9 \cdot 10^{-3} \sqrt{N_e} \quad \text{[Mhz]}$$

is valid.

Radiation below this "plasma frequency" or above the corresponding wave length $\lambda_o = c/\nu_o$ can not emerge, because then the refractive index becomes < 0.

Radiation temperature of the radio radiation: 1...3 × 10^6 degrees.

6.4 *Physics of the corona*

All observations yield about the same temperature of several million degrees.

⟶ Nearly isothermal sphere in thermal equilibrium.

| In spite of the high temperature the corona is not visible because of the low density.

Inner corona: 10^{-11} atm. (= very good vacuum)

| The high temparature sets in on account of the low density, because collisions and hence the emission are not sufficient to get rid of the energy supplied from below.

Dynamics

The corona is in a state of permanent hydrodynamic expansion, supported by heating from below (shock waves, mechanism see § 5;

1/10 000 of the kinetic energy of granules is sufficient to maintain the temperauture of the corona). Therefore, acceleration of the coronal plasma which causes the solar wind (see 2.9.5).

Energy output: a) radiation at high temperature

b) solar wind (see 2.9.5)

⟹ c) heat conduction by free electrons inward in the region of the steep temperature gradient between chromosphere and corona.

Origin of the continuous X-ray radiation < 20 Å

Free-bound transitions of C, N, O, Ne, ...

Temperature: 2 ... 3 × 10^6 degrees

In active regions (coronal condensations)

up to 4 × 10^6 °K or even higher

§ 7 Solar activity

Literature: E. Tandberg-Hanssen 1967, *Solar activity*, Blaisdell Publ. Co. London.

General remark:

The sun shows many variable and temporary visible phenomena which we summarize as "solar activity". The individual phenomena are connected with each other in a rather complicated way. A region of high activity shows spots, faculae, prominences, flares, bursts, corona condensations et. al., and shows itself in the whole spectral region from the radio- to the X-rays. This one should always keep in mind, even if in the following sections the individual phenomena are handled separately.

7.1 *Sunspots*

A) Statistics: Worldwide, practically uninterrupted survey

European center: Zürich (Swiss Federal Observatory)

World center: Boulder, Colorado

// Sunspot number: $\boxed{R = \text{const} \times (10g + f)}$

g = number of groups (a single spot counts as a group)

f = number of individual spots

const = individual constant for transformation to the Zürich system (original instrument with an aperture of 8 cm and a magnification of 64 ×)

Maximum values of R about 300

// Sunspot area: F in units of 10^{-6} of the solar hemisphere (used in the Greenwich series)

The two quantities are correlated: $F \approx 16.7\ R$

Solar cycle: Sunspot numbers fluctuate greatly from day to day, influenced by solar rotation. Have records of monthly means since 1749.

These show an obvious period = Solar cycle

Mean period: 11 years

Intervals between the individual maxima: 7 to 17 years,

correlated with the height of the maxima; high maxima with short periods and vice versa.

The maxima have been counted since 1760; in 1968 we were at the maximum of the 20th cycle. The varying height of the maxima indicates a superposed ⟶ period of about 80 years

Shape of individual cycles:

Area below the ascending branch nearly constant

Area below the descending branch proportional to R_{max}

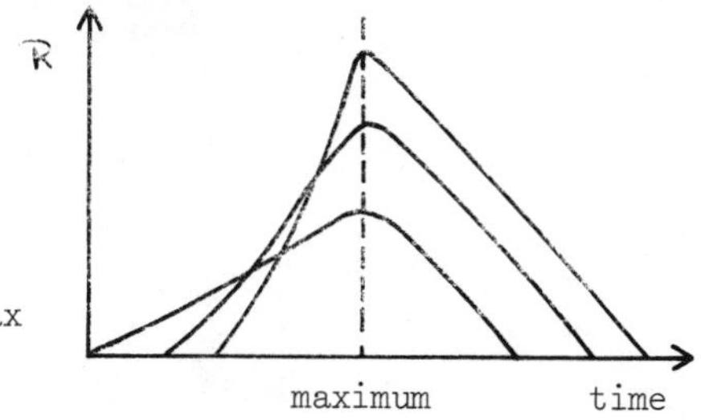

Spot zones:

During the 11 years cycle the activity regions (not the individual spots) show an equatorial migration, starting in the beginning of the cycle at about ± 35° and ending at about ± 8° heliographic latitude. This results in Maunder's "butterfly diagram" when time is plotted vertically, increasing upward, against sunspot latitudes as abscissa, see figure.

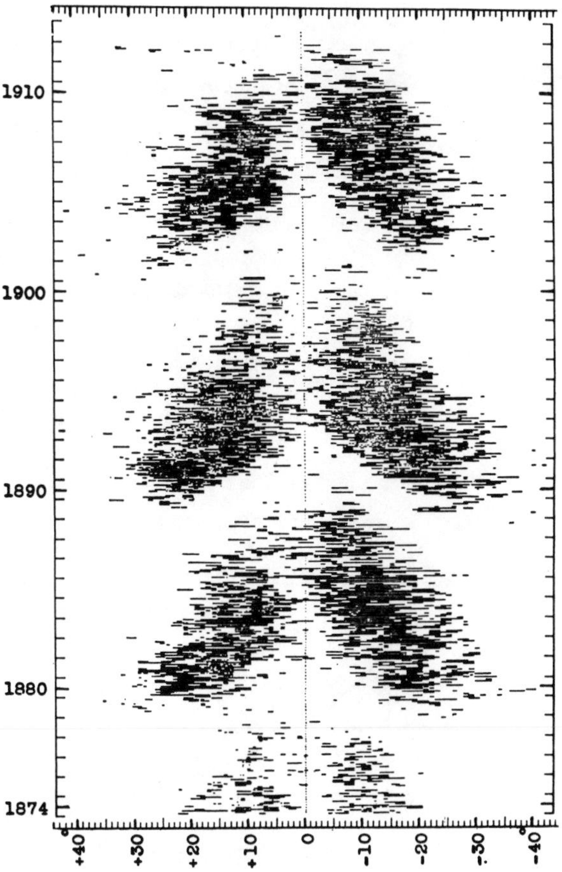

Up to two years of overlap; that is, when the last spots occur close to the equator, at high latitudes the first spots of a new cycle are already appearing.

Spots rare at latitudes > 40°; occur only with short lifetime. Record in 1915: spot at 60° latitude.

Symmetric to a group of spots on the northern hemisphere another one appears on the southern hemisphere; frequency significantly higher than due to chance. Occasionally also a group diametrically opposite (tetrapolar perturbation).

Occurrence of spots in preferred regions, fixed "spot sources", where new spots usually occur, ⟶ activity centers.

E.g., two sources are tracked from 1887 to 1889 and after the minimum again until 1893.

Surplus of newly formed spots on the east side of the sun, by a factor of ~3 (!) Reason: "predevelopment"

(a) It takes a certain time until the spot has grown from size 0 to detectable size F_d

(b) Detectable size $F_d = F_{true} \cdot \cos\theta$

(= geometrical fore-shortening; θ = angle between viewing direction and vertical on the sun)

E side: (a) and (b) in the same direction, F_d is reached rapidly.

W side: (a) and (b) in opposite direction, eventually compensate. Apparent growth of the spot is slowed by the geometrical foreshortening.

Analysis yields: $F_d \approx 500$ km

Predevelopment at the solar center: ≈ 0.8 days

B) Evolution of a single spot

Lifetime: On the average several days; short-lived spots are more frequent.

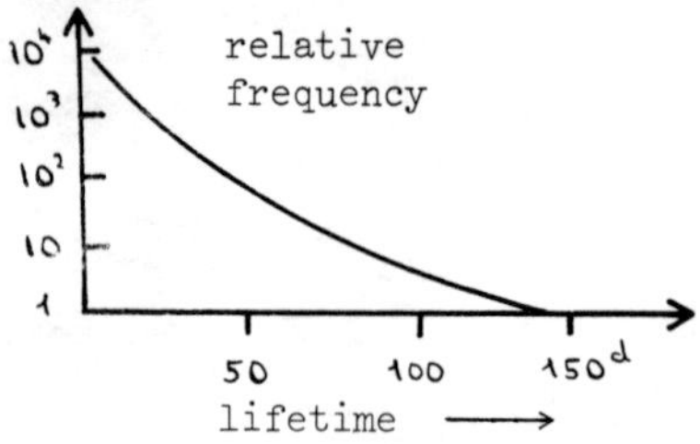

50% of all spots < 2^d

90% of all spots < 11^d

Large single spots: rare, but much more interesting

Lifetime several months

Structure: Umbra (= nucleus

Penumbra (= outer envelope)
with laminar structure

Spectroheliograms show a vortex structure in the surroundings of the spot (Coriolis forces)

Diameter of the umbra up to 50,000 km

Classification: 9-step classification (A through J excepting I) according to Waldmeier.

Major spots pass through many of these steps during their evolution.

Typical evolutionary path of a large group

(1) Group becomes elongated, two main spots develop.

P spot (preceding)
F spot (following) } relative to the solar rotation

In major groups *P* and *F* themselves are also groups.

Total extent up to more than 15°

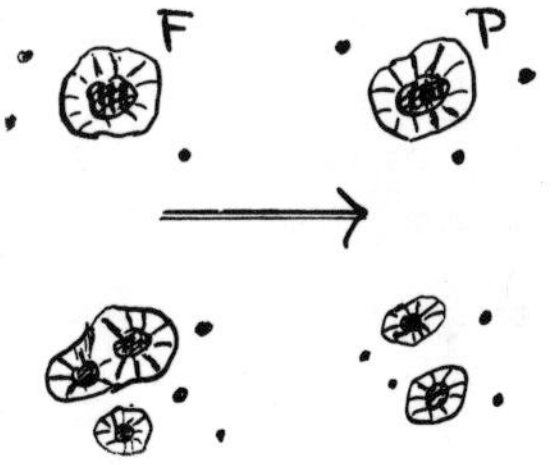

(2) The smaller spots disappear, a "bipolar group" (because of the different polarities of the magnetic field) remains. Usually *P* spot nearer to the equator.

The distances change because of the proper motions.

Individual spots migrate up to 5°

at $b > 16^{\circ}$ polewards; at $b < 16^{\circ}$ toward the equator

(3) *F* spot becomes smaller and disappears, the *P* spot survives, often for a long time.

Magnetic fields:

Observation

either: Direct observation of the splitting of the lines (Zeeman effect) in the spectra,

or : Photoelectrically by means of magnetographs. Two slits at the wings of the lines and corresponding polarization optics. Measurement of the polarization properties of the line components as caused by the Zeeman effect.

All spots show magnetic fields; up to 4000 gauss.

Field lines along solar radius at center of umbra, and have increasing inclination to vertical as penumbra-photosphere boundary is approached.

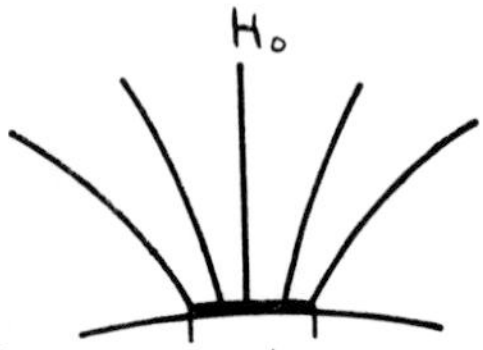

$H(r) \cong H_o (1-r^2)$

H_o = field at the center of the spot

r = distance from the center of the spot

Field actually merges with surrounding plage field at some distance outside optical penumbra.

Classification: (according to R. Richardson 1948)

91 % Bipolar groups
F and *P* spot with different polarities

8.6% Unipolar group
Single spot, group, or major spot with companion having the same polarity

0.4% Multipolar groups
Complex structure

Statistics: The *P* and the *F* spot always have opposite polarity; Relationship of polarities on the N and S hemisphere just opposite; in the following cycle all polarities exchanged.

E.g., cycle n :	N	*P* spot	+	*F* spot	-
	S	"	-	"	+
cycle $(n+1)$:	N	"	-	"	+
	S	"	+	"	-

$\Longrightarrow$ In fact total cycle 22 years

Often one observes:

Magnetic field without a spot

or magnetic field in the case of a single spot at position where the second spot would be expected

or magnetic field before the spot appears or after the spot has disappeared.

i.e., || the magnetic field is a more sensitive measure of a perturbation than the visible spot!

Magnetic knots

In the neighborhood of the spots numerous (invisible in integrated light) small regions (diameter several hundred km) with strong magnetic fields (~400 gauss)

Total magnetic flux (spot + magnetic knots) about the same in both polarities, i.e. the field lines starting from the spots end in part at the magnetic knots.

"General magnetic field"

Also the "general" magnetic field of the sun as observed with low resolution, very probably consists of local chromospheric fields and of rest fields of former sunspot regions. Therefore it varies with the sunspot cycle and changes its polarity.

Fine structure

Penumbra: consists of bright and dark filaments, presumably hot and cool streams of matter, extending radially from center of spot

Radial outflow and inflow becomes detectable by a strong asymmetry of the spectral lines, (due to doppler red and violet displacements) = Evershed effect

Umbra : High-resolution pictures show a granulation-like fine structure in the nucleus of the spot. Individual points (umbral dots) bright and long-lived (in excess of 30 minutes).

C) Physics and theory of the spots

Temperatures: About 4000°; 1600° cooler than photosphere

Intensity ratio: $I(\text{spot})/I(\text{phot.}) \begin{cases} = 0.13 \text{ at } \lambda \;\; 3{,}000 \text{ Å} \\ = 0.46 \text{ at } \lambda \;\; 10{,}000 \text{ Å} \end{cases}$

Spectrum: Corresponds - as far as it is comparable with a stellar spectrum - to that of a late K star (Temperatures and intensity ratios in large spots are even lower than given)

Observation of precise spectra is difficult because of the superposed scattered light of the photosphere.

Analyses of spectra, computation of spot models, etc., tried at several places, however, with large, still unexplained discrepancies.

Theory

Up to now no satisfactory theory exists either for the single spots or for the sunspot cycle.

Single spots: Thermodynamic considerations are not sufficient. Presumably the convective energy flux in the deeper layers is braked by the magnetic field.

Cycle: Origin certainly not, as previously occasionally presumed, outside the sun (related to Jupiter's orbital period), but magnetohydrodynamic processes in the hydrogen convection zone.

Plausible hypothesis:

Magnetic tubes, which are wound around sun by the differential rotation twisted into flux ropes by convective flow and occasionally get to the surface (Babcock).

7.2 *Faculae*

Structures seen in white light which have $\gtrsim 10\%$ contrast near limb called "photospheric faculae" or "faculae". Contrast very small at disk center. Structures seen in monochromatic photographs (e.g. H_α, Ca II K) called "chromospheric faculae" or "plages faculaires" or "plages", spatially similar to but but exactly coextensive with the white light faculae. All spots embedded in larger facular regions.

Statistics of faculae same as for spots (§ 7.1)

Granulation: The granules of faculae are brighter and more long-lived than the normal granules.

Polar faculae: In addition to the faculae areas in the spot zone very small polar faculae often consisting of only a few granules occur predominantly in the years before minimum and during minimum at high latitudes.

7.3 *Prominences, filaments*

Clouds or streams of gas (condensed coronal material) outside the photosphere embedded in the corona.

At the solar limb: bright against the dark sky; emission } $\Longrightarrow$ prominences

On the disk: dark against the bright photosphere; absorption } ⟹ filaments

A) Statistics, morphology, evolution

Also 11 year cycle, though less pronounced than for the spots.

Main zone: same statistics as for the spots

Polar zone: appear shortly before sunspot minimum at about 50° latitude, migrate polewards, increase in activity, reach maximum numbers near the pole about two years before the sun spot maximum

(1) Quiescent or long-lived prominences

stable or stationary situation
life time: several months to one year
appear in the main sunspot zone (Zone Royale) as well as in the polar zone

Great diversity in appearance

Thickness:	at average	7,000 km,	extreme	4,000 - 15,000 km
Height :	"	40,000 " ,	"	15,000 - 120,000 "
Length :	"	200,000 " ,	"	up to - 1,000,000 "

⟶ i.e., long, thin, high, approximately planar, laminar features including hanging curtains, hedgerows, etc.

Plane of prominence inclined 8° ... 10° to solar radius in the direction of rotation.

Often they are connected to the chromosphere, standing on individual "feet" (arches or arcades).

Evolution: Origin mostly in groups of spots or in regions of faculae. They grow by means of "extensions" polewards. Maximum is reached in months, after the spot already has disappeared. Prominence activity persists about three months after decline of spot group.

Because of the differential rotation of the sun the position of the prominences becomes more and more parallel to the equator

(2) Short-lived prominences

= active or eruptive prominences in connection with flares (see above) or active spots (see below)

Onset of activity very sudden, duration minutes to hours;

Very diverse shapes and phenomena:

Sprays: matter explosively rises into the corona with increasing velocity up to more than 1000 km/sec;

greatest height observed: $1.5 \cdot 10^6$ km (> solar diameter)

Surges: matter shoots upward like a jet ($v \sim 50$ to 200 km/sec).
In active sunspot groups small surges arise continuously

Coronal rain: after a flare matter from an "invisible" source in the corona falls back to the sun's surface like a rain.

Loops, arches: matter follows magnetic lines of forces, thus building nice loops and arches.

Also quiescent prominences sometimes undergo an active stage; matter streams down along magnetic lines of forces; prominence often rebuilds itself in the old shape (the magnetic "framework" remains preserved).

> Different classifications for prominences used in the literature are described by Tandberg-Hanssen in *Solar Activity* (loc. cit.).

B) Physics of prominences

Not amorphous masses, but open filamentary structure; threads of 1" diameter. Only a fraction of the external structure is actually filled by matter.

Ionized matter, which is held together by a "magnetic framework". If the matter streams away in an active state, new matter from the corona condenses on the remaining framework

> In quiescent prominences, too, the matter is in motion constantly, streams away and is replaced. Only the external shape remains at rest

Density about 100 to 1000 times larger than in the surrounding corona.

Temperature correspondingly lower

> One observes directly, that the corona in the surroundings is somewhat "diluted"

Prominences always appear between regions of opposite magnetic polarity where lines of forces in different hights are presumably horizontal.

Spectrum:

Emission lines: Balmer series, Ca II H + K, He - D_3, ...

At eclipses very many more faint lines are visible.
Qualitative = spectrum of the chromosphere.

Physical constitution in long-lived prominences similar to the spicules $T_{exc} \approx 4000^\circ$; $T_{kin} \approx 10{,}000^\circ$

Exciting radiation presumably from the transition region chromosphere - corona

In most lines the prominence is optically thin.
H_α shows self absorption. In L_α it is optically thick; L_α originates from a very thin layer.

Short-lived prominences show a somewhat "hotter" spectrum, the high-excited line 4686 Å of He II is enhanced, $T \approx 30{,}000^\circ$ (probably a transit stage if rising matter is heated to the coronal temperature or falling matter is cooling down).

Theory:

Many attempts, many detailed processes elaborated, many ideas; however, one can not yet speak of a general solution of the problem.

Spots – prominences – faculae are not related in a cause-and-effect way, but are different manifestations of disturbances in deeper layers.

7.4 *Flares*

Rapid release of 10^{28} ... 10^{32} ergs of energy

Appearance always in active regions in the chromosphere

According to the size one distinguishes types 1 to 3^+, designated "importance", with importance 1 having smallest area, etc.

"Flare" = the H_α brightening (or Ca II K). Associated phenoomena are said to "accompany" the flare.

Frequency: during periods of greatest activity one may observe

up to	1 large	flares per day
	10 average	
	100 small	

Lifetime depends roughly on the size: 5-10 minutes to ~7-10 hrs.

In rare events of large size, atomic nuclei are accelerated to cosmic ray energies.

Phenomena connected with flares

(a) Burst of short-wave length radiation $\lambda < 2000$ Å

Energy released typically $\sim 10^{29} - 10^{30}$ ergs

(b) X rays

In flares of greatest energy and area, X-ray photons observed to > 100 KeV energy, that is, down to 0.1 Å. Enhanced X rays (~1 Å wavelength) cause disturbances of the earth's ionosphere (Mögel-Dellinger effect).

Enhanced ionization of the *D* layer.
D layer damps radio waves, which - in order to be reflected by the *F* layer - must traverse the *D* layer twice ⟶ hindering broadcasting (fading results)

(c) Corpuscular radiation

With v = 1000 to 2000 km/sec. Arrives at the earth about 2 days or more later

⟶ Magnetic storms, ⟶ aurorae

(d) Bursts of radio radiation, see below,

in the meter-wave region increase up to 10^5 times!

(e) Cosmic rays (see 9.8.1)

Only during very large flares. Protons of energies up to 10^{10} ... 10^{11} eV in rare cases. (surge phenomenon)

Because of the practical importance (influence on the earth) continuous survey, ⟶ daily, broadcasted "URSI grams" (= Union Radio Scientifique Internationale)

Many phenomena accompany flares. Complex physics.
No fully acceptable theory.

Possible origins:

Instabilities of the magnetic field (pinch effect)

Suddenly greatly enhanced mechanical energy flow, so that the energy can not escape fast enough and leads to the flare.

7.4 *Disturbed radio radiation*

Phenomena of the disturbed radio radiation so manifold that a new branch of research has developed:

"solar radio astronomy"

A) Slowly varying component (S - component)

from sunspot regions, hence also called "spot component".

Originates in discrete regions of the solar atmosphere, which usually are connected with spot regions.

Radiation flux F closely correlated with the spot number R.

For $\lambda = 15$ cm: $F_{(R=200)} = 5\, F_{(R=0)}$

The optically visible spots are not themselves the location of the radio emission (it does not penetrate so far). Presumably due to thermal radiation from coronal condensations, i.e., overheated regions above the activity regions of the photosphere $T \sim 10^7$ degrees

Height of the emitting regions above the photosphere:

Depending on frequency: 20,000 ... 100,000 km

Spectral range: 1.2 to 100 cm, maximum at 15 cm

Duration of the radiation same as of the regions of activity, i.e., weeks to months.

B) Radio bursts

Most prominent phenomenon of the solar radio activity:

Occurring over the whole range: < 1 cm to 40 m

Intensity increase in the cm range of 20 to 40 times, in the meter range of 100,000 times the normal radiation.

Preliminary remark

According to 3.2.3 each electron density has a boundary frequency ν_o, below which no radio waves can get out, because then the refractive index < 0

(compare also 5.6.3)

$$\nu_o = \sqrt{\frac{e^2}{mc} N_e} = 9 \cdot 10^{-3} \sqrt{N_e} \quad \text{[Mhz] (lower boundary)}$$

or

$$\lambda_o = c/\nu_o = 0.3 \cdot 10^7 \frac{1}{\sqrt{N_e}} \quad \text{[cm] (upper boundary)}$$

These phenomena are very diverse; the relationships are not always known. Hence,

the classifications of the bursts used in the literature are not uniform

type I meter region

= short, rapidly increasing radiation shocks

| Maximum reached within $0\overset{s}{.}1$; total duration mostly < 1 sec.
| λ > 60 cm

They are the main contributor to the "noise storms" (see section C), but also frequently take place independently of noise storms.

Type II meter region

= emission in a narrow frequency band which drifts slowly with time from high to low frequencies

| Velocity of the frequency drift: 0.25 to 1 MHz/sec at ~100 - 200 MHz.
| Lifetime of the phenomenon on the average ~10 min;
| λ > 60 cm; increase of intensity factor 100 or more
| $F(125\text{ MHz}) > 200\ \text{Wm}^{-2}\ \text{Hz}^{-1}$

Frequently ($\gtrsim$60% of all cases) the harmonic 2:1 overtone wave occurs.

Representation in the time-frequency diagram

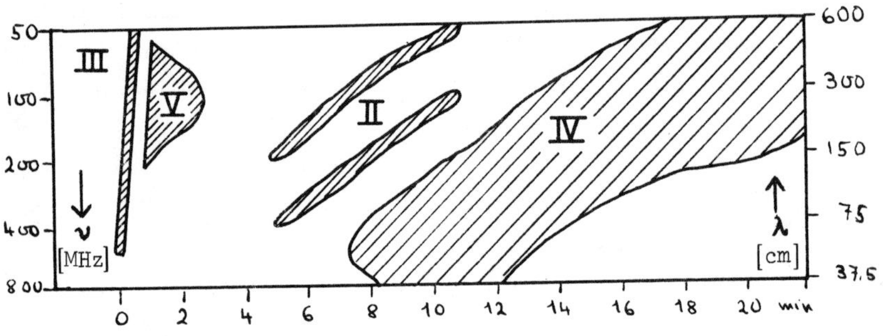

Abscissa: Variation with time at fixed frequency

Ordinate: Spectrum at a fixed time

Physical process

Ejected matter moves through the corona. The longer wave lengths always come later because of the "boundary frequency" (see preliminary remark). The frequency shifting, hence, directly reflects the altitude reached

→ rising velocity 400 to 1000 km/sec

(≈ velocity of the corpuscular radiation)

Mechanism: Presumably plasma frequency of the coronal plasma

Type II bursts are relatively rare; during the sunspot maximum about one burst per 50 hours.

Correlated with geomagnetic storms, which start about 2 to 3 days after the burst.

Type III meter region

= narrow-band emission, similar to type II,

but with very fast drifting of frequency of about 20 MHz/sec (Drift rate is frequency-dependent).

Lifetime of the phenomenon about 10 sec

Proper velocity of rise about 0.4 c (at an altitude of 1 $R_\odot$ above the photosphere).

Excitation evidently by high-speed electrons

The rapid ascending motion can be observed directly interferometrically.

Type III bursts are more frequent; at the sunspot maximum about 3 per hour. Close correlation with flares, occurs preferentially at the beginning of a flare.

Type IV over the whole radio region

= very broad-band emission with continuous spectrum.

Intensity increases slowly, reaches one or more maxima and decreases again slowly.

Emitting region very extended: 150,000 ... 350,000 km,

Altitude above the photosphere: 0.3 to 0.4 $R_\odot$

Type IV burst occurs only in connection with strong flares and, in that case, usually follows a type II burst. The radio emission may survive the optical flare.

Mechanism: synchrotron radiation of fast electrons

Type V meter region

= broad-band emission with continuous spectrum, which, when it occurs, is seen to follow a type III burst. Originates from the same physical region as the type III bursts.

Hence,

|| type II burst and type IV continuum ||
|| type III " and type V " ||

go together.

cm wave bursts

= totality of all phenomena in the region of 1 cm to 30 cm.

One can distinguish:

a) Simple peaks, half width (in time) 0.1 ... 7 min

b) types with slow increase and decrease,
duration 7 to 60 min (Gradual Rise and Fall = GRF)

c) forms made up of a) and b) having complex variations with time

Continuous spectrum: F_{max} = 10 ... >200 · 10^{-22} Wcm^{-2} Hz^{-1}

Mechanism: thermal emission and synchrotron radiation of fast electrons.

Close correlation to flares in the optical region

C) <u>"Noise storms"</u> in the meter-wave region

Great number of radiation bursts, which, often, overlie emission with continuous spectrum (storm continuum).

They often are restricted to a narrow frequency band of less than 100 MHz.

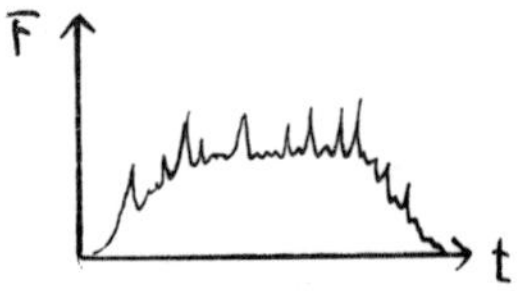

Duration: hours to several days

During sunspot maximum a frequent phenomenon, occurring up to 10% of the time.

In the case of single radiation bursts

<u>type I bursts</u> (see above) are involved.

During strong storms the frequency of the individual bursts is very high (more than 100/min), so that often one cannot decide whether the storm has its own continuum or if this is simulated by many unresolved individual bursts.

<u>Location</u> of radio emission in the corona, 0.3 to 1 $R_\odot$ above the photosphere; preferably above spot regions, but no close correlation

<u>Intensity</u> up to 100 times the normal radiation

<u>Origin</u>: Presumably synchrotron radiation of high-speed electrons.

INDEX